PEARSON ALWAYS LEARNING

William Sanborn Pfeiffer

Pocket Guide to Technical Communication

with Selections from Strategies for Business and Technical Writing

Custom Edition for
Western Michigan University's College of
Engineering and Applied Sciences

Taken from:
Pocket Guide to Technical Communication,
Fifth Edition
by William Sanborn Pfeiffer

Cover Art: Courtesy of brandXpictures.

Taken from:

Pocket Guide to Technical Communication, Fifth Edition
by William Sanborn Pfeiffer

Published by Prentice Hall
Upper Saddle River, New Jersey 07488

Pearson Learning Solutions, 501 Boylston Street, Suite 900,
Boston, MA 02116
A Pearson Education Company
www.pearsoned.com

Printed in the United States of America

5 18

000200010271887551

TF/AK

ISBN 10: 1-269-90744-1
ISBN 13: 978-1-269-90744-6

15 2023

Copyright Acknowledgements

Grateful acknowledgment is made to the following sources for permission to reprint material copyrighted or controlled by them:

"Evaluating and Testing as You Revise," by Linda Flower and John Ackerman, reprinted from *Writers at Work* (1977), by permission of Harcourt Brace College Publishers.

"Gobbledygook," by Stuart Chase, reprinted from *Power of Words* (1954), Houghton Mifflin Harcourt Publishing Company.

"What Do You Mean You Don't Like My Style?" by John S. Fielden, by permission of *Harvard Business Review* (May–June 1982).

"International Communication and Language," by Gwyneth Olofsson, reprinted from *When in Rome or Rio or Riyadh . . . Cultural Q & As for Successful Business Behavior Around the World* (2004), by permission of the author.

"The Importance of Memos, Letters, and E-Mail," by Sharon J. Gerson and Steven M. Gerson, reprinted from *Technical Communication: Process and Product* (2007), by permission of Pearson Education.

"How to use bottom-line writing in corporate communications," by John S. Fielden and Ronald E. Dulek, reprinted from *Business Horizons* (July–August 1984), by permission of Elsevier, Inc.

"Audience Analysis: The Problem and a Solution," by J. C. Mathes and Dwight W. Stevenson, reprinted from *Designing Technical Reports: Writing for Audiences in Organizations* (1991), by permission of the authors.

"How to Lie with Statistics," by Darrell Huff, reprinted from *How to Lie with Statistics* (1954), W.W. Norton & Company, Inc.

Preface

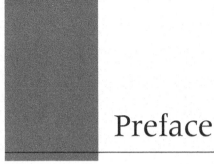

This little book aims to provide you with a handy reference for on-the-job and academic writing. It does not pretend to be the last word on the subject. There are plenty of longer books to serve that purpose. Instead, it gives you quick, easy-to-read answers to common writing problems you will face in school and on the job. This introduction includes information on the organization of the text, changes in the fifth edition, and the sources used in writing it.

NEW TO THIS EDITION

The fifth edition of the *Pocket Guide to Technical Communication* includes several additions and revisions that make the book even more useful to students and working professionals. The main changes are as follows.

- Figures have been updated, and several new figures have been added.
- The revision process has been expanded to include a review of layout and graphics.
- The Planning Form at the end of the book has been revised to make it applicable to both written discourse and oral presentations.
- The section on email has been expanded to include "helpful hints" related to readers, privacy, tone, format, ownership, editing/proofing, and cultures.
- An entirely new section on PowerPoint has been added to Chapter 4, with three sets of guidelines for planning, creating, and delivering speeches that use PowerPoint.
- Two editing exercises have been added to the end of the Appendix (Writing Handbook), so that users of the book can apply the guidelines in the Appendix.

ORGANIZATION OF TEXT

The *Pocket Guide* presents information on five main subjects, each with its own chapter or appendix:

Chapter 1	The Writing Process: Achieving Speed and Quality
Chapter 2	Structure: Achieving Order and Design
Chapter 3	ABC Formats and Examples
Chapter 4	Special Topics: Graphics and Oral Presentations
Appendix:	Writing Handbook

Each section gives you a jump start on planning, drafting, or revising when you are rushed to deliver a document. The appendix will be especially useful for immediate help with revision and editing. It contains alphabetized entries to assist with questions about style, grammar, and usage.

ACKNOWLEDGMENTS

I would like to thank the following individuals and companies for allowing me to incorporate their material into examples: Jefferson Alexander, Natalie Birnbaum, David Cox, Jeffrey Daxon, Rob Duggan, Fugro-McClelland, Inc., Chuck Keller, Becky Kelly, Steven Knapp, Law Companies Group, Alan Mitchell, Jeff Orr, Chris Owen, Ken Rainey, Sam Randell, Hattie Schumaker, Herb Smith, and James Stephens.

Additionally, I would like to thank the reviewers of this text for their attention and insight: Jackie Atkins, Pennsylvania State University–Dubois; Siobhan Brownson, Winthrop University; Mary Custureri, Embry Riddle Aeronautical University; Linda Eicken, Cape Fear Community College; Suzanne Karberg, Purdue University; and Julie McDade, Montana State University–Billings.

Also, many thanks to my wife, Evelyn, for her support on this pocket guide and on my other book projects over the years. Only she knows what that support has meant to me. My thanks also go to my son, Zachary, who made helpful comments on Chapter 4.

REQUEST FOR YOUR COMMENTS

In using the *Pocket Guide*, you may come up with suggested changes for another edition. Please send your ideas to me at pfeiffer@warren-wilson.edu. I'd be glad to hear from you.

ABOUT THE AUTHOR

William Sanborn Pfeiffer ("Sandy") has focused his academic career on two fields: technical and professional communication and international studies. With a Ph.D. in English, he helped develop graduate and undergraduate degree programs in technical communication at Southern Polytechnic State University, where he also served as a department head and later vice president of academic affairs. After retiring from Southern Poly, he was provost, vice president of academic affairs, professor of international studies, and interim president at Ramapo College of New Jersey. He is currently president of Warren Wilson College in Asheville, North Carolina.

Besides the *Pocket Guide*, Pfeiffer has written six editions of *Technical Communication: A Practical Approach*. The current 7th edition was coauthored with Kaye E. Adkins (Pearson 2010). The book is used in colleges and universities around the country. He also wrote *Proposal Writing: The Art of Friendly Persuasion* (Merrill, 1989); coauthored, with Chuck Keller, *Proposal Writing: The Act of Friendly and Winning Persuasion* (Prentice Hall, 2000); coauthored, with Steven Zwickel, *Pocket Guide to Technical Presentations & Professional Speaking* (Prentice Hall, 2006); and wrote *Pocket Guide to Public Speaking* (Prentice Hall, 2002).

Since 1979, Pfeiffer has taught communication seminars to business, industry, and government groups in the United States and overseas. Sample seminar topics include report writing, proposals, oral presentations, effective meetings, and technical editing.

You can contact Sandy Pfeiffer at the following address:

William Sanborn Pfeiffer, Ph.D.
Office of the President
Warren Wilson College
P.O. Box 9000

Brief Contents

The following chapters are taken from:
Pocket Guide to Technical Communication,
Fifth Edition
by William Sanborn Pfeiffer

1 The Writing Process
Achieving Speed and Quality

All writers want to write quickly and well. If there were magic pills to create good writing on demand, they would sell very well. Although there are no prose-producing pills, we do have simple techniques for dramatically increasing the speed and quality of on-the-job writing. This chapter presents techniques to improve the writing process.

The "writing process" can be defined as the steps you follow to complete a successful writing project. Process is indeed the key to good writing because it separates activity into manageable stages, each of which includes specific goals. To introduce you to the writing process, this chapter has three main sections:

- **Definition of Technical Writing**—giving basic information about purpose, writers, and readers in technical writing
- **Nine Steps to Better Writing**—explaining the main steps that help you plan, draft, and revise
- **Writing in Groups**—providing five guidelines for collaborative writing projects

This chapter gives most attention to the planning process. In fact, seven of the "Nine Steps to Better Writing" take place before you even begin a first draft. To assist you in the crucial planning process, at the end of the book you will find a Planning Form to use in preparing your strategy for completing each document.

DEFINITION OF TECHNICAL WRITING

At some point in our lives, we all do three main types of writing: academic, personal, and technical (see Figure 1–1). Yet for many of us, only technical writing remains the type that will determine our professional success.

The term *technical writing* includes all written communication done on the job. It originally referred only to writing done in fields of technology,

Type	Purpose	Audience	Example
Academic	Display knowledge	Teachers or colleagues	Research paper
Personal	Enlighten, entertain	Yourself or friends	Journal, letters
Technical	Get something done	Supervisors, subordinates, or customers	Reports

FIGURE 1–1
Three types of writing

engineering, and science, but it has come to mean writing done in *all* professions and organizations (see Figure 1–2). Technical writing can be distinguished from other prose by features related to its (1) purpose, (2) writer, and (3) readers.

Purpose: Getting Something Done

A practical purpose underlies all on-the-job writing. With such writing you strive to get something accomplished for your organization, for a customer, or for both. Academic writing displays knowledge, and personal writing entertains or enlightens. Although technical writing may sometimes have these goals too, its main purpose is *practical*—for example, to change a policy, offer a new product, or explain a procedure.

Writer: Conveying Your Knowledge to the Reader

As writer, you have something to teach your readers. Usually, you know more about the topic than they do—that's why *you're* writing to *them*. Readers benefit from knowledge you provide and make changes accordingly—for example, responding to problems you highlight, following recommendations you put forth, and buying products you are selling. Of course, your superior knowledge about the topic can sometimes create a problem. You must avoid talking over the heads of your readers. This challenge may be the greatest one you face in the writing process because there's a tendency to assume readers know more about the subject than they actually do.

Writer's Job #1: Write for the Reader, Not for Yourself

Correspondence: In-House or External
- Memos to your boss and to your subordinates
- Routine letters to customers, vendors, etc.
- "Good news" letters to customers
- "Bad news" letters to customers
- Sales letters to potential customers
- Electronic mail (email) messages to coworkers or customers over a computer network

Short Reports: In-House or External
- Analysis of a problem
- Recommendation
- Equipment evaluation
- Progress report on project or routine periodic report
- Report on the results of laboratory or field work
- Description of the results of a company trip

Long Reports: In-House or External
- Complex problem analysis, recommendation, or equipment evaluation
- Project report on field or laboratory work
- Feasibility study

Other Examples
- Proposal to boss for new product line
- Proposal to boss for change in procedures
- Proposal to customer to sell a product, a service, or an idea
- Proposal to funding agency for support of research project
- Abstract or summary of technical article
- Technical article or presentation
- Operation manual or other manual
- Web site

FIGURE 1–2
Examples of technical writing
Source: Technical Communication: A Practical Approach, 6th ed. (p. 5) by W. S. Pfeiffer, 2006, Upper Saddle River, NJ: Prentice Hall. Reprinted by permission.

Readers: Understanding Their Diverse Needs

Your job would be simple if each document were directed to just one reader. But actual technical writing is not that easy. Instead, a document often has *many* readers, who have mixed technical backgrounds and different needs. Even when a document goes to only one person, it may be read by other people later. This varied audience affects the structure and the language you select to drive home your message.

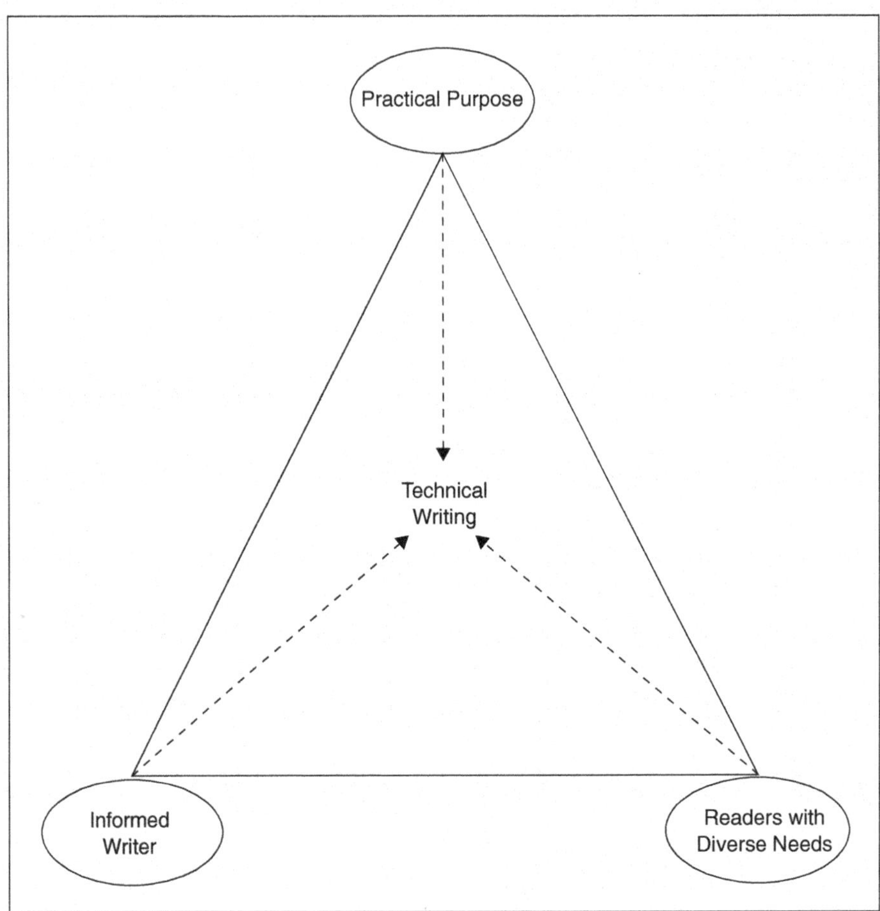

FIGURE 1–3
Technical writing triangle

Thus, the fabric of technical writing is formed by the combination of three elements, as shown in Figure 1–3:

1. A practical purpose
2. A writer more informed than the audience
3. Readers with diverse needs

Such writing will challenge you. The rest of this chapter shows how the challenge can be met most efficiently during the planning, drafting, and revision stages of writing.

NINE STEPS TO BETTER WRITING

Most good writers are made, not born. They work hard at perfecting the *process* of writing. The written *product* may appear to have been effortlessly produced, but in fact it results from a disciplined approach to composition. The discipline is embodied in a nine-step plan. If you follow this plan, you will learn for yourself that there is no mystery to improving the efficiency and quality of your writing.

Of the main stages of writing—planning, drafting, and revising—the first deserves the most attention but often receives the least. An extra hour spent planning can save two or three hours of rework during the drafting and revision stages. For that reason, Steps 1 through 7 concern the planning process. Then Steps 8 and 9 offer suggestions for drafting and revising your draft.

As noted earlier, you may choose to use the Planning Form at the end of this book to help you design the best strategy for planning a document.

Step 1: Write a Brief Purpose Statement

A one- or two-sentence purpose statement helps get you started. It becomes the lead-in to your outline and then often becomes the first words in the document itself. Writing a purpose statement forces you to decide (1) exactly why you are writing and (2) what response you want from your readers. It directs your effort and becomes the lens through which you view the entire writing project.

A purpose statement can begin with a simple phrase like "The purpose of this report is to . . . ," or it can include more subtle phrasing. Whatever wording you choose, strive to write a passage that clearly sets forth your intentions.

Purpose Statements

> **Example 1:** This report presents the findings of our fieldwork at Trinity Dam, along with our recommendation that the spillway be replaced.
>
> **Example 2:** The purpose of this report is to compare and contrast two computer systems being considered for Greenway, Inc. The report draws conclusions about the system best suited for Greenway's long-term needs.

Note that a purpose statement only indicates why you are writing. It does not present summary points such as conclusions or recommendations. It gives direction, not results, and intends only to get you started with the writing process.

Step 2: Consider the Obstacles Your Readers Face

In an ideal world, readers would eagerly await your documents and give them their undivided attention. That ideal rarely exists. In fact, you're better off making the following assumptions about the audience members.

They Are Always Interrupted
Meetings, phone calls, email, lunch, and even business trips may interrupt them as they attempt to read your document.

They Are Impatient
They want you to deliver the goods quickly and clearly. While they read, they are thinking, "What's the point?" or "So what?" or "What does this have to do with me?" This impatience may mean they will not, or cannot, read the document from beginning to end.

They Have a Different Background Than You Do
They may not understand the terms you use. Thus they'll feel insulted—or just plain lost—if you speak in language they cannot understand.

To add to your challenge as a writer, most documents are viewed by different readers who may share decision-making authority and who may have different needs. The next two steps give you a way to analyze the background of diverse readers. For now, consider asking the following questions of each reader to help design a document that meets his or her needs:

1. What is the reader's technical or educational background?
2. What main question does this person need answered?
3. What main action do you want this person to take?
4. What features of this person's personality might affect his or her reading?
5. What features does this person prefer in document style and organization?

These same questions are included on the Planning Form at the end of the book.

Step 3: Determine Technical Levels of Readers

How much do your readers know about the subject? To answer this question, you can place most readers into one of the four categories that follow.

Category 1: Managers
Managers often are removed from the hands-on details of the topic. They need brief summaries, background information, and definitions of technical terms.

Category 2: Experts
Experts have a good understanding of the technical aspects of your topic. They need supporting technical detail, helpful tables and figures, and even appendixes of supporting information.

Category 3: Operators
Operators—such as field technicians, office workers, or members of a sales force—apply the ideas in your document to their jobs. They need (1) clear organization so that they can find sections relevant to them, (2) well-written procedures, and (3) clarity about how the document affects their jobs.

Category 4: General Readers
General readers, also known as "laypersons," have the least amount of information on your topic and often are outside an organization—for example, citizens reading a report on the environmental impact of a factory proposed for their community. They need (1) definitions of technical terms, (2) frequent use of graphics, and (3) clear statements about how the document will affect them.

Step 4: Determine Decision-Making Levels of Readers

Your readers also can be classified by the degree to which they make decisions based on your document. During the planning process, you can classify your readers into the following three groups.

Decision-Makers
As managers, decision-makers translate your document into action. Decisions can be made by an individual or by a committee.

Advisers
Although advisers do not make decisions themselves, they have the ear of people who do. That is, busy managers often give engineers, accountants, and others the task of analyzing technical points of a document. Final decisions may rest on recommendations that flow from this analysis.

Receivers
Some readers are not part of the decision-making process. Instead, they receive information in the document and make adjustments in their jobs accordingly.

Figure 1–4 includes technical levels on the vertical axis and decision-making levels on the horizontal axis. It shows 12 basic categories of readers. Generally, the more categories that apply to any given writing project, the more challenging is your job in meeting the needs of a varied audience. Figure 1–4 is also part of the Planning Form included at the end of the book.

Technical Level	Decision-Making Level		
	Decision Makers	Advisers	Receivers
Managers			
Experts			
Operators			
General Readers			

FIGURE 1–4
Reader matrix
Source: Technical Communication: A Practical Approach, 6th ed. (p. 14) by W. S. Pfeiffer, 2006, Upper Saddle River, NJ: Prentice Hall. Reprinted by permission.

A fictional case study will demonstrate how a typical writing project can easily involve half the audience categories shown in the Figure 1–4 matrix. As the architect for a college, Megan Neeley is developing a proposal for a new entrance for the school where she works. The proposed project will include a massive stone arch, widened roadway, new traffic light, renovated bell tower, and expanded landscaping. The main goals are to enhance the appearance of the part of the college most seen by the public, improve safety and convenience for students and employees entering campus, and increase enrollment by improving the visibility of the school.

In her proposal, Megan should consider the needs of the following six categories represented in Figure 1–4:

1. Decision-Maker/Manager: the president of the college, who will make the decision for the college and whose main background and experience are in management
2. Decision-Maker/General Reader: the mayor of the town, who will make the decision for the city and is the owner of a small local business as well as a politician
3. Adviser/Expert: the chief accountant at the college, who will advise the president about the proposal and is an expert in matters of finance
4. Advisers/Operators: the two traffic coordinators of the town, who will advise the mayor about the road and stoplight proposals and who work every day on the town's traffic problems

5. Receivers/Managers: the three academic deans of the college, who will inform faculty about the proposal but who themselves are not part of the decision-making process
6. Receiver/General Reader: the editor of the college's student newspaper, who will write an article on the proposal for the paper but will not take part in the decision-making process

Note that in a different writing situation, the individuals listed would change decision-making roles. Indeed, the purpose of this case study is to demonstrate that information about readers must be based on facts of the particular context in which you are writing.

Step 5: Find Out What Decision-Makers Want

Knowing the technical and decision-making levels of your readers is a good first step. Next, you need to focus on the needs of the most important readers—those who make decisions. Three suggestions follow.

Write Down What You Know about Decision-Makers
Specifically, try to get answers to the questions listed previously in Step 2 (and also included on the Planning Form at the end of the book).

Talk with Colleagues Who Have Written to the Same Readers
Someone else in your organization may know the needs of the decision-makers for your document. Ask around the office to see if your colleagues can help you answer the questions about readers on the Planning Form.

Remember That All Readers Prefer Simplicity
When you just aren't able to find out much about the decision-makers, remember one essential point about all readers: They prefer documents to be as short and simple as possible. The popular KISS principle is the best rule to follow:

> Keep It Short and Simple!

Step 6: Collect and Document Information Carefully

Whether you gather information yourself or get it from other sources, be careful during the research phase of the planning process. First, your reader may want to know exactly how you developed supporting data. Second, your professional reputation, and even your job, may be at risk if you err in the way you handle borrowed information. Some suggestions follow.

Record Notes Carefully

Basic writing courses often stress the importance of taking careful notes on material borrowed from books, magazines, newspapers, interviews, or the Internet. This research step is also important in technical writing you produce in college and in your career. Only by preventing errors at the earliest stages of the writing process can you ensure that your final document will have used borrowed information correctly.

Start by writing a bibliography card for each source you use. Take special care in recording information with absolute accuracy because you will use information on the card—not the source itself—when you construct the final bibliography for your document. The second type of card is a notecard. Each one contains quotations, paraphrases, or summaries based on a particular source. Figure 1–5 includes a sample bibliography card and

Henry & McGrath :

The Insight has modest power but can't carry much weight.

Summary, p. 161

Henry & McGrath:

The Insight won't win any races, but it will get you safely on the freeway. Its load weight (365 pounds) is poor, however. Honda says that is wouldn't damage the car to overload it, but that performance and mileage would suffer.

paraphrase, p. 161

Henry & McGrath:

"Although the car [Insight] will never lead the pack at Indy, you won't fear for your life getting on the freeway. But not this. The Insight's 365-pound payload capacity means a couple of hefty passengers can overload [sic] the car. Honda says that wouldn't damage the vehicle, but would impede performance and mileage."

p. 161

FIGURE 1–5
Research cards

Adapted from *Technical Communication: A Practical Approach,* 6th ed. (pp. 546, 548) by W. S. Pfeiffer, 2006, Upper Saddle River, NJ: Prentice Hall. Reprinted by permission.

three notecards, all based on the same passage of borrowed material. Observe the following distinctions in the three types of notecards:

1. **Quotation** cards include the exact wording of the original passage. Requiring much time to write and much space on a card, they are useful only when you're convinced the precise words of the original will be needed in your document.
2. **Paraphrase** cards may use a few key words from the original but require words and sentence structures that are mostly your own. They are especially useful when you want to reflect the train of ideas in the source without getting bogged down in direct quotations.
3. **Summary** cards reduce a good deal of borrowed information to a few of your own sentences. Although they may mix summary with some direct quotations (clearly indicated with quotation marks), generally summary cards use your own words to distill a large amount of text from the source.

If in the past you have used regular notebooks instead of notecards to record your research, you will be pleasantly surprised at the flexibility provided by cards. For example, you can sort cards into topics with ease once you have written an outline (see the next step on writing an outline). Also, you can more conveniently carry them with you in a pocket or bag when you are conducting research at varied locations. Cards provide a simple, yet powerful, research strategy.

Transfer Information Carefully

Most errors in documentation result from careless work, not from intentional cheating. But whether an error in using borrowed information is unintentional or intentional, it may be considered *plagiarism*, that is, the parading of someone else's ideas, words, or graphics as your own. Unless information is considered "common knowledge"—namely, information generally available from many basic sources in the field—its use should include a citation to the source. In college, plagiarism can result in failing a paper or course. In a career, it can result in embarrassment at best, or lawsuits and job loss at worst. So it's worth taking some time at the notetaking stage to consider ways to avoid the problem. Here are a few pointers:

- Avoid changing the meaning of a quotation if you choose to replace some words with *ellipses* (series of spaced periods—see Quotation Card example in Figure 1–5). Although ellipses can prove helpful in removing words that are not essential to your purpose, their inclusion must not alter the meaning or context of the original.
- Circle quotation marks on cards and on early drafts. Using this technique, you can easily identify material taken directly from a source. In other

words, you want to make sure you don't make the error of assuming a direct quotation is one of your own paraphrases.

- Look away from your source for a few moments before you write a paraphrase or summary card. In this way you will be much more likely to use your own words and sentence structure. Then, after you have written the paraphrase or summary, compare your writing to the original to be sure you have not too closely paralleled the words or structure of the original.

Use the Right Citation System

In citations of borrowed information in the text, colleges and professional associations now favor simple systems that get the job done without fanfare. In most cases, borrowed information is identified with short parenthetical notations that occur within the text after the borrowed information (as opposed to footnotes). The references may include the author's last name, possibly the year of publication, and a page reference. Such references should follow any borrowed information—whether quotation, paraphrase, or summary—that is not considered common knowledge. For example, if you were paraphrasing some of the material in this chapter, your reference might look something like the following:

> The author indicates that writers are required to include a parenthetical reference to all borrowed information unless the information is understood to be "common knowledge" (Pfeiffer, 2010, 10–12).

Besides the parenthetical references, documentation systems usually include, at the end of the document, a list of all references cited. Systems may vary considerably, especially in the style of individual entries and lists of works cited. Use the system most acceptable to your audience or most appropriate in your professional context. Some organizations that have developed their own systems include the Modern Language Association (MLA) and American Psychological Association (APA). Another common source is the *Chicago Manual of Style*. All these systems recommend some form of parenthetical documentation and some type of list of references at the end of the document. Figure 1–6 shows one approach to a list that closely resembles the systems mentioned. You may want to use it if you are not using another system.

Step 7: Write an Outline

Completing an outline is the single best way to write both quickly and well. This section answers three main questions: (1) Why is an outline so important? (2) What should it look like? and (3) What steps should you use in writing it?

First, why is an outline so important? Here are the main reasons.

- **Organization:** An outline forces you to grapple with matters of organization at a time when it is easy to change the structure of the document,

Book with two or more authors: Note that the second author's name is given in normal order, with a comma between the two authors' names.

Andrews, T. S., and L. Kelly. 1965a. *Geography of central Oregon,* 4th ed. New York: Jones and Caliber Press.

Book by same authors: Note that the blank line indicates another source by same authors. The "b" is used because the same authors published two cited books in the same year. Also, the state abbreviation is used for clarity, since Hiram is a small town.

_____. 1965b. *Geography today.* Hiram, OH: Pixie Publishers.

Journal article: Note that there are no spaces between the first page number of this journal article and the colon that follows the volume number. Also, there is only a space, but no punctuation, between the journal title and the volume number.

Cranberg, E. V. 1986. Fossils are fun: The life of a geologist in the 1980s. *Geology Issues* 34:233–344.

Article in collection: This entry is for an article that appears in a collection, with a general editor. Note the comma and "ed." (for "edited by") after the collection title. This same format would be used in other cases where you were referring to a piece from a collection, such as a paper in a conference proceeding.

Fandell, C. N., L. Guest, H. M. Smith, and Z. H. Taylor. 1976. Achieving purity in your sampling techniques. In *Geotechnical Engineering Practices,* ed. J. Schwartz, 23–67. Cleveland: Hapsburg Press.

Interview: Refer to yourself in the third person as the "author."

Iris, J. G. 1988. Resident of Summer Hills Subdivision. Interview with the author at site of toxic-waste dump, 23 March.

Newspaper article: This reference includes the day, section, and page number of the article. If no author had been listed, the entry would have begun with the article title.

Mongo, G. P. 1989. Sinkhole psychology: The ground is falling, Chicken Little. *Dayton Gazette,* 12 July, sec. D, 5.

Article from popular magazine: This reference is handled like a journal article except that the date of the particular issue is also included, after the volume number. Note that there is no extra spacing around the parentheses.

Runyon, D. G., and L. P. Moss. 1967. Sinkholes are coming to your area soon. *Timely News* 123 (15 July):65–66.

Information from personal email message: This entry concerning a personal email message contains information on both sender and receiver, as well as the date and subject of the message.

Jankowski, S. X. (sjan@spdu.edu). Nature of the Mahikari movement. Personal email to Matthew B. Knob (mknob@aol.com). 22 Dec. 1999.

CD-ROM citation: Reference to a CD-ROM does not require inclusion of the date you consulted the source.

Jasic, H. D. (1972). Japanese religions today [CD-ROM]. Available: USD Quest File Ondisc Item QF 54/4.

FIGURE 1–6 (pp. 13–14)
Sample list of references

Source: Technical Writing: A Practical Approach, 5th ed. (pp. 537–538) by W. S. Pfeiffer, 2003, Upper Saddle River, NJ. Prentice Hall. Reprinted by permission.

Database and Web citations: Note that Web citations must include the date that the information was found.

Traeger, C. (n.d.) The will of the Prius. *Carlist.com.* Retrieved 10 August 2001 from the World Wide Web: *http://www.carlist.com/newcars/2001/toyotaprius.html*

Einstein, P. (1999, October 29). The benefits of Insight. *Professional Engineering,* 12.19, 23. Retrieved August 3, 2001 from GALILEO, All databases, ProQuest: *http://www.galileo.peachnet.edu*

Glynn, M. (2001, January 19). Automakers will offer "2 for the price of 1": Many major manufacturers are hoping gas-electric hybrids can power future sales. *Seattle Times,* F1. Retrieved August 4, 2001 from GALILEO, All databases, ProQuest: *http://www.galileo.peachnet.edu*

FIGURE 1–6 (*continued*)

that is, before you have committed words to draft. As you add and delete ideas on the page and shift points from main to secondary topics, you are thinking about the best way to satisfy the readers' needs.

- **Visualization:** An outline shows you—visibly—whether you have enough supporting information. For example, if your outline includes only one subheading for a topic, you know that you need to do more research or to delete the topic.
- **Review:** An outline speeds up the review process when your documents must be approved by someone else in your organization. It is much easier to make changes at this stage than later, after you have invested time in the draft. Indeed, reviewers who sign off on your outline are much less likely to request major changes during the drafting or revision process.

Second, what should an outline look like? You may remember a teacher requiring you to submit a neat and orderly outline with ideal format. Such an outline is rarely the first version,. Instead, each outline will (1) start as points spread over a page without any recognizable hierarchy, (2) evolve to a recognizable list of main and supporting points, and (3) change shape during the drafting process as you adjust points of emphasis. Outlining is a messy business because it reflects the thinking you do *before* you write.

Third, what steps should you use in writing an outline? Follow the sequence below. Figure 1–7 shows the result of the first two steps. Figure 1–8 shows a later outline resulting from the third step.

Record Random Ideas Quickly

This "nonlinear" (translate: messy) process involves the free association of ideas. To stay on track, write your purpose statement at the top of the page. Then quickly write as many points as possible that relate to the topic.

Problems/Solutions: M-Global's Cafeteria

- High prices P#2
- Poor selection P#1
- Soft drinks - $1.39 $1.99 each
- Hamburgers are now $3.19
- Average lunch now $7 - $8
- Offer lease to another vendor S#3

-PBJ/Tuna/Egg salad are only sandwiches
no bread choices besides white

- Excel - good regional reputation
- APG - local with good price

- Only one hot meal entree each day
- No low-fat milk products
- No options for those on restricted diets

- Sally Ann's, Country Corner, Mother's Palace, Peaceful Platter all expressed interest

P#3
- Inflexible current staff
- Haven't changed hours to accommodate "flextime"
Not responsive to suggestions

Dont handle special events

- Operated by M-Global, it would be non-profit
— Would hire food service manager and use students in food service management from Maryland Shore C.C.

Current contract expires in 2 months

Now have chance to develop contract conditions turned down by current company

- Have M-Global take over restaurant S#1

S#2 Have meals catered in

Talked with Good Food, Inc. - does several other M-Global offices in U.S.

Higher quality likely with these restaurants

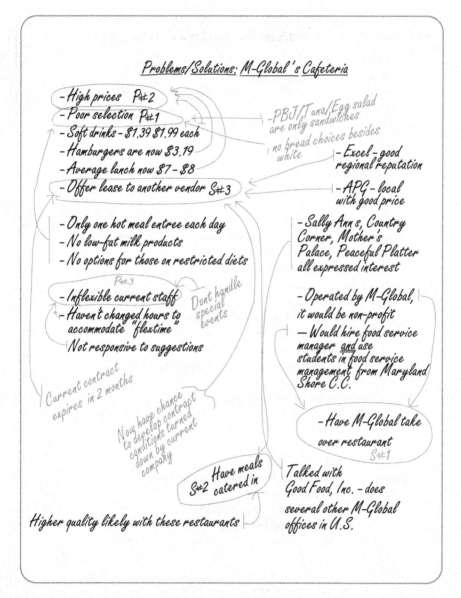

FIGURE 1–7
The outlining process: Early stage

Source: Technical Communication: A Practical Approach, 6th ed. (p. 19) by W. S. Pfeiffer, 2006, Upper Saddle River, NJ: Prentice Hall. Reprinted by permission.

PROBLEMS AND SOLUTIONS: CURRENT CAFETERIA IN BUILDING

I. Problem #1: Poor selection
   A. Only one hot meal entree each day
   B. Only three sandwiches—PBJ, egg salad, and tuna
   C. Only one bread—white
   D. No low-fat milk products (milk, yogurt, LF cheeses, etc.)
   E. No options for those with restricted diets

II. Problem #2: High prices
   A. Soft drinks from $1.39 to $1.99 each
   B. Hamburgers now $3.19
   C. Average lunch now $7-$8

III. Problem #3: Inflexible staff
   A. Unwilling to change hours to meet M-Global's flexible work schedule
   B. Have not acted on suggestions
   C. Not willing to cater special events in building

IV. Solution #1: End lease and make food service an M-Global department
   A. Hire food service manager
   B. Use students enrolled in food service management program at Maryland Shore Community College
   C. Operate as nonprofit operation—just cover expenses

V. Solution #2: Hire outside restaurant to cater meals in to building
   A. Higher quality likely
   B. Initial interest by four nearby restaurants
      1. Sally Ann's
      2. Country Corner
      3. Mother's Palace
      4. Peaceful Platter

VI. Solution #3: Continue leasing space but change companies
   A. Initial interest by three vendors
      1. Excel—good regional reputation for quality
      2. APG—close by and local, with best price
      3. Good Food, Inc.—used by two other M-Global offices with good results
   B. Current contract over in two months
   C. Chance to develop contract not acceptable to current company

FIGURE 1–8
The outlining process: Later stage
Source: Technical Communication: A Practical Approach, 6th ed. (p. 20) by W. S. Pfeiffer, 2006, Upper Saddle River, NJ: Prentice Hall. Reprinted by permission.

Show Relationships
Surveying your page of ideas, locate the three or four main points that indicate the direction your document will take. Circle them. Then draw lines to connect these main points to their many supporting points, as shown in Figure 1–7.

Draft a Final Outline
Your messy outline now must be cleaned up to make it useful to you as you write. You can either use the traditional format with roman numerals, and so forth (see Figure 1–8), or you can simply use dashes and indent to indicate outline levels. Whatever format you choose, the final outline should reflect three main features:

- **Depth:** Be sure the entire outline has enough support to develop the draft.
- **Balance:** Include adequate detail for all of your main points. When you subdivide a point, have at least two breakdowns—any object divided has at least two parts.
- **Parallel Form:** Give points in the same grouping the same grammatical form, both to make the outline easier to read and to ease the transition to writing the corresponding text in the first draft. In fact, consider keeping the entire outline consistent in form; that is, use either full sentences or fragments for your points. Fragments are preferable because they take up less space and don't lock you into sentences too early.

With outline in hand, you are ready to begin the second part of the three-part writing process—drafting.

Step 8: Write Your First Draft Quickly

The first draft offers you another chance to speed up the writing process. Unfortunately, this is when many writers encounter "writer's block" and slow down. Note the following suggestions for capturing time often wasted at this stage. Of course, the most important suggestion was covered in the previous step: *Always* enter the drafting stage with a complete outline in hand.

Schedule Blocks of Drafting Time
Writing requires concentration. Close your door if you have one, head to an empty office, or write at home—just do whatever you must to keep from being interrupted for at least 30 to 60 minutes. By giving writing a priority, you will finish drafts quickly. However, if you allow every other activity to upset your drafting schedule, writing even a simple document will consume your day.

Don't Stop to Edit
Editing uses a different part of your brain than drafting does. When you stop to correct grammar or spelling errors, you derail the drafting effort. With each interruption, it becomes harder and harder to regain the concentration needed to write the draft. Save editing for later.

Begin with the Easiest Section
A well-structured outline gives you the luxury of starting with almost any part of the document. Skip around if doing so allows you to write the draft more quickly.

Write Summaries Last
Summary sections, such as the executive summary for a formal report, usually get written last. They require the kind of thoughtful overviews and careful wording that you can write best after you've seen where the entire document is going. Of course, you can write a summary at any time if you have a good outline. It's just that you will write the *best* one when you have the chance to view a completed draft of the rest of the document.

Your goal is to get words on paper quickly. Following the suggestions above will save you hours each week, days each year, and weeks over a career. The ideas are simple, but they work.

Step 9: Revise in Stages

Producing a carefully revised and scrupulously edited document is absolutely essential to your success as a writer. During revision, you must attend to matters of content, style, grammar, and mechanics. The trick to solving a variety of editing problems is to adopt a "divide and conquer" approach. Review the draft several times, correcting a different set of problems on each run-through. This effort to focus your attention on specific problems yields the best results. Five stages of revision follow.

Adjust and Reorganize Content
This task could be considered either the first stage of revision or the last stage of drafting. Here you expand sections that need more development, shorten some sections, and change the location of some passages.

Edit for Style
Style refers to changes that make your writing smoother, more readable, and more interesting. Here are options to consider:

- Shorten sentences.
- Improve clarity (for example, by adding transitional words and improving the logical flow of ideas).

- Change passive voice sentences to active.
- Define technical terms.
- Add headings, lists, and graphics.
- Replace longer words with synonyms that are shorter or easier to understand.

Edit for Grammar

Grammar haunts all of us. Your head may be filled with dozens of half-remembered rules and terms from school days—comma splices, sentence fragments, subject-verb agreement, and dangling participles, to name just a few. Here's a simple strategy to ensure that your writing will be grammatically sound.

- First, use your own self-reflection or the editorial advice of a colleague to determine the most common grammatical errors in your writing. Focus mainly on this short list—*not* on all grammatical errors—when you edit.
- Second, use the Appendix of this book as an editing resource while you write.

Edit for Mechanics

Examples of mechanical errors include the following:

- Omitted words or phrases
- Misspelled words
- Inconsistent margins
- Wrong paging
- Nonparallel format in headings or subheadings

Word processing programs have made such errors less common and much easier to correct. But technology also has lulled us into a false sense of security. You need to remain vigilant in spotting potentially embarrassing errors that may have worked their way into your draft.

Review Layout and Graphics

The last stage of revision requires that you review the visual elements of the document. Check that all illustrations are mentioned in the text and that their location is appropriate. Further, make certain that you have been consistent in the format of headings, lists, fonts, white space, and other elements of design.

A Nine-Step Strategy

The nine steps to better writing provide a strategy for writing every kind of on-the-job document. These steps require you to apply to writing the same degree of organization that you would apply to other parts of your job. After

Directions: The following checklist addresses the nine guidelines in this chapter. The only change here is that the guidelines are written as questions for you to consider as you are writing.

PLANNING

1. Have you written a brief purpose statement? ______
2. Have you considered the obstacles your readers face? ______
3. Do you know the technical levels of your readers? ______
4. Do you know the decision-making levels of your readers? ______
5. Do you know exactly what decision-makers want? ______
6. Have you collected and documented information carefully? ______
7. Have you written an outline? ______

DRAFTING

8. Have you written the first draft quickly? ______

REVISING

9. Have you revised in stages? ______

FIGURE 1–9
Writing checklist

all, how much of your average day do you spend writing?—20%? 30%? Or 50%? Using a disciplined method will help you use that time more efficiently while producing better work.

Figure 1–9 compresses the nine guidelines in this chapter into a writing checklist to use for any document.

WRITING IN GROUPS

Group writing is common in today's organizations, which emphasize teamwork at all levels and in all activities. For example, a successful proposal or technical manual may result from the combined effort of technical specialists, marketing experts, graphic artists, writers, editors, and administrative assistants. At its best, group writing benefits from the collective experience and specialties of participants. This section describes five pointers for keeping a collaborative writing project on track:

1. Get to know your group.
2. Set clear goals and ground rules.
3. Use brainstorming techniques.

4. Agree on a revision process.
5. Use computers to communicate.

Guideline 1: Get to Know Your Group

If you're used to being a "lone ranger"—that is, a solitary writer—you have some adjustments to make in reaching consensus during a group project. The best way to open the channels of communication is to learn as much as possible about your colleagues. Here are two techniques for doing so:

- Spend time talking to group members before the project begins, establishing personal relationships.
- Use the first session for informal chatting before you get down to business.

The point is this: The success of your group project may depend as much on having a good working relationship as it does on the technical specialties each member brings to the table.

Guideline 2: Set Clear Goals and Ground Rules

All groups should set goals and establish operating rules. For example, questions such as those below should be answered either before or during the first meeting:

- What is the main objective?
- How will tasks be distributed?
- How will differences of opinion be resolved?
- What's the schedule for the work?

Guideline 3: Use Brainstorming Techniques

The most common error in group work is getting too judgmental too quickly. Just as an individual writer needs the chance to spill ideas onto paper during the outline stage, members of a group need a chance to share ideas openly, without concern for criticism. This opportunity for a nonjudgmental pooling of ideas—or "brainstorming"—comes at the beginning of the group's work. Here's one strategy for brainstorming:

1. Ask the group recorder to take down ideas as quickly as possible.
2. Write ideas on large pieces of paper affixed to the walls in a room.
3. Use ideas written on the wall sheets to suggest additional ideas.
4. Distribute results of the exercise to group members after the meeting.
5. Meet again to choose ideas of most use in the project.

Guideline 4: Agree on a Revision Process

Group drafting and editing can be difficult. Some people who are used to writing in solitude find it hard to reach consensus on matters of style. Follow these suggestions for keeping the collaborative process on track:

1. Avoid making changes for the sake of individual preferences.
2. Search for areas of agreement among members, not areas of disagreement.
3. Make only those style and grammar changes that can be supported by rules of style, grammar, and word usage (see Appendix).
4. Ask the group's all-around best stylist to complete a final edit.

Your goal should be a document that sounds, as much as possible, as if it were written by one person.

Guideline 5: Use Computers to Communicate

Whether group members are in the same building or spread out across the world, they can benefit from using computers to communicate about the project. This technology, though changing constantly, falls into two general categories:

- **Asynchronous:** Such software permits members to post messages to each other and to alter a document, though not at the same time that other group members are making contributions.
- **Synchronous:** Software of this type allows group members to carry on simultaneous computer "conversations" about a document in real time. With several windows on their screens, they can place messages on the screen at the same time they edit a document that appears on the screen of all participants involved in the computer conversation.

Computer conversations can go well beyond email. Perhaps the greatest advantage they lend to group work is the openness encouraged by such online discussions. When coordinated with face-to-face sessions, such computer meetings produce results.

2 Structure
Achieving Order and Design

Your readers will respond well to inviting, easy-to-read, and well-structured documents. This chapter will help you apply simple rules about structure to everything you write.

Structure is defined here as both the arrangement of information within the document *(organization)* and the techniques used to highlight information *(page design)*. Included in this chapter are guidelines on both aspects of structure, in the following three main sections:

- **Basics of Organization**—describes the main rule of technical writing and the three principles that flow from it
- **ABC Format**—outlines a three-part pattern of organization—abstract, body, conclusion—that applies to all technical documents
- **Page Design**—explains simple formatting techniques that can improve any technical document

Together, the three sections provide an "executive summary" about structure in technical writing. Then Chapter 3 provides ABC Format outlines and accompanying models for many common documents, which can serve as starting points for your on-the-job writing projects.

BASICS OF ORGANIZATION

As noted in Chapter 1, your readers may differ greatly in technical background and decision-making authority. Yet most will share four features: (1) They are interrupted while reading, (2) they are impatient to find important information, (3) they lack your knowledge of the topic, and (4) the documents they read are seen by others too. Any principles of organization must respond to this set of features, for there is one cardinal rule of all technical writing:

Write for your reader, not for yourself.

This rule sounds sensible and obvious enough. However, subscribing to it will challenge you when there are readers with varying needs. Sometimes it is hard to find the one approach that works for many readers. This section presents three guidelines to remember as you plan, draft, and revise documents for readers of mixed technical backgrounds.

Structure Rule 1: Write Different Parts for Different Readers

The longer the document, the less likely it is that anyone will read it from beginning to end. This fact is especially true for documents such as formal reports (see ABC Format and example on pages 39–107 in Chapter 3). Readers often use a "speed-read" approach that includes these steps:

Step 1: **Quick scan.** Readers scan easy-to-read sections like executive summaries, introductory summaries, introductions, tables of contents, conclusions, and recommendations. They pay special attention to the beginning and ending sections, especially in documents longer than a page or two, and to illustrations.

Step 2: **Focused search.** Readers go directly to parts of the document body that will give them what they need at the moment. To find information quickly, they search for format devices like subheadings, listings, and white space in margins to guide their reading.

Step 3: **Short follow-ups.** Readers return to the document, when time permits, to read or re-read important sections.

In other words, readers often won't digest information in the same order you present it. Fortunately, you can use this fact to your advantage by writing different sections of documents for different readers. For example, the lead-off summary for a report may respond especially to the needs of managers, whereas technical sections in the body may be directed toward various groups of experts.

Writing different parts for different readers does present one hazard. If you go too far in tailoring sections for selected readers, the document may become fragmented. To avoid such fragmentation, use the common threads of organization, theme, and style to hold all sections together as one piece of work. For example, each section of a long proposal could begin with a purpose statement, emphasize related selling points, use frequent headings, and include more active voice than passive voice sentences—even though the different sections were directed toward different readers.

Structure Rule 2: Emphasize Beginnings and Endings

Most of us read fiction and essays much differently than we read technical writing. With fiction and essays, we read patiently until plot information and new knowledge come our way. With technical writing, we rush to find essential information and are impatient when we don't find it quickly.

In technical writing you must accommodate impatient readers by placing important information where they want it—at the beginning and end of the document. Figure 2–1 shows how this emphasis on beginnings and endings responds to the interest level of readers. Note that interest peaks at the beginning. Here is where the reader needs you to answer the classic "so what" question:

> "So what does this document mean to me?"

As explained in the next section, the beginning part presents an overview of important information, not details. Then, specifics of major interest, such as detailed lists of conclusions and recommendations, come at the end.

Structure Rule 3: Repeat Key Points

Most people will read your document selectively, not sequentially from beginning to end. Thus, important information should be repeated, especially in longer documents.

For example, a formal report may mention a key recommendation in the cover letter, in the executive summary, and in the conclusions and

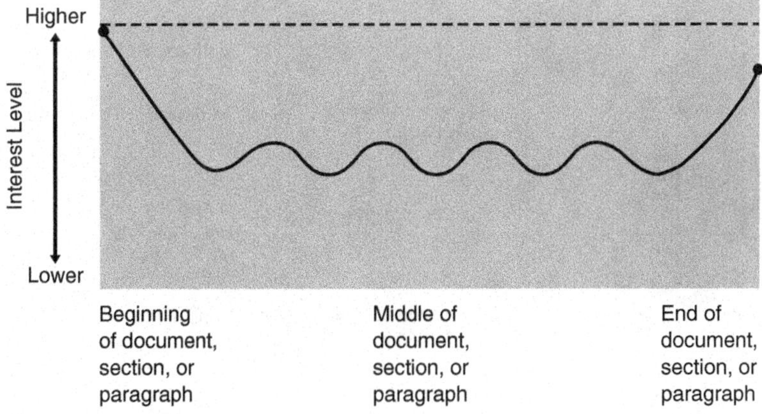

FIGURE 2–1
Reader interest curve

Source: Technical Communication: A Practical Approach, 6th ed. (p. 81) by W. S. Pfeiffer, 2006, Upper Saddle River, NJ: Prentice Hall. Reprinted by permission.

recommendations section. Or a purpose statement for the report may show up, perhaps with different wording, in the cover letter, executive summary, and introduction. Needless repetition is not being advocated here. But strategic repetition makes sense if you are delivering key information to different sets of readers.

The main principle of technical writing—write for your reader, not for yourself—and the three guidelines just covered lead directly to a pattern of organization you can use in all career writing.

ABC FORMAT

In the *Poetics,* Aristotle claimed that a literary work, to be considered "whole," must have a beginning, middle, and end. And so it is true more than 2,300 years later with technical writing. Here, the simple three-part structure of technical writing is labeled the ABC Format (for abstract, body, and conclusion).

Figure 2–2 gives a visual representation of the ABC Format; it also shows how the sections of the report in Figure 2–3 "map" on to this ABC Format.

The diamond pattern is used because it implies the following important points about the abstract, body, and conclusion sections:

- **Abstract**—provides introductory and summary information. It is represented by the narrow top of the diamond because it is brief and leads into the body.

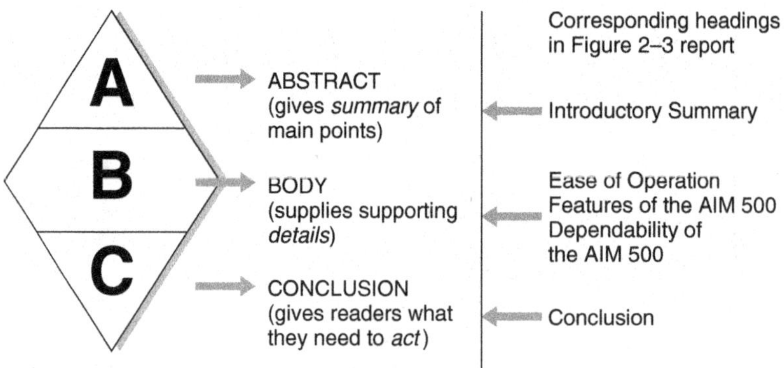

FIGURE 2–2
ABC Format for all documents
Adapted from *Technical Communication: A Practical Approach,* 6th ed. (p. 84) by W. S. Pfeiffer, 2006, Upper Saddle River, NJ: Prentice Hall. Reprinted by permission.

MEMORANDUM

DATE: September 5, 2006
TO: Danielle Firestein
FROM: Barbara Ralston *BR*
SUBJECT: Recommendation for AIM 500 Fax

INTRODUCTORY SUMMARY

The purpose of this report is to present the results of the study you requested on the AIM 500 facsimile (fax) machine. I recommend purchase of additional AIM 500 machines, when needed, because they deliver fast, dependable service and include features we need most. This report includes the following sections: Ease of Operation, Features of the AIM 500, Dependability of the AIM 500, and Conclusion.

EASE OF OPERATION

The AIM 500 is so easy to operate that a novice can learn to transmit a document to another location in about two minutes. Here's the basic procedure:

1. Press the button marked TEL on the face of the fax machine. You then hear a dial tone.
2. Press the telephone number of the person receiving the fax on the number pad on the face of the machine.
3. Lay the document facedown on the tray at the back of the machine.

At this point, just wait for the document to be transmitted—about 18 seconds per page to transmit. The fax machine will even signal the user with a beep and a message on its LCD display when the document has been transmitted. Other more advanced operations are equally simple to use and require little training. Provided with the machine are two different charts that illustrate the machine's main functions.

The size of the AIM 500 makes it easy to set up almost anywhere in an office. The dimensions are 13 inches in width, 15 inches in length, and 9.5 inches in height. The narrow width, in particular, allows the machine to fit on most desks, file cabinets, or shelves.

FEATURES OF THE AIM 500

The AIM 500 has many features that will be beneficial to our employees. In the two years of use in our department, the following features were found to be most helpful:

Automatic redial
Last number redial memory
LCD display

FIGURE 2–3 (pp. 27–28)
Short report in ABC Format

Ralston to Firestein, 2

Preset dialing
Group dialing
Use as a phone

Automatic Redial. Often when sending a fax, the sender finds the receiving line busy. The redial feature will automatically redial the busy number at 30-second intervals until the busy line is reached, saving the sender considerable time.

Last Number Redial Memory. Occasionally there may be interference on the telephone line or some other technical problem with the transmissions. The last number memory feature allows the user to press one button to automatically trigger the machine to retry the number.

LCD Display. This display feature clearly shows pertinent information, such as error messages that tell a user exactly why a transmission was not completed.

Preset Dialing. The AIM 500 can store 16 preset numbers that can be engaged with one-touch dialing. This feature makes the unit as fast and efficient as a sophisticated telephone.

Group Dialing. Upon selecting two or more of the preset telephone numbers, the user can transmit a document to all of the preset numbers at once.

Use as a Phone. The AIM 500 can also be used as a telephone, providing the user with more flexibility and convenience.

DEPENDABILITY OF THE AIM 500

Over the entire two years our department has used this machine, there have been no complaints. We always receive clear copies from the machine, and we never hear complaints about the documents we send out. This record is all the more impressive in light of the fact that we average 32 outgoing and 15 incoming transmissions a day. Obviously, we depend heavily on this machine.

So far, the only required maintenance has been to change the paper and dust the cover.

CONCLUSION

The success our department has enjoyed with the AIM 500 compels me to recommend it highly for additional future purchases. The ease of operation, many exceptional features, and record of dependability are all good reasons to buy additional units. If you have further questions about the AIM 500, please contact me at extension 3646.

FIGURE 2–3 (*continued*)

- **Body**—supplies all supporting details for the document. It is represented by the broad expansive section of the diamond because it is the longest part of a document.
- **Conclusion**—gives readers what they need to act. It is represented by the narrow bottom section of the diamond because it is brief and leads away from the body section.

In this model, note that the terms *abstract, body,* and *conclusion* refer to *generalized* parts of a document, *not* to specific headings. The exact headings used to represent these sections in documents will vary, depending on the document you're writing and the organization where you work (see Figure 2–3). Think of the ABC Format as a *general* organizational pattern. Within it you can fit the diverse sections of any document. Guidelines for writing each of the sections follow. Remember that Chapter 3 presents ABC Formats and models for many common documents.

ABC Rule 1: The Abstract Gives the "Big Picture"

The abstract component gives readers, especially decision-makers, both introductory and summary information. Specifically, it answers four questions:

1. **Purpose:** Why are you writing?
2. **Scope:** What work did you do?
3. **Results:** What main point do decision-makers want to know?
4. **Contents:** What main sections follow?

If you answer these four questions at the outset, you have given readers a capsule version of the entire document. Put another way, you have attracted the attention of the readers, appealed to their logic and/or emotions, and given them a reason to keep reading.

In a short report or letter, the abstract might be embodied in the first few sentences. It may have a heading like "introduction" or "introductory summary" (see Figure 2–3) or it may have no heading at all. In a long report, the abstract may encompass several sections, such as the letter of transmittal, executive summary, and introduction. Thus, the term *abstract,* as used in this book, is a construct to help you write. It can, and often does, include several document sections that, when viewed together, make up an overview.

The two paragraphs that follow satisfy the criteria for an abstract. They are from a short in-house report.

> This report describes the results of a study that compared two laser printers being considered for bulk purchase: the CopyX 3000 and Printeze 101. We studied the marketing brochures, talked to users at several firms, and tried several models loaned to us by the manufacturers.
>
> On the basis of our study, we recommend the Printeze 101. The following sections support our recommendation with information about reliability, economy of operation, and print quality. The appendix includes technical data and testimonials from three users.

ABC Rule 2: The Body Gives Supporting Details

The document body relates details of your work. It is especially useful to technical readers who want to see support for your conclusions or recommendations. As such, it answers these kinds of questions:

- **Background:** What led up to the project?
- **Methods:** How did you gather information?
- **Data:** What information resulted from the field, lab, or office work conducted during the study?

In some documents, the body can also include detailed conclusions and recommendations—especially if such conclusions and recommendations are the main thrust of the document. In other documents, conclusions and recommendations are a brief capstone for the document and thus are reserved for a final short section. In any case, follow four general guidelines for the document body.

Use Lead-Ins at the Beginning of Sections

Lead-ins give readers a road map for what follows. They can be as simple as a list of the subsections that follow in a section. Readers need such direction finders in the same way they need an overview at the beginning of the whole document.

Include Listings

Almost any series of three or more points should make you consider using a listing. (See the Lists entries in the Appendix.) Bulleted or numbered lists are easier to read than long paragraphs of text, as long as you keep lists from becoming too long. One rule of thumb is to include no more than nine items.

Use Graphics

Graphics draw attention to important points. They are especially useful in presenting data to technical readers, most of whom expect effective graphics.

Separate Facts from Opinions

Be clear about where opinions begin and end. Body sections usually move from facts to opinions, just like technical projects themselves. To make distinctions clear, preface your opinions with phrases like "We believe that" or "I think that."

In summary, the body sections of each document should present supporting information with clarity, structure, and interest.

ABC Rule 3: The Conclusion Provides a Wrap-Up

The conclusion component varies considerably from document to document. Generally, it answers questions like the following:

- **Results:** What are your conclusions and recommendations?
- **Action:** What happens next?
- **Emphasis:** What single point would you like to leave with readers?
- **Personal Note:** What can you add that will enhance your relationship with readers?

Because readers focus on beginnings and endings, you must exploit the opportunity provided by the conclusion part of the ABC Format.

As with abstract and body, the term *conclusion* is an umbrella term for various heading labels used at the end of documents. Possible headings are Conclusions, Recommendations, Conclusions and Recommendations, Closing, and Closing Remarks. Extremely short documents, like letters or memos, may end with a closing paragraph that has no heading. In any case, the conclusion component of the ABC Format provides the document with closure, that is, the sense of an ending.

PAGE DESIGN

The previous section covered organization, or the arrangement of information within a document. This section deals with the other element of structure—that is, the "look" of the document, or page design.

> **Page Design:** Page design is the collection of formatting techniques used to draw attention to your writing and engage the interest of readers. Examples include use of white space, headings, lists, and varied typefaces.

Here's one way to view page design: The ABC Format forms the *deep* structure of your document, whereas page design forms the *surface* structure. Deep structure takes precedence and provides the raw material for designing pages. Yet, page design can greatly influence readers. If you can capture their attention with well-designed pages, you will be more likely to engage their long-term interest in the document. This section covers four basic rules of page design.

Design Rule 1: Use White Space Liberally

White space refers to spaces devoid of text or graphics. Empty space on the page acts like a magnet to draw the reader's eye to text. It can also relieve visual monotony of printed words. Here are some suggestions for using white space effectively; Figure 2–4 shows these suggestions put to use.

Frame Text with 1″ to 1 1/2″ Margins
You may want to use an even greater margin at the bottom of the page. If your document is bound, remember to add extra margin space on the left.

Experiment with Double Columns
Long lines of text can tire the eyes, so you may want to try double columns in some documents. The extra space between the columns can help readers move down the page. However, the double-column look can also present problems: (1) It may look too stilted for informal documents like short letter reports, (2) its "newspaper" appearance may encourage a cursory reading, and (3) the placement of graphics becomes challenging.

Skip Lines between Paragraphs in Single-Spaced Text
The extra line space provides visual relief in a sea of text. You should continue to indent paragraphs, however. Most readers prefer the visual break that paragraph indenting adds.

Use Ragged Right Margins in Short Documents
The uneven edge adds visual variety needed to keep the reader's attention. Reserve a right-justified margin for some formal documents where a book-like appearance is expected.

Use Slightly More Space above Headings than below Them
The additional space helps to separate a heading and related text from the text that came before it.

Design Rule 2: Use Headings and Subheadings Often

Headings are labels used to introduce new sections and subsections. Besides helping readers stay on track, they provide visual relief from the monotony of text and assist in finding specific information later. Following are some suggestions for producing an effective heading structure.

Use Your Outline to Create Headings and Subheadings
A well-organized outline provides the headings and subheadings for the text. Use the following general rules for headings:

- Avoid single subheadings for a heading (because anything divided must have at least two parts).

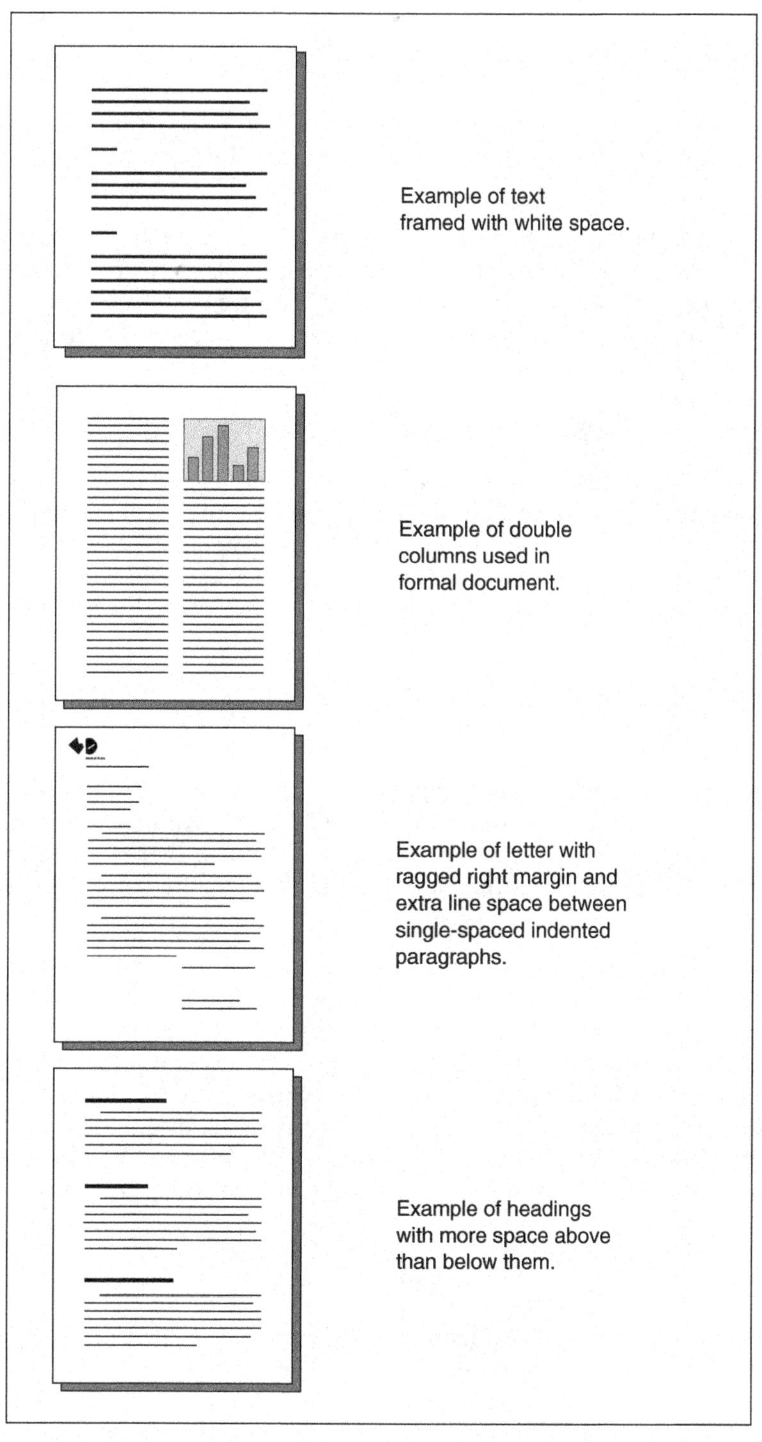

Example of text
framed with white space.
Example of double
columns used in
formal document.
Example of letter with
ragged right margin and
extra line space between
single-spaced indented
paragraphs.
Example of headings
with more space above
than below them.

FIGURE 2–4
Use of white space
Adapted from *Technical Writing: A Practical Approach*, 4th ed. (pp. 104–105) by W. S. Pfeiffer, 2000, Upper Saddle River, NJ: Prentice Hall. Reprinted by permission.

- Maintain parallel grammatical form in headings of equal importance.
- Try to have at least one heading on each page of text.

Use Substantive Wording

Readers prefer headings that reflect content. Use concrete language rather than abstract nouns, even if the heading ends up being longer. Thus, "Surveying the Graduates" would be preferable to "Methodology," and "Background on the Bentley Dam Failure" would be preferable to "Background."

Establish a Clear Visual Ranking of Headings

Readers should be able to identify heading levels quite easily as they scan a document. That is, each level should be distinctive. Figure 2–5 shows a few alternative systems for headings. There are no hard-and-fast rules for heading format. In general, keep the structure simple and neat—with a hierarchy that is clear to readers.

Design Rule 3: Use Lists Frequently

As a design element, lists distinguish technical writing from other types of documents such as magazine essays and fiction. Almost by definition, tech writing invites you to cluster information in lists of bulleted and numbered items. Follow the suggestions below for the most effective use of lists.

Keep Lists Short

Experts say that the maximum length of a list should reflect the number of items people retain in their short-term memory: no more than nine items. (Three is the usual minimum for a list.) If you have more than nine items, create a grouped list with several major categories—almost in the form of an outline. This format gives readers a way to grasp information. For example, the many suggestions for page design in this section are grouped under four main rules.

Use Bullets and Numbers

Bullets (usually enlarged dots or squares) work best in short lists where there is no sequence. Numbers are useful when items reflect a sequence (steps in a process) or ranking (priorities for a selection). Avoid using numbers simply because a list is long, for readers will infer sequence even if you don't intend it.

1. Four levels, formal report	**LEVEL-1 HEADING** **LEVEL-2 HEADING** **Level-3 Heading** **Level-4 Heading.**
2. Three levels, formal report: Option A	**Level-1 Heading** **Level-2 Heading** **Level-3 Heading.**
3. Three levels, formal report: Option B	**LEVEL-1 HEADING** **LEVEL-2 HEADING** **Level-3 Heading**

FIGURE 2–5 (pp. 35–36)
Some heading options

Adapted from *Technical Writing: A Practical Approach,* 4th ed. (pp. 109–111) by W. S. Pfeiffer, 2000, Upper Saddle River, NJ: Prentice Hall. Reprinted by permission.

4. Three levels, informal (letter or memo) report	**Level-1 Heading** **Level-2 Heading** **Level-3 Heading.**
5. Two levels, informal (letter or memo) report: Option A	**LEVEL-1 HEADING** **Level-2 Heading**
6. Two levels, informal (letter or memo) report: Option B	**Level-1 Heading** **Level-2 Heading.**
7. One level, informal (letter or memo) report: Option A	**LEVEL-1 HEADING**
8. One level, informal (letter or memo) report: Option B	**Level-1 Heading**

FIGURE 2–5 (*continued*)

Punctuate, Space, and Capitalize Lists Properly
An entry in the Appendix (Lists: Punctuation) presents several punctuation options for listings. The most common approach is (1) to avoid punctuation between items in a list made up of sentence fragments and (2) to capitalize the first word of each item in a list.

Use Proper Lead-Ins and Parallel Structure
Like headings, lists are preceded by lead-ins that should be complete grammatical units followed by colons. For example, "We have planned to" should be replaced by "We have planned the following activities:" Also, items in the same list should have parallel grammatical form. (For more information, see Lists: General Pointers, an entry in the Appendix. Also, see Figure 2–3 for an illustration of how lists are introduced.)

Design Rule 4: Use Fonts Effectively

Another design option you have is font size and type. Font size is measured in "points" (72 points to an inch). Your computer's font-selection menu may list sizes such as 9, 10, 12, 18, and so on. As for font types, they are classified into two main groups: serif, a typeface with "tails" at the ends of letters; and "sans serif," which has no tails. Figure 2–6 shows three different font types in different point sizes. New Century Schoolbook and Times Roman are serif; Helvetica is sans serif.

If you are choosing the font yourself, consider criteria such as the purpose of the document, the image you want to convey, and any information you have about reader preferences. The following are additional guidelines:

1. **Use serif fonts for regular text in your documents.** The tails on letters make letters and entire words more visually interesting to the reader's eye. In this sense, they serve the same purpose as ragged-edge copy—that is, they help your reader move smoothly through the document.
2. **Consider using another typeface—sans serif—for headings.** Headings benefit from a clean look that emphasizes the white space around letters. Sans serif type helps attract attention to these elements of organization within your text.
3. **Avoid too many font variations in the same document.** There is a fine line between interesting font variations and busy and distracting text. But there *is* a line. Your general rule might be to use no more than two fonts per document—one for text and another for headings and subheadings.

New Century Schoolbook (serif font)
9 point
10 point
12 point
14 point
18 point
24 point

Times Roman (serif font)
9 point
10 point
12 point
14 point
18 point
24 point

Helvetica (sans serif font)
9 point
10 point
12 point
14 point
18 point
24 point

FIGURE 2–6
Examples of font size and types
Adapted from: *Technical Communication: A Practical Approach*, 5th ed. (p. 119) by W. S. Pfeiffer, 2003, Upper Saddle River, NJ: Prentice Hall. Reprinted by permission.

This chapter has presented only the "big picture" about structure, format, and page design. As you apply the basic rules included here, refer to the document models in Chapter 3 to assist you in specific on-the-job tasks.

3 ABC Formats and Examples

Chapter 2 covered the ABC Format (abstract, body, conclusion) in general. This chapter gets down to specifics by applying the ABC Format to 17 on-the-job documents. You can use this chapter as a desk reference while outlining and writing your drafts. Remember, however, that the formats and examples in this chapter are only recommendations, *not* prescriptions. You may need to adjust formats and even overall organizational structures to meet the needs of your readers and your specific purpose.

Each of the 17 sections contains two parts: (1) an ABC outline for the document, along with some "Helpful Hints," and (2) a document example that follows the outline. Documents are provided for the following ABC models:

1. Email
2. Memorandum
3. Positive letter
4. Negative letter
5. Neutral letter
6. Sales letter
7. Job letters and résumés
8. Instructions
9. Problem analysis
10. Recommendation report
11. Equipment evaluation
12. Lab report
13. Trip report
14. Proposal
15. Feasibility study
16. Progress report
17. Formal report

ABC Format 1: Email

Abstract

- Casual, friendly greeting if justified by relationship
- Short, clear statement of purpose for writing
- List of the main topics to be covered

Body

- Supporting information for points mentioned in abstract
- Use of short paragraphs that start with the main ideas
- Use of headings and lists
- Use of abbreviations and jargon only when understood by all readers

Conclusion

- Summary of the main points
- Clarity about action that comes next

Helpful Hints

Email rivals all forms of technical communication in the time it consumes during the average working day. While it's hard to imagine operating without email, it should not replace other forms of communication—like letters and phone calls—that still work best in many situations. The following are some hints about when and how to use email properly, in your role as both a sender and receiver of email:

1. **READERS:** The speed and ease of mail makes it far too easy to copy people who may not need to see the message. HINT: Think carefully about who should be your main audience and who should receive copies. Don't copy people unless they truly need to know what you're conveying. Also, avoid keeping people in an email exchange who no longer need to partake of the conversation. In particular, don't hit "reply all" instead of "reply" unless you're certain everyone on the list needs to see your response.
2. **PRIVACY:** Unlike conventional correspondence, email can easily go to unintended readers anywhere and anytime. HINT: Do not send any email that would embarrass you if it were to be read by someone for whom it was not intended, and do not forward another person's email unless you know the writer would agree to such use. Also, avoid using the automatic "reader receipt" message—some readers believe it violates their privacy to record their opening of email, or they consider it a nuisance, or both.
3. **TONE:** Although the immediacy of email is convenient, it can be your undoing if you tend to send messages prematurely. HINT: When an email must relate opinions that could be misunderstood or even offensive, wait at least a day to respond so that you've had time to make sure your tone is constructive and appropriate. Also, remember that complex or emotional messages might best be conveyed in a phone call or meeting, if they are to be conveyed at all. Email is no substitute for conversation.
4. **FORMAT:** Email is not as easy to read as hard copy because it does not allow you to use a full range of graphic techniques. HINT: Exploit the few attention-keeping tactics email does permit. Besides those mentioned in the ABC Format above (lists, headings, and short paragraphs), use white space liberally (such as including line spaces between paragraphs) and

avoid full capitalization of text (except for emphasis of an occasional word). Also, choose engaging subject lines that invite readers to open rather than delete the message and that help them scan and use email files later.

5. **OWNERSHIP:** You don't "own" email written at work. Indeed, it might be read by an employer, and it might be requested and used in legal proceedings long after you have written it. HINT: Find out your employer's guidelines for electronic communication the first day on the job, and make sure to follow them. Also, write every email as if it might some day be used in a company inquiry or in a court of law.
6. **EDITING/PROOFING:** Although email can include a level of informality not permitted in more formal documents, most readers still expect well-edited text. The email should be professional and should represent you well. HINT: Use spell-checking and editing software to correct errors, and keep passages concise and clear. Also, double-check to make sure you have the correct person in the "TO" line before you push "send."
7. **CULTURES:** Your email may be viewed by readers from diverse cultures, both inside and outside your country. HINT: Be sensitive to cultural differences among potential readers. Some obvious pointers are to choose wording that is unambiguous, define technical terms that might not be universally understood, leave out humor because it's often culture-bound or tied to a context hard to convey through email, and avoid slang terms and idioms. Also, do not use emoticons (such as a "smiley face"), both because they are unprofessional unless you know the reader quite well and because they don't "translate" well to readers from diverse cultures.

TO: Lab, Marketing, and Administrative Staff in U.S. Offices
FROM: Janice Simmons, Benefits Manager
SUBJECT: Training Funds for Fiscal Year 2006
DATE: January 2, 2006

Happy New Year to all of you! I hope you had a good break. I'm writing to announce some guidelines for approved training for the next twelve months—including an increased reimbursement. Please read on to see how these changes affect all lab, marketing, and administrative staff.

1. **Lab Staff**
   Maximum Reimbursement: $3,000 (up from $2,000)
   Approval Process: Discuss with your manager 21 days before trip
   Trip Purpose: To improve lab procedures

2. **Marketing Staff**
   Maximum Reimbursement: $4,000 (up from $3,500)
   Approval Process: Discuss with your manager 21 days before trip
   Trip Purpose: To learn new sales techniques

3. **Administrative Staff**
   Maximum Reimbursement: $4,500 (up from $4,000)
   Approval Process: Discuss with your manager 21 days before trip
   Trip Purpose: To improve productivity of office procedures

I encourage all of you to seek training opportunities that fit the guidelines listed above. **Please note the required 21-day lead time in the approval process!**

Just send me an email if you have any questions about the procedure.

Janice

EXAMPLE 1

Email message

Adapted from *Technical Communication: A Practical Approach,* 6th ed. (p. 253) by W. S. Pfeiffer, 2006, Upper Saddle River, NJ: Prentice Hall. Reprinted by permission.

ABC Format 2: Memorandum

Abstract

- Clear statement of memo's purpose
- Outline of the main parts of memo

Body

- Absolute clarity about what memo has to do with reader
- Tactful presentation of any negative news
- Supporting points, with strong points at the beginning or end
- Frequent use of short paragraphs or lists
- Reference to attachments, when much detail is required

Conclusion

- Clear statement of what step should occur next
- An effort to retain goodwill and cooperation of readers

Helpful Hints

We spend more time reading and writing memos (including email) than we want to admit. The main rule is to be clear, brief, and tactful. Because many activities are competing for your readers' time, memos should be written so that they can be understood immediately. Use headings and lists. Also, put the main point at the beginning, with a brief buffer if you are delivering bad news.

MEMORANDUM

DATE: August 1, 2006
TO: Technical Staff
FROM: Gini Preston, Chair, Word-Processing Committee GP
SUBJECT: Word-Processing Suggestions

The Word-Processing Committee has met for six weeks to consider changes in Totally Teak's Word-Processing Center. This memo highlights the recommendations that have been approved by management.

1. **Document status:** Documents will be designated either "rush" or "regular" status, depending on what you request. If at all possible, rush documents will be returned within four hours. Regular documents will be returned within one working day.

2. **Draft stages:** Both users and operators should make every effort to produce no more than three hard-copy drafts of any document. Typically, these would include the following:

   - **First typed draft** (typed from writer's handwritten or cut-and-paste copy)
   - **Second typed draft** (produced after user makes editing corrections on first-draft copy)
   - **Final typed draft** (produced after user makes final editing changes, after proofreader makes a pass through the document, and after operator incorporates final changes into the copy)

3. **New proofreader:** A company proofreader has been hired to improve the quality of our documents. This individual will have an office in the Word-Processing Center and will review all documents produced by the word-processing operators.

These changes will take effect August 15. Your efforts to implement them will help improve the efficiency of the center, the quality of your documents, and the productivity of the company.

Feel free to call me at ext. 567 if you have any questions.

Copy: Rob Ahab

EXAMPLE 2
Memorandum
Adapted from *Technical Writing: A Practical Approach,* 5th ed. (p. 255) by W. S. Pfeiffer, 2003, Upper Saddle River, NJ: Prentice Hall. Reprinted by permission.

ABC Format 3: Positive Letter

Abstract

- Bridge between this letter and the last communication with reader
- Clear statement of good news you have to report

Body

- Supporting data for the main point mentioned in abstract
- Clarification of any questions reader may have
- Qualification, if any, of the good news

Conclusion

- Statement of eagerness to continue relationship, complete project, etc.
- Clear statement of what step should come next

Helpful Hints

In the "bridge" (see Abstract), refer to your last contact with the reader or to the situation that prompted the letter (for example, "Thank you for your letter asking for a sample of our new Glide-Way bearings"). The good news comes immediately after the bridge—and sometimes even before it (for example, "Yes, we'll be glad to send you a free sample immediately"). In other words, good news always comes early in the letter. Any delay can cause confusion about the letter's purpose and can make the reader think, wrongly, that bad news is ahead.

Note: See Figures 1, 2, and 3 in the Appendix: Writing Handbook (pp. 197–199) for a description of three common letter formats.

12 Post Street
Houston, Texas 77000
(713) 555-9781

July 23, 2006

The Reverend John C. Davidson
Maxwell Street Church
Canyon Valley, TX 79195

Dear Reverend Davidson:

We have received your letter asking to reschedule the church project from mid-August to another, more convenient time. Yes, we'll be able to do the project on one of two possible dates in September, as explained below.

As you know, Carruthers originally planned to fit your foundation investigation between two other projects planned for the Canyon Valley area. In making every effort to lessen church costs, we would be saving money by having a crew already on site in your area—rather than having to charge you mobilization costs to and from Canyon Valley.

As it happens, we have just agreed to perform another large project in the Canyon Valley area beginning on September 18. We would be glad to schedule your project either before or after that job. Specifically, we could be at the church site for our one-day field investigation on either September 17 or September 25, whatever date you prefer.

Please call me by September 2 to let me know your scheduling preference for the project. In the meantime, have a productive and enjoyable conference at the church next month.

Sincerely,

Nancy Slade

Nancy Slade, P.E.
Project Manager

NS/mh

EXAMPLE 3
Positive letter
Adapted from *Technical Writing: A Practical Approach,* 5th ed. (p. 250) by W. S. Pfeiffer, 2003, Upper Saddle River, NJ: Prentice Hall. Reprinted by permission.

ABC Format 4: Negative Letter

Abstract

- Bridge between your letter and previous communication
- General statement of purpose or appreciation—in an effort to find a common bond or an area of agreement

Body

- Strong emphasis on what can be done, when possible
- Buffered (yet clear) statement of what cannot be done, with reasons
- Facts that support your views

Conclusion

- Closing remarks that express interest in continued association
- Statement of what will happen next

Helpful Hints

In negative letters, buffer the bad news but still be clear. Use the abstract to convey information that will help preserve goodwill and your relationship with the reader. Then use the body of the letter to state what can, and what cannot, be done. This approach assumes you want to retain your relationship with the reader and avoid "burning bridges." In the few cases where the relationship with the reader is gone—such as a request for payment that has been repeatedly ignored—a more direct approach may be necessary.

Note: See Figures 1, 2, and 3 in the Appendix: Writing Handbook (pp. 197–199) for a description of three common letter formats.

12 Post Street
Houston, Texas 77000
(713) 555-9781

July 23, 2006

The Reverend John C. Davidson
Maxwell Street Church
Canyon Valley, TX 79195

Dear Reverend Davidson:

We have received your letter asking to reschedule the foundation project at your church from mid-August to late August, because of the regional conference.

One reason for our original schedule, as you may recall, was to save the travel costs for a project crew going back and forth between Houston and Canyon Valley. Because Carruthers has several other jobs in the area, we had planned not to charge you for travel.

We can reschedule the project, as you request, to a more convenient date in late August, but the change will increase project costs from $1,500 to $1,800 to cover travel. At this point, we don't have any other projects scheduled in your area in late August that would defray the additional expenses. Given our low profit margin on such jobs, that additional $300 would make the difference between our firm making or losing money on the foundation investigation at your church.

I'll call you next week to select a new date that would be most suitable. We look forward to our association with the Maxwell Street Church and to a successful project in late August.

Sincerely,

Nancy Slade

Nancy Slade, P.E.
Project Manager

NS/mh

EXAMPLE 4

Negative letter

Adapted from *Technical Writing: A Practical Approach*, 5th ed. (p. 251) by W. S. Pfeiffer, 2003, Upper Saddle River, NJ: Prentice Hall. Reprinted by permission.

ABC Format 5: Neutral Letter

Abstract

- Bridge or transition between letter and previous communication
- Exact purpose of letter (request, invitation, etc.)

Body

- Details that support purpose statement, for example,
  —Description of item(s) requested
  —Requirements related to the invitation
  —Description of item(s) sent

Conclusion

- Statement of appreciation
- Description of actions that should occur next

Helpful Hints

Neutral letters must be absolutely clear about your inquiry or response. As with positive letters, make your point early so that there is no confusion about the message. Your first paragraph can include a bridge or transition sentence (for example, "Yesterday I called your warehouse to find out what calculators you have in stock"). It can be followed by a direct reference to the request (for example, "Using information provided by your staff, I want to order the nine calculators listed below").

Note: See Figures 1, 2, and 3 in the Appendix: Writing Handbook (pp. 197–199) for a description of three common letter formats.

January 4, 2006

Mr. Timothy Fu, Personnel Director
The Franklin Group
127 Rainbow Lane
St. Louis, MO 63103

Dear Mr. Fu:

The Franklin Group has hired 35 graduates of River College since 1975. To help continue that tradition, we would like to invite you to the college's first Career Fair, to be held February 21, 2006, from 8 a.m. until noon.

Sponsored by the Student Government Association, the Career Fair gives juniors and seniors the opportunity to get to know more about a number of potential employers. We give special attention to organizations, like The Franklin Group, that have already had success in hiring River College graduates. Indeed, we have already had a number of inquiries about whether your firm will be represented at the fair.

Participating in the Career Fair is simple. We will provide you with a booth where one or two Franklin representatives can talk with students who come by to ask about your firm's career opportunities. Feel free to bring along whatever brochures or other written information that would help our students learn more about Franklin's products and services.

I will call you next week, Mr. Fu, to give more details about the fair and to offer a specific booth location. We at River College look forward to building on our already strong association with The Franklin Group.

Sincerely,

Faron G. Abdullah

Faron G. Abdullah, President
Student Government Association

56 New Lane
Bolt, Missouri
65101
(314) 555-0272

EXAMPLE 5

Neutral letter

Adapted from *Technical Communication: A Practical Approach,* 6th ed. (p. 248) by W. S. Pfeiffer, 2006, Upper Saddle River, NJ: Prentice Hall. Reprinted by permission.

ABC Format 6: Sales Letter

Abstract

- Choose one or two of the following strategies for capturing attention:
  —Cite a surprising fact
  —Announce a new product or service
  —Ask a question
  —Show understanding of client's problem
  —Show potential for solving client's problem
  —Summarize results of a meeting
  —Answer a question reader previously asked

Body

- Choose one or two of the following strategies for convincing the reader:
  —Stress one main problem reader has concern about
  —Stress one main selling point of your solution
  —Emphasize what is unique about your solution
  —Focus on value and quality, rather than price
  —Put details in enclosures
  —Briefly explain the value of any enclosures

Conclusion

- Keep control of the next step by doing the following:
  —Leave the reader with one crucial point to remember
  —Offer to call (first choice) or ask reader to call you (second choice)

Helpful Hints

The key words above are *capture*, *convince*, and *control*—the "3Cs." Capture the readers' attention at the beginning, convince them in the middle, and control the next step at the end. Sales letters work together with personal contacts to build continuing relationships with customers.

Note: See Figures 1, 2, and 3 in the Appendix: Writing Handbook (pp. 197–199) for a description of three common letter formats.

August 21, 2006

Mr. James Swartz, Safety Director
Jessup County School System
1111 Clay Street
Smiley, MO 64607

NEW ASBESTOS-ABATEMENT SERVICE NOW AVAILABLE

We enjoyed working with you last year, James, to update your entire fire alarm system. Given the current concern in the country about another safety issue, asbestos, we wanted you to know that our staff now does abatement work.

As you know, many of the state's school buildings were constructed during years when asbestos was used as a primary insulator. No one knew then, of course, that the material can cause illness and even premature death for those who work in buildings where asbestos was used in construction. Now we know that just a small portion of asbestos produces a major health hazard.

Fortunately, there's a way to tell whether you have a problem: the asbestos survey. This procedure, done by our certified asbestos-abatement professionals, results in a report that tells whether your buildings are affected. If we find asbestos, we can remove it for you.

Jessup showed foresight in modernizing its alarm system last year, James. Your desire for a thorough job on that project was matched, as you know, by the approach we take to our business. Now we'd like to give you the peace of mind that will come from knowing that either (1) there is no asbestos problem in your 35 structures or (2) you have removed the material.

The enclosed brochure outlines our asbestos services. I'll call you in a few days to see how Mastman can help you.

Barbara Feinstein

Barbara H. Feinstein
Certified Industrial Hygienist

EXAMPLE 6

Sales letter

Adapted from *Technical Communication: A Practical Approach,* 6th ed. (p. 250) by W. S. Pfeiffer, 2006, Upper Saddle River, NJ: Prentice Hall. Reprinted by permission.

ABC Format 7: Job Letter and Résumé

Abstract

- Apply for a specific job
- Refer to ad, mutual friend, or other source of information about the job
- (Optional) Briefly state how you can meet the main need of your potential employer

Body

- Specify your understanding of the reader's main needs
- Provide the main qualifications that satisfy these needs (but only highlight points from your résumé—do *not* simply repeat all résumé information)
- Avoid mentioning weak points or deficiencies
- Keep body paragraphs to six or fewer lines
- Use a bulleted or numbered list if it helps draw attention to three or four main points
- Maintain the "you" attitude throughout

Conclusion

- Tie the letter together with one main theme or selling point, as you would a sales letter
- Refer to your résumé
- Explain how and when the reader can contact you for an interview

Helpful Hints

In the examples of job letters and résumés that follow, note that three résumés are in what is called chronological format and two are in functional format. Also included are two résumés that combine the two formats. All résumés reflect a clear presentation of basic information about education, work experience, skills, and interests. However, they differ in what they emphasize, as explained below:

- James Sistrunk's résumé is chronological. Because he has relevant full-time job experience, he gives it priority, with his most recent work listed first.
- Denise Sanborn's résumé is functional. Because she has limited work experience, she wants to focus instead on the functional skills acquired in her part-time and summer jobs.
- Donald Vizano's résumé is chronological and gives special emphasis to his major and related coursework in college.
- Todd Fisher's résumé is functional, with considerable attention given to three sets of skills that may be valuable to a potential employer.
- Susan Martin's résumé is in a combined functional and chronological format, yet most focus is placed on skills attained.
- Leslie Highland's résumé is chronological, emphasizing a history of relevant experience with no time gaps.
- Karen Patel's combined format résumé lists two main skill sets as her main categories, under which particular full- and part-time jobs and their time periods are included.

Use the résumé format that best matches your background. Above all, keep your résumé looking clean. Remember that its purpose is only to get you to the next stage of the job process: the interview.

Note: See Figures 1, 2, and 3 in the Appendix: Writing Handbook (pp. 197–199) for a description of three common letter formats.

1523 River Lane
Worthville, OH 43804
August 6, 2006

Mr. Willard Yancy
Director, Automotive Systems
XYZ Motor Company, Product Development Division
Charlotte, NC 28202

Dear Mr. Yancy:

Recently I have been researching the leading national companies in automotive computer systems. Your job ad in the July 6 *National Business Employment Weekly* caught my eye because of XYZ's innovations in computer-controlled safety systems. I would like to apply for the automotive computer engineer job.

Your advertisement notes that experience in computer systems for machinery or robotic systems would be a plus. I have had extensive experience in the military with computer systems, ranging from a digital communications computer to an air traffic control training simulator. In addition, my college experience includes courses in computer engineering that have broadened my experience. I am eager to apply what I have learned to your company.

My mechanical knowledge was gained from growing up on my family's dairy farm. After watching and learning from my father, I learned to repair internal combustion engines, diesel engines, and hydraulic systems. Then for five years I managed the entire dairy operation.

With my training and hands-on experience, I believe I can contribute to your company. Please contact me at (614) 882-2731 if you wish to arrange an interview.

Sincerely,

James M. Sistrunk

James M. Sistrunk

Enclosure: Resume

EXAMPLE 7a, part 1

Job letter and résumé (letter in block style)

Examples 7a through 7g adapted from *Technical Communication: A Practical Approach,* 6th ed. (pp. 595–605) by W. S. Pfeiffer, 2006, Upper Saddle River, NJ: Prentice Hall. Reprinted by permission.

James M. Sistrunk
1523 River Lane
Worthville, OH 43804
(614) 882-2731

Professional Objective:

To contribute to the research, design, and development of automotive computer control systems

Education:

B.S., Computer Engineering, 1999–present

Columbus College, Columbus, Ohio
Major concentration in Control Systems with minor in Industrial Engineering. Courses included Microcomputer Systems, Digital Control Systems, and several different programming courses.

Computer Repair Technician Certification Training, 1999–2000
U.S. Air Force Technical Training Center, Keesler Air Force Base, Biloxi, Mississippi
General Computer Systems Option with emphasis on mainframe computers. Student leader in charge of processing and orientation for new students from basic training.

Career Development:

Computer Repair Technician, U.S. Air Force, 1999–2002
Secret Clearance

Responsibilities and duties included:

- Repair of computer systems
- Preventative maintenance inspections
- Diagnostics and troubleshooting of equipment

Accomplishments included:

- "Excellent" score during skills evaluation
- Award of an Air Force Specialty Code "5" skill level

Assistant Manager, Spring Farm, Wootan, Ohio, 1993–1998
Responsible for dairy operations on this 500-acre farm. Developed management and technical skills; learned to repair sophisticated farm equipment.

Special Skills:

Macintosh desk-top publishing
Microsoft Word
Assembly Language
C++ Programming

References:

Available upon request

EXAMPLE 7a, part 2
Job letter and résumé (résumé in chronological format)

456 Cantor Way, #245
Gallop, MN 55002
September 3, 2005

Ms. Judith R. Gonzalez
American Hospital Systems
3023 Center Avenue
Randolf, MN 55440

Dear Ms. Gonzalez:

My placement center recently informed me about the Management Trainee opening with Mercy Hospital. As a business major with experience working in hospitals, I wish to apply for the position.

Your job advertisement notes that you seek candidates with a broad academic background in business and an interest in hospital management. At Central State College, I've taken extensive coursework in three major areas in business: finance, marketing, and personnel management. This broad-based academic curriculum has provided a solid foundation for a wide variety of management tasks at Mercy Hospital.

My summer and part-time employment also matches the needs of your position. While attending Central State, I've worked part-time and summers as an assistant in the Business Office at Grady Hospital. That experience has acquainted me with the basics of business management within the context of a mid-sized hospital, much like Mercy.

The enclosed resume highlights the skills that match your Management Trainee opening. I would like the opportunity to talk with you in person and can be reached at (612) 111-1111 for an interview.

Sincerely,

Denise Ware Sanborn

Denise Ware Sanborn

EXAMPLE 7b, part 1
Job letter and résumé (letter in modified block style)

Denise Ware Sanborn
456 Cantor Way, #245
Gallop, MN 55002
(612) 111-1111

Objective
Entry-level management position in the health care industry. Seek position that includes exposure to a wide variety of management and business-related tasks.

Education
Bachelor of Arts Degree, June 2004
Central State College
Gallop, Minnesota

Major: Business Administration
Grade Point Average: 3.26 of possible 4.0, with 3.56 in all major courses
All college expenses financed by part-time and summer work at Grady Hospital in St. Paul, Minnesota

Skills and Experience
Finance
Helped with research for three fiscal year budgets
Developed new spreadsheet for monthly budget reports
Wrote accounts payable correspondence
Marketing
Solicited copy from managers for new brochure
Designed and edited new brochure
Participated in team visits to ten area physicians
Personnel
Designed new performance appraisal form for secretarial staff
Interviewed applicants for Maintenance Department jobs
Coordinated annual training program for nursing staff

Awards
2003 Arden Award for best senior project in the Business Administration Department (paper that examined Total Quality Management)

Dean's list for six semesters

References
Academic and work references available upon request

EXAMPLE 7b, part 2
Job letter and résumé (résumé in functional format)

201 Edge Drive
Norcross, PA 17001
March 15, 2006

Mr. James Vernon, Personnel Director
McDuff, Inc.
105 Halsey Street
Baltimore, MD 21212

Dear Mr. Vernon:

My academic advisor, Professor Sam Singleton, informed me about an electrical engineering opening at McDuff, where he worked until last year. I am writing to apply for the job.

I understand that McDuff is making a major effort to build a full-scale equipment development laboratory. That prospect interests me greatly, because of my academic background in electrical engineering. At Northern Tech, I took courses in several subjects that might be useful in the lab's work—for example, microprocessor applications, artificial intelligence, and fiber optics.

Also, related work at Jones Energy & Automation, Inc., has given me experience building and developing new electronics systems. In particular, my work as an assembler taught me the importance of precision and quality control. I'd like the opportunity to apply this knowledge at McDuff.

Personal business will take me to Baltimore April 8 to 10. Could you meet with me on one of those days to discuss how McDuff might use my skills? Please let me know if an interview would be convenient at that time.

Enclosed is a résumé that highlights my credentials. I hope to be talking with you in April.

Sincerely,

Donald Vizano

Donald Vizano

Enclosure: Résumé

EXAMPLE 7c, part 1
Job letter and résumé (letter in modified block style)

Donald Vizano
201 Edge Drive
Norcross, PA 17001
(300) 555–7861
dvizano@nct.edu

OBJECTIVE: A full-time position in electrical engineering, with emphasis on designing new equipment in automation and microprocessing

EDUCATION: 2000–2006 Bachelor of Science in Electrical Engineering (expected June 2006) Northern College of Technology, Shipley, PA 3.5 GPA (4.0 scale)

Selected Major Courses:

Artificial Machine Intelligence
Communication Control Systems
Microcomputer Applications
Digital Control Systems
Semiconductor Circuits & Devices

Selected Related Courses:

FORTRAN
Engineering Economy
Technical Communication

ACTIVITIES AND HONORS: Institute of Electrical and Electronic Engineering (IEEE)
Dean's List, 8 quarters.

EMPLOYMENT:

2002–2006 Electronic Assembler (part-time)
Jones Energy & Automation, Inc.
Banner, PA

2001–2002 Lab Monitor (part-time)
Computer Services
Northern College of Technology
Shipley, PA

PERSONAL: Willing to travel, fluent in Spanish

REFERENCES: Available upon request

EXAMPLE 7c, part 2
Job letter and résumé (résumé in chronological format)

2389 Jenson Court
Gulfton, MS 39200
(601) 111–1111
February 17, 2006.

Mr. Nigel Pierce, Personnel Director
Structural Systems, Inc.
105 Paisley Way
Jackson, MS 39236.

Dear Mr. Pierce:

I am writing in response to your ad for a technical representative in the July 13 (Sunday) edition of the *Jackson Journal*. I believe my experience and education make me an excellent candidate for this position.

I am very familiar with your products for the wood construction market. The laminated beams and floor joists your company manufactures were specified by many of the architects I have worked with during my co-op experience at Mississippi Technical College. Work I have done in the residential and small commercial construction industry convinced me of the advantages of your products over nominal lumber.

Enclosed is my résumé, which focuses on the skills gained from my co-op work that would transfer to your firm. I look forward to meeting you and discussing my future with your company.

Sincerely,

Todd L. Fisher

Todd L. Fisher

Enclosure: Résumé

EXAMPLE 7d, part 1
Job letter and résumé (letter in modified block style)

Todd L. Fisher
2389 Jenson Court
Gulfton, MS 39200
(601) 111–1111
tlfish@ail.com

PROFESSIONAL OBJECTIVE	Use my education in civil engineering technology and my construction experience to assume a technical advisory position.
EDUCATION	Mississippi Technical College Hart, Mississippi; Associate of Science, Civil Engineering Technology June 2004, GPA: 3.00 (out of 4.00)
PROFESSIONAL EXPERIENCE	Financed education by working as co-op student for two Jackson construction firms for 18 months.
Design Skills	Assisted with the layout and design of wall panels for Ridge Development condominium project. Created layout and design for complete roof and floor systems for numerous churches and small commercial projects.
Computer Skills	Introduced computerization to the design offices of a major construction company (HP hardware in HP basic operating system). Designed trusses on Sun workstations in the UNIX operating system. Operated as the system administrator for the office.
Leadership Skills	Instructed new CAD (computer-assisted design) operators on the operation of design software for panel layout and design. Designed and implemented management system for tracking jobs in plant.
INTERESTS	Family, gardening, sailing, travel
REFERENCES	References available upon request.

EXAMPLE 7d, part 2
Job letter and résumé (résumé in functional format)

SUSAN A. MARTIN

PRESENT ADDRESS	**PERMANENT ADDRESS**
540 Wood Drive	30 Avon Place
Bama, CA 90012	Atlas, CA 90000
(901) 666–2222	(901) 555–6074

PROFESSIONAL OBJECTIVE:	Analyze and solve problems involving natural and pollution control systems as an Environmental Scientist.
EDUCATION:	Pierce College, Bama, California Bachelor of Science, Environmental Science May 2003, GPA: 3.15 (out of 4.00) Pleasant Valley College, Barnes, Nevada Associate in Applied Science, Engineering Science May 2001, GPA: 3.15 (out of 4.00)
PROFESSIONAL EXPERIENCE:	
Research Skills:	• Worked as lab assistant in a research project to analyze the effect of acid rain on frog reproduction in Lake Lane. • Designed Pierce College computer program to analyze data on ozone depletion.
Leadership Skills:	• Taught inventory procedures to new employees of Zane's Office Supply. • Helped incoming freshmen and transfer students adjust to Pierce College (as dormitory resident assistant).
Organizational Skills:	• Maintained academic department files as student assistant in Environmental Science Department.
HONORS AND ACTIVITIES:	• Dean's List (five semesters) • President of Cycling Club • Campus newspaper reporter (three years) • Habitat for Humanity Club (two years)
EMPLOYMENT:	*Dormitory Resident Assistant*, Pierce College, Bama, CA, 2002–2003 *Trainer,* Zane's Office Supply, Bama, CA, 2001–2002
REFERENCES:	References and transcripts available upon request

EXAMPLE 7e
Résumé (combined chronological and functional format)

Leslie Highland
997 Simmons Drive
Boise, Idaho 88822

OBJECTIVE:	A full-time position in architectural design with emphasis on model-making and renderings for future buildings.
EDUCATION:	**Boise Architectural College** Boise, Idaho Bachelor of Science Architectural Engineering Technology June 2003
	Harvard University Cambridge, Massachusetts Certificate in Advance Architectural Delineation August 1997
ACTIVITIES AND HONORS:	**Boise Architectural College** Winner of Senior Design Project Architectural Engineering Technology
	Charter Member of American Society of Architectural Perspectives
EMPLOYMENT:	
1997–2003	**Architectural Designer and Delineator** Dorsey-Hudson, Architects Boise, Idaho
1995–1997	**Architectural Designer and Renderer** Windsor and Associates, Architects St. Lake, Utah
1992–1995	**Architectural Renderer and Drafter** Sanders and Associates, Architects Provo, Utah
1990–1992	**Architectural Drafter** Brown Engineering St. Lake, Utah
REFERENCES:	References and portfolio available upon request.

EXAMPLE 7f
Résumé (chronological format)

Karen S. Patel
300 Park Drive
Burtingdale, NY 20092

Home: (210) 400-2112 **Messages:** (210) 400-0111

OBJECTIVE	Position as in-house technical writer and as trainer in communication skills
EDUCATION	**Sumpter College, Marist, Vermont** M.S. in Technical Communication, GPA: 4.0 December 2000
	Warren College, Aurora, New York M.A. in English, Cum Laude, June 1997
	University of Bombay, India B.A. in English, First Class Honors, June 1994
EMPLOYMENT *Editing/ Writing*	**Public Relations Office, Sumpter College, 2000–present** Administrative Assistant: Write press releases and conduct interviews. Publish news stories in local newspapers and in *Sumpter Express.* Edit daily campus newsletter.
	Hawk Newspapers, Albany, New York, 1995–1996 Warren College Internship: Covered and reported special events; conducted interviews; assisted with proofreading, layout, headline count. Scanned newspapers for current events; conducted research for stories. Published feature stories.
Teaching/ Research	**Sumpter College, Marist, Vermont, 1999–2000** Teaching Assistant: Tutored English at the Writing Center; answered "Grammar Hotline" phone questions; edited and critiqued student papers; taught English to non-English speakers; helped students prepare for Regents exams.
	Warren College, Aurora, New York, 1996–1997 Teaching Assistant: Taught business writing; supervised peer editing and in-class discussions; held student conferences; graded student papers.
	Research Assistant: Verified material by checking facts; wrote brief reports related to research; researched information and bibliographies.
COMPUTER SKILLS	WordPerfect, Microsoft Word, PageMaker, UNIX, Excel
REFERENCES	Available upon request

EXAMPLE 7g
Résumé (combined chronological and functional format)

ABC Format 8: Instructions

Abstract

- Clear purpose statement for instructions
- Summary of the main steps
- List of materials or equipment needed (or reference to list or graphic)

Body

- Helpful pointers or definitions
- Well-placed references to (1) Cautions (possibility of damage to things), (2) Warnings (possibility of injury), and (3) Dangers (probability of injury or death)
- Numbered steps
  —Steps grouped under main tasks, not presented in one laundry list
  —Limit of one action in each step
  —Use of verbs rather than nouns (for example, "Check the meter reading")
- Separation of essential information (in steps) from helpful information (in "Notes" and "Results")

Conclusion

- Statement, or restatement, about importance of procedure

Helpful Hints

Instructions can be either freestanding documents or part of another document. In either case, the most common error is to make them too complicated for the audience. Carefully consider the technical level of your readers. Use white space, graphics, and other design elements to make the instructions appealing. Most important, be sure to include Caution, Warning, and Danger references *before* the steps to which they apply.

MEMORANDUM

DATE: June 23, 2006
TO: Employees Receiving New Message Recorders
FROM: Matthew Edwards, Purchasing Agent *ME*
SUBJECT: Instructions for New Message Recorders

INTRODUCTORY SUMMARY

We have just received the new phone message recorder you ordered. After processing, it will be delivered to your office within the week. The machine is one of the best on the market, but the instructions that accompany it are somewhat hard to follow. To help you begin using the recorder as soon as possible, I have simplified the instructions for setting up and operating the machine.

The illustration below labels the machine's parts. Following the illustration are seven easy steps you need to operate the recorder.

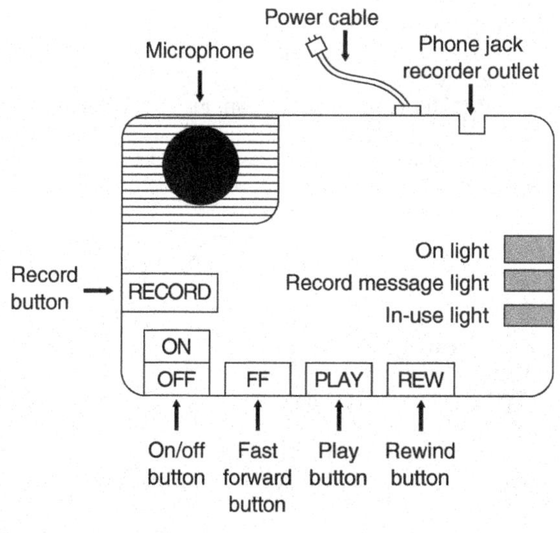

EXAMPLE 8 (pp. 65–67)
Instructions

Adapted from *Technical Writing: A Practical Approach,* 5th ed. (pp. 207–209) by W. S. Pfeiffer, 2006, Upper Saddle River, NJ: Prentice Hall. Reprinted by permission.

Memo to: Employees receiving new message recorders Page 2
June 23, 2006

SETTING UP AND USING YOUR NEW RECORDER

If you devote about 15 minutes to these 7 tasks, you can learn to operate your new message recorder.

1. Hooking Up Your Recorder

a. Plug the recorder into any wall outlet using the *power cable.*
b. Plug the *phone jack* into the *recorder outlet* located at the back of the unit.

2. Preparing Your Message

a. Write down your:
Greeting
Name and department
Time of return
b. Write down the request you want to leave on the machine.
NOTE: A sample request might be as follows: "Please leave your name, phone number, and a brief message after you hear the tone."

3. Recording Your Message

a. Press the *ON* button.
RESULT: The red *on* light will come on.
b. Press and hold down the *RECORD* button, and keep holding it down for the entire time you record.
RESULT: While the button is held down, the red *record message* light will come on.
c. Record your message directly into the *microphone.*
d. Release the *RECORD* button when you are finished recording.
e. Do you need to record the message again?
If *yes,* repeat steps a through d (your previous message will be erased each time you record).
If *no,* go on to the next step.

4. Turning On and Testing Your Recorder

a. Press the *ON* button.
RESULT: The red *on* light will come on.
b. Press the *PLAY* button.
RESULT: The red *in-use* light will come on.
c. Call in your message from another phone to make sure the unit is recording properly.

EXAMPLE 8 (*continued*)

Memo to: Employees receiving new message recorders Page 3
June 23, 2006

5. Playing Back Messages

a. Look at the red *record message* light to see if it is blinking.
NOTE: The number of times the light blinks in succession indicates the number of messages you have received.

b. Press the *REW* (rewind) button.
NOTE: The tape will stop automatically when it is completely rewound.

CAUTION: Do not press *PLAY* and *FF* (fast forward) at the same time! Doing so will break the tape. See the manufacturer's manual for process of replacing broken tape.

c. Press *PLAY* and listen to the messages.

d. Do you want to replay messages?
If *yes,* repeat steps b and c.
If *no,* go on to the next step.

e. Do you want to skip ahead to other messages?
If *yes,* push the *FF* (fast forward) button.
If *no,* go on to the next step.

6. Erasing Received Messages

a. Press and continue holding down the *PLAY* and *REW* (rewind) buttons at the same time.

b. Release the buttons when you hear a click.
NOTE: The tape automatically stops when the messages are erased.

7. Turning Off Your Recorder

a. Press the *OFF* button.
RESULT: All red lights will go off.

CONCLUSION

These new recorders are fully guaranteed for three years, so please report any problems right away. Paul Hansey (ext. 765) will be glad to help fix the machine or return the machine to the manufacturer for repair. In particular, you need to report these problems to Paul:

- Lost or incomplete messages
- Interference or noise on line
- Faulty equipment
- Inability to record

EXAMPLE 8 (*continued*)

ABC Format 9: Problem Analysis

Abstract

- Purpose of report
- Capsule summary of problems covered in report discussion

Body

- Background on source of problems
- Well-organized description of problems observed
- Data that support your observations
- Consequences of the problems

Conclusion

- Brief restatement of the main problems (unless report is so short that restatement would be repetitious)
- Degree of urgency required in handling problems
- Suggested next step

Helpful Hints

Problem analyses must provide an *objective* presentation of information, so that the readers (who are often decision-makers) can decide upon the next step. Any opinions set forth must be well supported by facts.

MEMORANDUM

DATE: October 15, 2006
TO: Jan Stillwright, Vice President of Research and Training
FROM: Harold Marshal, Technical Supervisor *HM*
SUBJECT: Boat Problems during Summer Season

INTRODUCTORY SUMMARY

We have just completed a one-month project in the Pacific Ocean aboard the leased ship, *Seeker II*. All work went just about as planned, with very few delays caused by weather or equipment failure.

However, there were some boat problems that need to be solved before we lease *Seeker II* again this season. This report highlights the problems so that they can be brought to the owner's attention. My comments focus on four areas of the boat: drill rig, engineering lab, main engine, and crew quarters.

DRILL RIG

Thus far the rig has operated without incident. Yet on one occasion, I noticed that the elevator for lifting pipe up the derrick swung too close to the derrick itself. A quick gust of wind or a sudden increase in sea height caused these shifts. If the elevator were to hit the derrick, causing the elevator door to open, pipe sections might fall to the deck below.

I believe the whole rig assembly must be checked by someone knowledgeable about its design. Before we put workers near that rig again, we need to know that their safety would not be jeopardized by the possibility of falling pipe.

ENGINEERING LAB

Quite frankly, it is a tribute to our technicians that they were able to complete all lab tests with *Seeker II*'s limited facilities. Several weeks into the voyage, four main problems became apparent:

1. Ceiling leaks
2. Poor water pressure in the cleanup sink
3. Leaks around the window near the electronics corner
4. Two broken outlet plugs

Although we were able to devise a solution to the window leaks, the other problems stayed with us for the entire trip.

EXAMPLE 9 (pp. 69–70)

Problem analysis

Adapted from *Technical Writing: A Practical Approach*, 5th ed. (pp. 289–290) by W. S. Pfeiffer, 2006, Upper Saddle River, NJ: Prentice Hall. Reprinted by permission.

Jan Stillwright Page 2
October 15, 2006

MAIN ENGINE

On this trip, we had three valve failures on three different cylinder heads. Our experience on other ships indicates that it is very unusual to have one valve fail, let alone three. Fortunately for us, these failures occurred between projects, so we did not lose time on a job. And fortunately for the owner, the broken valve parts did not destroy the engine's expensive turbocharger.

Only an expert will be able to tell whether these engine problems were flukes or if the entire motor needs to be rebuilt. In my opinion, the most prudent course of action is to have the engine checked over carefully before the next voyage.

CREW QUARTERS

When 15 men live in one room for three months, it is important that basic facilities work. On *Seeker II* we experienced problems with the bedroom, bathroom, and laundry room that caused some tension.

Bedroom

Three of the top bunks had such poor springs that the occupants sank 6 to 12 in. toward the bottom bunks. More important, five of the bunks are not structurally sound enough to keep from swaying in medium to high seas. Finally, most of the locker handles are either broken or about to break.

Bathroom

Poor pressure in three of the commodes made them almost unusable during the last two weeks. Our amateur repairs did not solve the problem, so I think the plumbing leading to the holding tank might be defective.

Laundry Room

We discovered early that the filtering system could not screen the large amount of rust in the old 10,000-gallon tank. Consequently, undergarments and other white clothes turned a yellow-red color and were ruined.

CONCLUSION

As noted at the outset, none of these problems kept us from accomplishing the major goals of this voyage. But they did make the trip much more uncomfortable than it had to be. Moreover, in the case of the rig and engine problems, we were fortunate that injuries and downtime did not occur.

I strongly urge that the owner be asked to correct these deficiencies before we consider using *Seeker II* for additional projects this season.

EXAMPLE 9 (*continued*)

ABC Format 10: Recommendation Report

Abstract

- Purpose of report
- Brief reference to problem to which recommendations respond
- Capsule summary of recommendations covered in report

Body

- Details about problem
- Well-organized description of recommendations
- Data that support recommendations (with reference to attachments)
- The main benefits of recommendations
- Any possible drawbacks

Conclusion

- Brief restatement of the main recommendations
- The main benefit of recommended change
- Your offer to help with the next step

Helpful Hints

Recommendation reports must be more persuasive than reports such as problem analyses. Yet any recommendations in your report must be well supported by facts and analysis. You want readers to see your recommendations as ideas that flow naturally and inevitably from facts in the report.

677 Rothrock Way
Fairfax, VA 22030
(703) 555-6273

April 22, 2006

Big Muddy Oil Company, Inc.
12 Rankin Street
Abilene, TX 79224

ATTENTION: Mr. James Smith, Engineering Manager

SHARK PASS STUDY
BLOCK 15, AREA 43-B, GULF OF MEXICO

INTRODUCTORY SUMMARY

You recently asked our firm to complete a preliminary soils investigation at an offshore rig site. This report presents the tentative results of our study, including major conclusions and recommendations. A longer, formal report will follow at the end of the project.

On the basis of what we have learned so far, we believe that you can safely place an oil platform at the Shark Pass site. To limit the chance of a rig leg punching into the seafloor, however, we suggest you follow the recommendations in this report.

WORK AT THE PROJECT SITE

On April 16 and 17, 2006, GCC's engineers and technicians worked at the Block 15 site in the Shark Pass region of the gulf. Using GCC's leased drill ship, *Atlantis,* as a base of operations, our crew performed these main tasks:

- Seismic survey of the project study area
- Two soil borings of 40 feet each

Both seismic data and soil samples were brought to our Houston office for laboratory analysis.

LABORATORY ANALYSIS

On April 18 and 19, our lab staff examined the soil samples, completed bearing capacity tests, and evaluated seismic data. Here are the results of that analysis.

Soil Layers

Our initial evaluation of the soil samples reveals a 7–9 ft layer of weak clay starting a few feet below the seafloor. Other than that layer, the composition of the soils seems fairly typical of other sites nearby.

EXAMPLE 10 (pp. 72–73)
Recommendation report
Adapted from *Technical Writing: A Practical Approach,* 5th ed. (pp. 285–286) by W. S. Pfeiffer, 2006, Upper Saddle River, NJ: Prentice Hall. Reprinted by permission.

James Smith
April 22, 2006

Page 2

Bearing Capacity

We used the most reliable procedure available, the XYZ method, to determine the soil's bearing capacity (that is, its ability to withstand the weight of a loaded oil rig). That method required that we apply the following formula:

Q	=	cNv + tY, where
Q	=	ultimate bearing capacity
c	=	average cohesive shear strength
Nv	=	the dimensionless bearing capacity factor
t	=	footing displacement
Y	=	weight of the soil unit

The final bearing capacity figure will be submitted in the final report, after we repeat the tests.

Seafloor Surface

By pulling our underwater seismometer back and forth across the project site, we developed a seismic "map" of the seafloor surface. That map seems typical of the flat floor expected in that area of the gulf. The only exception is the presence of what appears to be a small sunken boat. This wreck, however, is not in the immediate area of the proposed platform site.

CONCLUSIONS AND RECOMMENDATIONS

On the basis of our analysis, we conclude that there is only a slight risk of instability at the site. Although unlikely, it is possible that a rig leg could punch through the seafloor, either during or after loading. We base this opinion on (1) the existence of the weak clay layer, and (2) the marginal bearing capacity.

Nevertheless, we believe you can still place your platform if you follow careful rig-loading procedures. Specifically, take these precautions to reduce your risk:

1. Load the rig in 10-ton increments, waiting 1 hour between loadings.
2. Allow the rig to stand 24 hours after the loading and before placement of workers on board.
3. Have a soils specialist observe the entire loading process, to assist with any emergency decisions if problems arise.

As noted at the outset, these conclusions and recommendations are based on preliminary data and analysis. We will complete our final study in three weeks and submit a formal report shortly thereafter.

GCC enjoyed working once again for Big Muddy Oil at its Gulf of Mexico lease holdings. I will phone you this week to see if you have any questions about our study. If you need information before then, please give me a call.

Sincerely,

Bartley Hopkins

Bartley Hopkins, Project Manager

EXAMPLE 10 (*continued*)

ABC Format 11: Equipment Evaluation

Abstract

- Purpose of report
- Capsule summary of what report says about the equipment

Body

- Thorough description of equipment being evaluated
- Well-organized critique, either analyzing the parts of one piece of equipment or contrasting several pieces of similar equipment
- Additional supporting data, with reference to attachments

Conclusion

- Brief restatement of major findings, conclusions, or recommendations

Helpful Hints

Equipment evaluations give objective critiques about how equipment has functioned. Possible topics include machinery, tools, vehicles, software, and office supplies. Like a problem analysis, the equipment evaluation may focus on problems. Or, like a recommendation report, it may suggest a change. In any case, it must provide well-documented observations of the manner in which equipment has performed.

MEMORANDUM

DATE: July 26, 2006
TO: Melanie Frank, Office Manager
FROM: Hank Worley, Project Manager *HW*
SUBJECT: Evaluation of Best Choice Software

INTRODUCTORY SUMMARY

When the office purchased one copy of Best Choice Software last month, you suggested I send you an evaluation after 30 days' use. Having now used Best Choice for a month, I have concluded that it meets all our performance expectations. This memo presents our evaluation of the main features of Best Choice.

HOW BEST CHOICE HAS HELPED US

Best Choice provides five primary features: word processing, file management, spreadsheet, graphics, and a user's guide. Here is my critique of all five.

Word Processing

The system contains an excellent word-processing package that the engineers as well as the secretaries have been able to learn easily. This package can handle both our routine correspondence and the lengthy reports that our group generates. Of particular help is the system's 90,000-word dictionary, which can be updated at any time. The spelling correction feature has already saved much effort that was previously devoted to mechanical editing.

File Management

The file-manager function allows the user to enter information and then to manipulate it quickly. During one three-day site visit, for example, a field engineer recorded a series of problems observed in the field. Then she rearranged the data to highlight specific points I asked her to study, such as I-beam welds and concrete cracks.

Spreadsheet

Like the system's word-processing package, the spreadsheet is efficient and quickly learned. Because Best Choice is a multipurpose software package, spreadsheet data can be incorporated into letter or report format. In other words, spreadsheet information can be merged with our document format to create a final draft for submission to clients or supervisors, with a real savings in time. For example, the memo I sent you last week on budget projections for field equipment took me only an hour to complete; last quarter, the identical project took four hours.

EXAMPLE 11 (pp. 75–76)

Equipment evaluation

Adapted from *Technical Writing: A Practical Approach*, 5th ed. (pp. 287–288) by W. S. Pfeiffer, 2006, Upper Saddle River, NJ: Prentice Hall. Reprinted by permission.

Melanie Frank
July 26, 2006
Page 2

Graphics

The graphics package permits visuals to be drawn from the data contained in the spreadsheet. For example, a pie chart that shows the breakdown of a project budget can be created easily by merging spreadsheet data with the graphics software. With visuals becoming such an important part of reports, we have used this feature of Best Choice quite frequently.

User's Guide

Eight employees in my group have now used the Best Choice user's guide. All have found it well laid out and thorough. Perhaps the best indication of this fact is that in 30 days of daily use, we have placed only three calls to the Best Choice customer-service number.

CONCLUSION

Best Choice seems to contain just the right combination of tools to help us do our job, both in the field and in the office. These are the system's main benefits:

- Versatility—it has diverse functions
- Simplicity—it is easy to master

The people in our group have been very pleased with the package during this 30-day trial. If you'd like, we would be glad to evaluate Best Choice for a longer period.

EXAMPLE 11 (*continued*)

ABC Format 12: Lab Report

Abstract

- Purpose of report
- Capsule summary of results

Body

- Purpose or hypothesis of lab work
- Equipment needed
- Procedures or methods used in the lab test
- Unusual problems or occurrences
- Results of the test with reference to your expectations (results may appear in conclusion, instead)

Conclusion

- Restatement of the main results
- Implications of lab test for further work

Helpful Hints

Like procedures, lab reports may stand on their own or be part of a larger report that uses lab work for supporting detail. Lab reports usually include topics such as procedures, equipment, problems, results, and implications.

12 Post Street
Houston, Texas 77000
(713) 555-9781

December 12, 2006

Mr. Andrew Hawkes
Monson Coal Company
2139 Lasiter Drive
Baltimore, MD 21222

LABORATORY REPORT
BOREHOLE FOSSIL SAMPLES
BRAINTREE CREEK SITE, WEST VIRGINIA

INTRODUCTORY SUMMARY

Last week you sent us six fossil samples from the Braintree Creek site. Having analyzed the samples in our lab, we believe they suggest the presence of coal-bearing rock. As you requested, this report will give a summary of the materials and procedures we used in this project, along with any problems we had.

As you know, our methodology is to identify microfossils in the samples, estimate the age of the rock by when the microfossils existed, and then make assumptions about whether the surrounding rock might contain coal.

LAB MATERIALS

Our lab analysis relies on only one piece of specialized equipment: a Piketon electron microscope. Besides the Piketon, we use a simple 400-power manual microscope. Other equipment is similar to that included in any basic geology lab, such as filtering screens and burners.

LAB PROCEDURE

Once we receive a sample, we first try to identify the kinds of microfossils the rocks contain. Our specific lab procedure for your samples consisted of two steps:

Step 1

We used a 400-power microscope to visually classify the microfossils that were present. Upon inspection of the samples, we concluded that there were two main types of microfossils: nannoplankton and foraminifera.

EXAMPLE 12 (pp. 78–79)

Lab report

Adapted from *Technical Writing: A Practical Approach,* 5th ed. (pp. 294–295) by W. S. Pfeiffer, 2006, Upper Saddle River, NJ: Prentice Hall. Reprinted by permission.

Andrew Hawkes
December 12, 2006
Page 2

Step 2

Next, we had to extract the microfossils from the core samples you provided. We used two different techniques:

Nannoplankton Extraction Technique

a. Selected a pebble-sized piece of the sample
b. Thoroughly crushed the piece under water
c. Used a dropper to remove some of the material that floats to the surface (it contains the nannoplankton)
d. Dried the nannoplankton-water combination
e. Placed the nannoplankton on a slide

Foraminifera Extraction Technique

a. Boiled a small portion of the sample
b. Used a microscreen to remove clay and other unwanted material
c. Dried remaining material (foraminifera)
d. Placed foraminifera on slide

PROBLEMS ENCOUNTERED

The entire lab procedure went as planned. The only problem was minor and occurred when we removed one of the samples from its shipping container. As the bag was taken from the shipping box, it broke open. The sample shattered when it fell onto the table. Fortunately, we had an extra sample from the same location.

CONCLUSION

Judging by the types of fossils present in the sample, we believe they come from rock of an age that might contain coal. This conclusion is based on limited testing, so we suggest you test more samples at the site. We would be glad to help with additional sampling and testing.

I will call you this week to discuss our study and any possible follow-up you may wish us to do.

Sincerely,

Joseph Rappaport

Joseph Rappaport
Senior Geologist

EXAMPLE 12 (*continued*)

ABC Format 13: Trip Report

Abstract

- Destination, dates, and purpose of trip
- Brief overview of results of trip
- The main sections of the report

Body

- Major accomplishments, grouped by task
- Any conclusions that flow from your work
- Any recommendations you developed
- Administrative details, such as trip expenses

Conclusion

- Wrap-up that refers to overall usefulness of the trip
- Follow-up activities that may be required

Helpful Hints

Trip reports can be so routine at some organizations that forms are used. In other organizations they are anything but routine. In any case, your organization has invested in your trip and expects you to be able to describe your accomplishments.

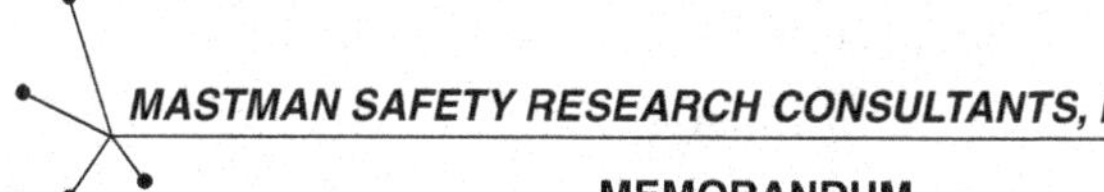

MEMORANDUM

DATE: July 15, 2006
TO: Susan Newton, Manager of Marketing
FROM: Stone Prentice, Marketing Specialist *SP*
SUBJECT: Report on Trip to Seattle

Last Friday I visited Seattle to explore several marketing opportunities for our firm. Having met with two potential clients, I believe we should strongly consider entering the Seattle market. This report highlights the results of my trip and proposes some follow-up activities for your review.

MEETINGS WITH POTENTIAL CLIENTS
In Seattle I met with officials from the two companies you asked me to contact. Both expressed interest in Mastman's services, as noted below.

Meeting with Josh McDonald, Pacific Retro Services
I spent the morning of July 11 with Mr. McDonald, reviewing his firm's projects for the next two years. He wants us to submit proposals for three upcoming projects to improve the indoor air quality (IAQ) of several downtown buildings. Further, he noted he has heard good comments about our patented IAQ equipment.

Meeting with Maureen Hemphill, the Builders Group
In the afternoon of July 11, I met with Ms. Hemphill at one of her firm's largest current projects, the 110 Jackson Building. She noted that her executive staff has been unhappy with delays in construction; it would like to consider hiring a firm like ours to manage construction for future projects. In fact, the Builders Group will issue two major requests for proposals before September.

PROPOSED PLAN OF ACTION
Pacific Retro Services and the Builders Group may offer us a lucrative Seattle market for our services. I suggest a threefold plan of action:

1. Submit proposals for all future projects for which we are qualified
2. Study the feasibility of starting a small branch in Seattle
3. Conduct future marketing trips in Seattle

CLOSING
I would be glad to help with the follow-up activities listed above. Seattle offers us a good opportunity to expand our work and provide a useful service.

EXAMPLE 13
Trip report

ABC Format 14: Proposal

Abstract

- Purpose of proposal
- The main need of readers
- The main feature of what you are offering
- The main benefit to reader of the feature noted above
- The main sections to follow

Body

- Problem or need and its significance
- Proposed solution or approach
- People to be used and their qualifications
- Schedule to be followed
- Cost of what is being proposed

Conclusion

- Restatement of a main feature or benefit or both
- Clarification of your interest in the work
- Statement about what should happen next

Helpful Hints

Long and short proposals cover the same basic topics—needs, features, and benefits. Long proposals, however, respond to more complex projects and are presented as formal documents, much like formal reports (see ABC Format 17). Whether long or short, proposals can be either in-house documents or sales proposals directed at customers.

DATE: October 6, 2006
TO: Gary Lane
FROM: Jeff Bilstrom JB
SUBJECT: Logo Proposal for Montrose Senior Citizens Center

My job as director of public relations is to get the Montrose name firmly entrenched in the minds of metro Atlanta residents. Having reviewed the contacts we have with the public, I believe we are sending a confusing message about the many services we offer retired citizens.

To remedy the problem, I propose we adopt a logo to serve as an umbrella for all services and agencies supported by the Montrose Senior Citizens Center. This proposal gives details about the problem and the proposed solution, including costs.

The Problem

The lack of a logo presents a number of problems related to marketing the center's services and informing the public. Here are a few:

- The letterhead mentions the organization's name in small type, with none of the impact that an accompanying logo would have.
- The current brochure needs the flair that could be provided by a logo on the cover page, rather than just the page of text and headings we now have.
- Our 14 vehicles are difficult to identify because there is only the lettered organization name on the sides, without any readily identifiable graphic.
- The sign in front of our campus, a main piece of free advertising, could better spread the word about Montrose if it contained a catchy logo.
- Other signs around campus could display the logo, as a way of reinforcing our identity and labeling buildings.

It's clear that without a logo, the Montrose Senior Citizens Center misses an excellent opportunity to educate the public about its services.

The Solution

A professionally designed logo could provide the Montrose Senior Citizens Center with a more distinct identity. Helping to tie together all branches of our operation, it would give the public an easy-to-recognize symbol. As a result, there would be a stronger awareness of the center on the part of users and financial contributors.

EXAMPLE 14 (pp. 83–84)

Proposal

Adapted from *Technical Communication: A Practical Approach,* 6th ed. (pp. 370–371) by W. S. Pfeiffer, 2006, Upper Saddle River, NJ: Prentice Hall. Reprinted by permission.

Gary Lane
October 6, 2006
Page 2

The new logo could be used immediately to do the following:

- Design and print letterhead, envelopes, business cards, and a new brochure.
- Develop a decal for all company vehicles that would identify them as belonging to Montrose.
- Develop new signs for the entire campus, to include a new sign for the entrance to the campus, one sign at the entrance to the Blane Workshop, and one sign at the entrance to the Administration Building.

Cost

Developing a new logo can be quite expensive. However, I have been able to get the name of a well-respected graphic artist willing to donate his services in the creation of a new logo. We need only give him some general guidelines to follow and then choose from among eight to ten rough sketches. Once a decision is made, the artist will provide a camera-ready copy of the new logo.

■ Design charge	$ 0.00
■ Charge for new letterhead, envelopes, business cards, and brochures (min. order)	545.65
■ Decal for vehicles (14 @ $50.00 + 4%)	728.00
■ Signs for campus	415.28
Total Cost	$1,688.93

Conclusion

As the retirement population of Atlanta increases in the next few years, there will be a much greater need for the services of the Montrose Senior Citizens Center. Because of that need, it's in our best interest to keep this growing market informed about the organization.

I'll stop by later this week to discuss any questions you might have about this proposal.

EXAMPLE 14 (*continued*)

ABC Format 15: Feasibility Study

Abstract

- Brief statement about who authorized the study and for what purpose
- Brief statement of the overall recommendation
- Reference to the main parts of report

Body

- Description of methods used in study
- Description of evaluation criteria (cost, schedule, quality, etc.)
- Analysis of item or items, according to the evaluation criteria
- Detailed information about advantages and disadvantages of adopting the change
- Other alternatives to consider, if any

Conclusion

- Major conclusions and recommendations resulting from the study
- Follow-up tasks that may be needed to acquire additional data

Helpful Hints

Although proposals may be solicited or unsolicited by the reader, feasibility studies are always solicited. The reader needs the study to determine the practicality—that is, feasibility—of a proposed policy, product, or service. Readers need information from the study to make decisions.

MEMORANDUM

DATE: July 22, 2006
TO: Greg Bass
FROM: Mike Tran MT
SUBJECT: Replacement of In-House File Server

INTRODUCTORY SUMMARY

The purpose of this feasibility study is to determine if the NTR PC905 would make a practical replacement for our in-house file server. As we agreed in our weekly staff meeting, our current file-serving computer is damaged beyond repair and must be replaced by the end of the week. This study shows that the NTR PC905 is a suitable replacement that we can purchase within our budget and install by Friday afternoon.

FEASIBILITY CRITERIA

There are three major criteria that I addressed. First, the computer we buy must be able to perform the tasks of a file-serving computer on our in-house network. Second, it must be priced within our $4,000 budget for the project. Third, it must be delivered and installed by Friday afternoon.

Performance

As a file server, the computer we buy must be able to satisfy these criteria:

- Store all programs used by network computers
- Store the source code and customer-specific files for Xtracheck
- Provide fast transfer of files between computers while serving as host to the network
- Serve as the printing station for the network laser printer

The NTR PC905 comes with a 120MB hard drive. This capacity will provide an adequate amount of storage for all programs that will reside on the file server. Our requirements are for 30MB of storage for programs used by network computers and 35MB of storage for source code and customer-specific programs. The 120MB drive will leave us with 55MB of storage for future growth.

The PC905 can transfer files and execute programs across our network. It can do so at speeds up to five times faster than our current file server. Productivity should increase because of less time spent waiting for transfer.

EXAMPLE 15 (pp. 86–87)

Feasibility study

Adapted from *Technical Writing: A Practical Approach,* 5th ed. (pp. 407–408) by W. S. Pfeiffer, 2006, Upper Saddle River, NJ: Prentice Hall. Reprinted by permission.

Greg Bass
July 22, 2006
Page 2

The computer we choose as the file server must also serve as the printing station for our network laser printer. The PC905 is compatible with our Hewy Packer laser printer. It also has 2.0MB more memory than our current server. As a result, it can store larger documents in memory and print with greater speed.

Budget

The budget for the new file server is $4,000. The cost of the PC905 is as follows:

PC905 with 120MB Hard Drive	$2,910
Keyboard	112
Monitor	159
Total	$3,181

No new network boards need to be purchased because we can use those that are in the current server. We also have all additional hardware and cables that will be required for installation. Thus the PC905 can be purchased for $800 under budget.

Time Frame

Our sales representative at NTR guarantees delivery of the system by Friday morning. With this assurance, we can have the system in operation by Friday afternoon.

Additional Benefits

We are now using NTR PCs at our customer sites. I am very familiar with the setup and installation of these machines. By purchasing a brand of computer currently in use, we will not have to worry about extra time spent learning new installation and operation procedures. In addition, we know that all our software is fully compatible with NTR products.

The warranty on the PC905 is for one year. After the warranty period, the equipment is covered by the service plan we have for other computers and printers.

CONCLUSION

I recommend that we purchase the NTR PC905 to replace our file server. It meets or exceeds all criteria for performance, price, and installation.

EXAMPLE 15 (*continued*)

ABC Format 16: Progress Report

Abstract

- Purpose of report
- Overview of project
- Survey of progress since the last report

Body

- Tasks completed since the last report—organized by task or time or both
- Clear reference to dead ends that have taken time but yielded no results
- Explanation of delays or incomplete work
- Work remaining on project(s)—organized by task or time or both
- Reference to attachments that may contain more specific information

Conclusion

- Brief restatement of work since the last reporting period
- Expression of confidence, or concern, about overall work on project
- Indication of willingness to make adjustments the reader may suggest

Helpful Hints

Progress reports are usually organized by task or by time. The reader, perhaps your supervisor or your customer, wants details about the status of a project. Although you should put forth the best case for the work you have completed, be certain not to overstate what you have done.

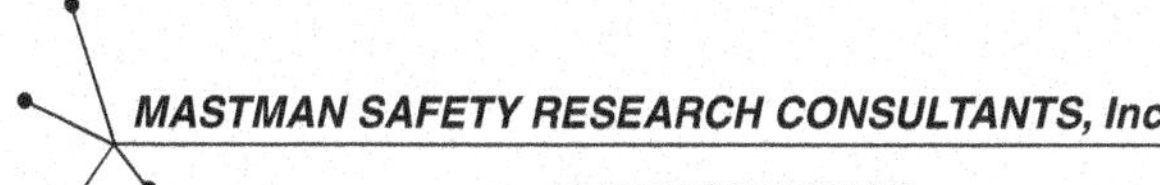

MEMORANDUM

DATE: June 11, 2006
TO: Kerry Camp, Vice President of Domestic Operations
FROM: Scott Sampson, Manager of Personnel *SS*
SUBJECT: Progress Report on Training Project

INTRODUCTORY SUMMARY

On May 21 you asked that I study ways our firm can improve training for technical employees in all domestic offices. We agreed that the project would take about six or seven weeks and involve three phases:

Phase 1: Make phone inquiries to competing firms
Phase 2: Send a survey to our technical people
Phase 3: Interview a cross section of our technical employees

I have now completed Phase 1 and part of Phase 2. My observation thus far is that the project will offer many new directions to consider for our technical training program.

WORK COMPLETED

In the first week of the project, I had extensive phone conversations with people at three competing firms about their training programs. Then in the second week, I wrote and sent out a training survey to all technical employees in Mastman's domestic offices.

Phone Interviews

I contacted three firms for whom we have done similar favors in the past: Simkins Consultants, Judd & Associates, and ABG Engineering. Here is a summary of my conversations:

1. Simkins Consultants

   Talked with Harry Roland, training director, on May 23. Harry said that his firm has most success with internal training seminars. Each technical person completes several one- or two-day seminars every year. These courses are conducted by in-house experts or external consultants, depending on the specialty.

EXAMPLE 16 (pp. 89–90)
Progress report

Adapted from *Technical Writing: A Practical Approach,* 5th ed. (pp. 291–292) by W. S. Pfeiffer, 2006, Upper Saddle River, NJ: Prentice Hall. Reprinted by permission.

Kerry Camp
June 11, 2006

Page 2

2. Judd & Associates
   Talked with Jan Tyler, manager of engineering, on May 23. Jan said that Judd, like Simkins, depends mostly on internal seminars. But Judd spreads these seminars over one or two weeks, rather than teaching intensive courses in one or two days. Judd also offers short "technical awareness" sessions at the lunch hour every two weeks. In-house technical experts give informal presentations on some aspect of their research or fieldwork.
3. ABG Engineering
   Talked with Newt Mosely, personnel coordinator, on May 27. According to Newt, ABG's training program is much as it was two decades ago. Most technical people at high levels go to one seminar a year, usually sponsored by professional societies or local colleges. Other technical people get little training beyond what is provided on the job. In-house training has not worked well, mainly because of schedule conflicts with engineering jobs.

Internal Survey

After completing the phone interviews noted, I began the survey phase of the project. Last week, I finished writing the survey, had it reproduced, and sent it with a cover memo to all 450 technical employees in domestic offices. The deadline for returning it to me is June 17.

WORK PLANNED

With phone interviews finished and the survey mailed, I foresee the following schedule for completing the project:

June 17:	Surveys returned
June 18–21:	Surveys evaluated
June 24–28:	Trips taken to all domestic offices to interview a cross section of technical employees
July 3:	Submission of final project report to you

CONCLUSION

My interviews with competitors gave me a good feel for what technical training might be appropriate for our staff. Now I am hoping for a high-percentage return on the internal survey. That phase will prepare a good foundation for my on-site interviews later this month. I believe this major corporate effort will upgrade our technical training considerably.

I would be glad to hear any suggestions you may have about my work on the rest of the project. In particular, please call if you have any specific questions you want asked during the on-site interviews (ext. 348).

EXAMPLE 16 (*continued*)

ABC Format 17: Formal Report

Abstract

- Cover/title page
- Letter or memo of transmittal
- Table of contents
- List of illustrations
- Executive summary
- Introduction

Body

- Discussion sections
- [Appendixes—that appear after text but that support the body section]

Conclusion

- Conclusions
- Recommendations

Helpful Hints

The term *formal report* refers to documents of a certain length (usually at least 6 to 10 pages of text) and degree of formality (usually bound, with formal covers and graphics). Formal reports cover complex projects and can include one or more types of information noted in previous ABC models. One part of the formal report—the executive summary—is especially important to decision-makers.

STUDY OF WILDWOOD CREEK

WINSLOW, GEORGIA

Prepared for:

The City of Winslow

Prepared by:

Christopher S. Rice, Hydro/Environmental Engineer
McDuff, Inc.

November 30, 2006

EXAMPLE 17 (pp. 92–107)
Formal report
Adapted from *Technical Communication: A Practical Approach,* 6th ed. (pp. 321–336) by W. S. Pfeiffer, 2006, Upper Saddle River, NJ: Prentice Hall. Reprinted by permission.

12 Peachtree Street
Atlanta, GA 30056
(404) 555-7524

McDuff Project #99-119
November 30, 2006

Adopt-a-Stream Program
City of Winslow
300 Lawrence Street
Winslow, GA 30000

Attention: Ms. Elaine Sykes, Director

STUDY OF WILDWOOD CREEK
WINSLOW, GEORGIA

We have completed our seven-month project on the pollution study of Wildwood Creek. This project was authorized on May 18, 2006. We performed the study in accordance with our original proposal, No. 14-P72, dated April 24, 2006.

This report mentions all completed tests and discusses the test results. Wildwood Creek scored well on many of the tests, but we are concerned about several problems, for example, the level of phosphates in the stream. The few problems we observed during our study have led us to recommend that several additional tests be completed.

Thank you for the opportunity to complete this project. We look forward to working with you on further tests for Wildwood Creek and other waterways in Winslow.

Sincerely,

Christopher S. Rice, P.E.

Christopher S. Rice, P.E.
Hydro/Environmental Engineer

EXAMPLE 17 (*continued*)

TABLE OF CONTENTS

APPENDIXES

EXAMPLE 17 (*continued*)

1

LIST OF ILLUSTRATIONS

EXAMPLE 17 (*continued*)

EXECUTIVE SUMMARY

The City of Winslow hired McDuff, Inc., to perform a pollution study of Wildwood Creek. The section of the creek that was studied is a one-mile-long area in Burns Nature Park, from Newell College to U.S. Highway 42. The study lasted seven months.

McDuff completed 13 tests on 4 different test dates. Wildwood scored fairly well on many of the tests, but there were some problem areas. For example, high levels of phosphates were uncovered in the water. The phosphates were derived either from fertilizer or from animal and plant matter and waste. Also uncovered were small amounts of undesirable water organisms that are tolerant to pollutants and can survive in harsh environments.

McDuff recommends that (1) the tests done in this study be conducted two more times, through spring 2007; (2) other environmental tests be conducted, as listed in the conclusions and recommendations section; and (3) a voluntary cleanup of the creek be scheduled. With these steps, we can better analyze the environmental integrity of Wildwood Creek.

EXAMPLE 17 (*continued*)

3

INTRODUCTION

McDuff, Inc., has conducted a follow-up to a study completed in 1993 by Ware County on the health of Wildwood Creek. This introduction describes the project site, scope of our study, and format for this report.

PROJECT DESCRIPTION

By law, all states must clean up their waterways. The State of Georgia shares this responsibility with its counties. Ware County has certain waterways that are threatened and must be cleaned. Wildwood Creek is one of the more endangered waterways. The portion of the creek that was studied for this report is a one-mile stretch in Burns Nature Park between Newell College and U.S. Highway 42.

SCOPE OF STUDY

The purpose of this project was to determine whether the health of the creek has changed since the previous study in 1993. Both physical and chemical tests were completed. The nine physical tests were as follows:

- Air temperature
- Water temperature
- Water flow
- Water appearance
- Habitat description
- Algae appearance
- Algae location
- Visible litter
- Bug count

The four chemical tests were as follows:

- pH
- Dissolved oxygen (DO)
- Turbidity
- Phosphate

REPORT FORMAT

This report includes three main sections:

1. Field Investigation: a complete discussion of all the tests that were performed
2. Test Comparison: charts of the test results and comparisons
3. Conclusions and Recommendations

EXAMPLE 17 (*continued*)

4

FIELD INVESTIGATION

Wildwood Creek has been cited repeatedly for environmental violations in the pollution of its water. Many factors can generate pollution and affect the overall health of the creek. In 1993, the creek was studied in the context of all water systems in Ware County. Wildwood Creek was determined to be one of the more threatened creeks in the county.

The city needed to learn if much has changed in the past 13 years, so McDuff was hired to perform a variety of tests on the creek. Our effort involved a more in-depth study than that done in 1993. Tests were conducted four times over a seven-month period. The 1993 study lasted only one day.

The field investigation included two categories of tests: physical tests and chemical tests.

PHYSICAL TESTS

The physical tests covered a broad range of environmental features. This section will discuss the importance of the tests and some major findings. The Test Comparison section on page 9 includes a table that lists results of the tests and the completion dates. The test types were as follows: air temperature, water temperature, water flow, water appearance, habitat description, algae appearance, algae location, visible litter, and bug count.

Air Temperature

The temperature of the air surrounding the creek will affect life in the water. Unusual air temperature for the seasons will determine if life can grow in or out of the water.

Three of the four tests were performed in the warmer months. Only one was completed on a cool day. The difference in temperature from the warmest to coolest day was 10.5°C, an acceptable range.

Water Temperature

The temperature of the water determines which species will be present. Also affected are the feeding, reproduction, and metabolism of these species. If there are one or two weeks of high temperature, the stream is unsuitable for most species. If water temperature changes more than 1° to 2°C in 24 hours, thermal stress and shock can occur, killing much of the life in the creek.

During our study, the temperature of the water averaged 1°C cooler than the temperature of the air. The water temperature did not get above 23°C or below 13°C. These ranges are acceptable by law.

EXAMPLE 17 (*continued*)

5

Water Flow

The flow of the water will influence the type of life in the stream. Periods of high flow can cause erosion to occur on the banks and sediment to cover the streambed. Low water flow can decrease the living space and deplete the oxygen supply.

The flow of water was at the correct level for the times of year the tests were done—except for June, which had a high rainfall. With continual rain and sudden flash floods, the creek was almost too dangerous for the study to be performed that month.

In fact, in June we witnessed the aftermath of one flash flood. Figure 1 shows the creek with an average flow of water, and Figure 2 shows the creek during the flood. The water's average depth is 10 inches. During the flash flood, the water level rose and fell 10 feet in about 1 hour. Much dirt and debris were washed into the creek, while some small fish were left on dry land as the water receded.

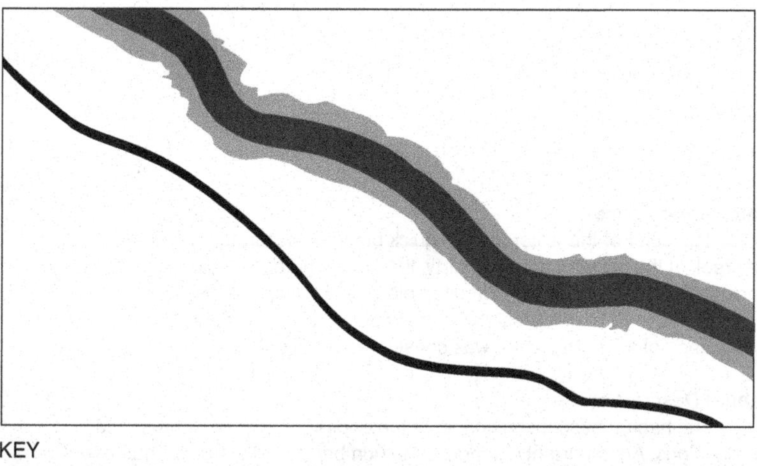

KEY

water

stream bed

running track

FIGURE 1 Wildwood Creek—Normal Water Level

EXAMPLE 17 (*continued*)

6

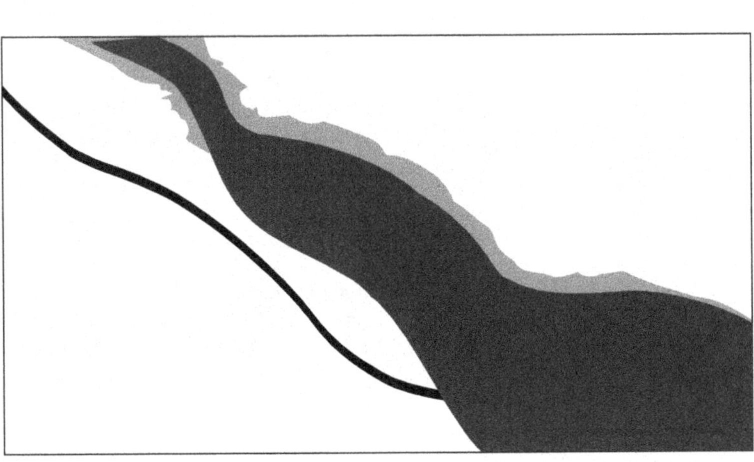

KEY

water

stream bed

running track

FIGURE 2 Wildwood Creek—Flash Flood Water Level

Water Appearance

The color of the water gives a quick but fairly accurate view of the health of the creek. If the water is brown or dirty, then silt or human waste may be present. Black areas of water may contain oil or other chemical products.

On each of the four test days, the water was always clear. Thus the appearance of the creek water was considered excellent.

Habitat Description

The habitat description concerns the appearance of the stream and its surroundings. An important criterion is the number of pools and the number of ripples—that is, points where water flows quickly over a rocky area. Both pools and ripples provide good locations for fish and other stream creatures to live and breed.

In describing habitat, McDuff also evaluates the amount of sediment at the bottom of the stream. Too much sediment tends to cover up areas where aquatic life lays eggs and hides them from predators. We also evaluate the stability of the stream banks; a stable bank indicates that erosion has not damaged the habitat. Finally, we observe the amount of stream cover. Such vegetation helps keep soil in place on the banks.

EXAMPLE 17 (*continued*)

Wildwood Creek tested fairly well for habitat. The number of pools and ripples was about average for such creeks. Stream deposits and stream bank stability were average to good, and stream cover was good to excellent. For more detail about test results, see the chart in the Test Comparison section on page 9.

Algae Appearance and Location

Algae is naturally present in any creek. The amount of algae can be a warning of pollution in the water. If algae is growing out of control, disproportionate amounts of nutrients such as nitrogen or phosphate could be present. These chemicals could come from fertilizer washed into the creek. Excessive amounts of algae cause the oxygen level to drop when they die and decompose.

During the four studies, algae was everywhere, but it was especially heavy on the rocks in the ripples of the creek. The algae was always brown and sometimes hairy.

Visible Litter

Litter can affect the habitat of a creek. Some litter has chemicals that can pollute the water; other litter can cover nesting areas and suffocate small animals. Whether the litter is harmful or not, it is always an eyesore.

On all four test dates, the litter we saw was heavy and ranged from tires to plastic bags. Some of the same trash that was at the site on the first visit was still there seven months later.

Bug Count

The bug count is a procedure that begins by washing dirt and water onto a screen. As water drains, the dirt with organisms is left on the screen. The bugs are removed and classified. Generally, the lower the bug count, the higher the pollution levels. Bug counts were considered low to average.

Two types of aquatic worms were discovered every time during our count, but in relatively small numbers. In addition, the worms we observed are very tolerant of pollution and can live in most conditions. Finally, we observed only two crayfish, animals that are somewhat sensitive to pollution.

CHEMICAL TESTS

Physical tests cover areas seen with the naked eye, but chemical tests can uncover pollutants that are not so recognizable. Certain chemicals can wipe out all life in a creek. Other chemicals can cause an overabundance of one life-form, which in turn could kill more sensitive animals.

A chart of results of chemical tests is included in the Test Comparison section on page 9. The chemical tests that McDuff performed were pH, dissolved oxygen (DO), turbidity, and phosphate.

EXAMPLE 17 (*continued*)

8

pH

The pH test is a measure of active hydrogen ions in a sample. The range of the pH test is 0–14. If the sample is in the range of 0–7, it is acidic; but if the sample is in the range of 7.0–14, it is basic. By law, the pH of a water sample must be within the range of 6.0–8.5.

For the tests we completed, the water sample was always 7.0, which is very good for a creek.

Dissolved Oxygen (DO)

Normally, oxygen dissolves readily into water from surface air. Once dissolved, it diffuses slowly in the water and is distributed throughout the creek. The amount of DO depends on different circumstances. Oxygen is always highest in choppy water, just after noon, and in cooler temperatures.

In many streams, the level of DO can become critically low during the summer months. When the temperature is warm, organisms are highly active and consume the oxygen supply. If the amount of DO drops below 3.0 ppm (parts per million), the area can become stressful for the organisms. An amount of oxygen that is 2.0 ppm or below will not support fish. DO that is 5.0 ppm to 6.0 ppm is usually required for growth and activity of organisms in the water.

According to the Water Quality Criteria for Georgia, average daily amounts of DO should be 5.0 ppm, with a minimum of 4.0 ppm. Wildwood Creek scored well on this test. The average amount of DO in the water was 6.9 ppm, with the highest amount being 9.0 ppm on November 11, 2006.

Turbidity

Turbidity is the discoloration of water due to sediment, microscopic organisms, and other matter. One major factor of turbidity is the level of rainfall before a test.

Three of our tests were performed on clear days with little rainfall. On these dates, the turbidity of Wildwood Creek was always 1.0, the best that creek water can score on the test. The fourth test, which scored worse, occurred during a rainy period.

Phosphate

Phosphorus occurs naturally as phosphates—for example, orthophosphates and organically bound phosphates. Orthophosphates are phosphates that are formed in fertilizer, whereas organically bound phosphates can form in plant and animal matter and waste.

Phosphate levels higher than 0.03 ppm contribute to an increase in plant growth. If phosphate levels are above 0.1 ppm, plants may be stimulated to grow out of control. The phosphate level of Wildwood was always 0.5 ppm, considerably higher than is desirable.

EXAMPLE 17 (*continued*)

9

TEST COMPARISON

There was little change from each of the four test dates. The only tests that varied greatly from one test to another were air temperature, water temperature, water flow, and DO. On the basis of these results, it would appear that Wildwood Creek is a relatively stable environment.

TABLE 1 Physical Tests

TEST DATES	**5/26/06**	**6/25/06**	**9/24/06**	**11/19/06**
Air Temperature in °C	21.5	23.0	24.0	13.5
Water Temperature in °C	20.0	22.0	23.0	13.0
Water Flow	Normal	High	Normal	Normal
Water Appearance	Clear	Clear	Clear	Clear
Habitat Description				
Number of Pools	2.0	3.0	2.0	5.0
Number of Ripples	1.0	2.0	2.0	2.0
Amount of Sediment Deposit	Average	Average	Good	Average
Stream Bank Stability	Average	Good	Good	Good
Stream Cover	Excellent	Good	Excellent	Good
Algae Appearance	Brown	Brown/hairy	Brown	Brown
Algae Location	Everywhere	Everywhere	Attached	Everywhere
Visible Litter	Heavy	Heavy	Heavy	Heavy
Bug Count	Low	Average	Low	Average

TABLE 2 Chemical Tests

Test	**5/26/06**	**6/25/06**	**9/24/06**	**11/19/06**
pH	7.0	7.0	7.0	7.0
Dissolved Oxygen (DO)	6.8	6.0	5.6	9.0
Turbidity	1.0	3.0	1.0	1.0
Phosphate	0.50	0.50	0.50	0.50

EXAMPLE 17 (*continued*)

10

CONCLUSIONS AND RECOMMENDATIONS

This section includes the major conclusions and recommendations from our study of Wildwood Creek.

CONCLUSIONS

Generally, we were pleased with the health of the stream bank and its floodplain. The area studied has large amounts of vegetation along the stream, and the banks seem to be sturdy. The floodplain has been turned into a park, which handles floods in a natural way. Floodwater in this area comes in contact with vegetation and some dirt. Floodwater also drains quickly, which keeps sediment from building up in the creek.

However, we are concerned with the number and types of animals uncovered in our bug counts. Only two bug types were discovered, and these were types quite tolerant to pollutants. The time of year these tests were performed could affect the discovery of some animals. However, the low count still should be considered a possible warning sign about water quality. Phosphate levels were also high and probably are the cause of the large amount of algae.

We believe something in the water is keeping sensitive animals from developing. One factor that affects the number of animals discovered is the pollutant problems in the past (see Appendix A). The creek may still be in a redevelopment stage, thus explaining the small numbers of animals.

RECOMMENDATIONS

On the basis of these conclusions, we recommend the following actions for Wildwood Creek:

1. Conduct the current tests two more times, through spring 2007. Spring is the time of year that most aquatic insects are hatched. If sensitive organisms are found then, the health of the creek could be considered to have improved.
2. Add testing for nitrogen. With the phosphate level being so high, nitrogen might also be present. If it is, then fertilizer could be in the water.
3. Add testing for human waste. Some contamination may still be occurring.
4. Add testing for metals, such as mercury, that can pollute the water.
5. Add testing for runoff water from drainage pipes that flow into the creek.
6. Schedule a volunteer cleanup of the creek.

With a full year of study and additional tests, the problems of Wildwood Creek can be better understood.

EXAMPLE 17 (*continued*)

11

APPENDIX A

Background on Wildwood Creek

Wildwood Creek begins from tributaries on the northeast side of the city of Winslow. From this point, the creek flows southwest to the Chattahoochee River. Winslow Wastewater Treatment Plant has severely polluted the creek in the past with discharge of wastewater directly into the creek. Wildwood became so contaminated that signs warning of excessive pollution were posted along the creek to alert the public.

Today, all known wastewater discharge has been removed. The stream's condition has dramatically improved, but non-point contamination sources continue to lower the creek's water quality. Non-point contamination includes sewer breaks, chemical dumping, and storm sewers.

Another problem for Wildwood Creek is siltration. Rainfall combines with bank erosion and habitat destruction to wash excess dirt into the creek. This harsh action destroys most of the macroinvertebrates. At the present time, Wildwood Creek may be one of the more threatened creeks in Ware County.

EXAMPLE 17 (*continued*)

12

APPENDIX B

Water Quality Criteria for Georgia

All waterways in Georgia are classified in one of the following categories: fishing, recreation, drinking, and wild and scenic. Different protection levels apply to the different uses. For example, the protection level for dissolved oxygen is stricter in drinking water than fishing water. All water is supposed to be free from all types of waste and sewage that can settle and form sludge deposits.

In Ware County, all waterways are classified as "fishing," according to Chapter 391-3-6.03 of "Water Use Classifications and Water Quality Standards" in the Georgia Department of Natural Resources *Rules and Regulations for Water Quality Control.* The only exception is the Chattahoochee River, which is classified as "drinking water supply" and "recreational."

EXAMPLE 17 (*continued*)

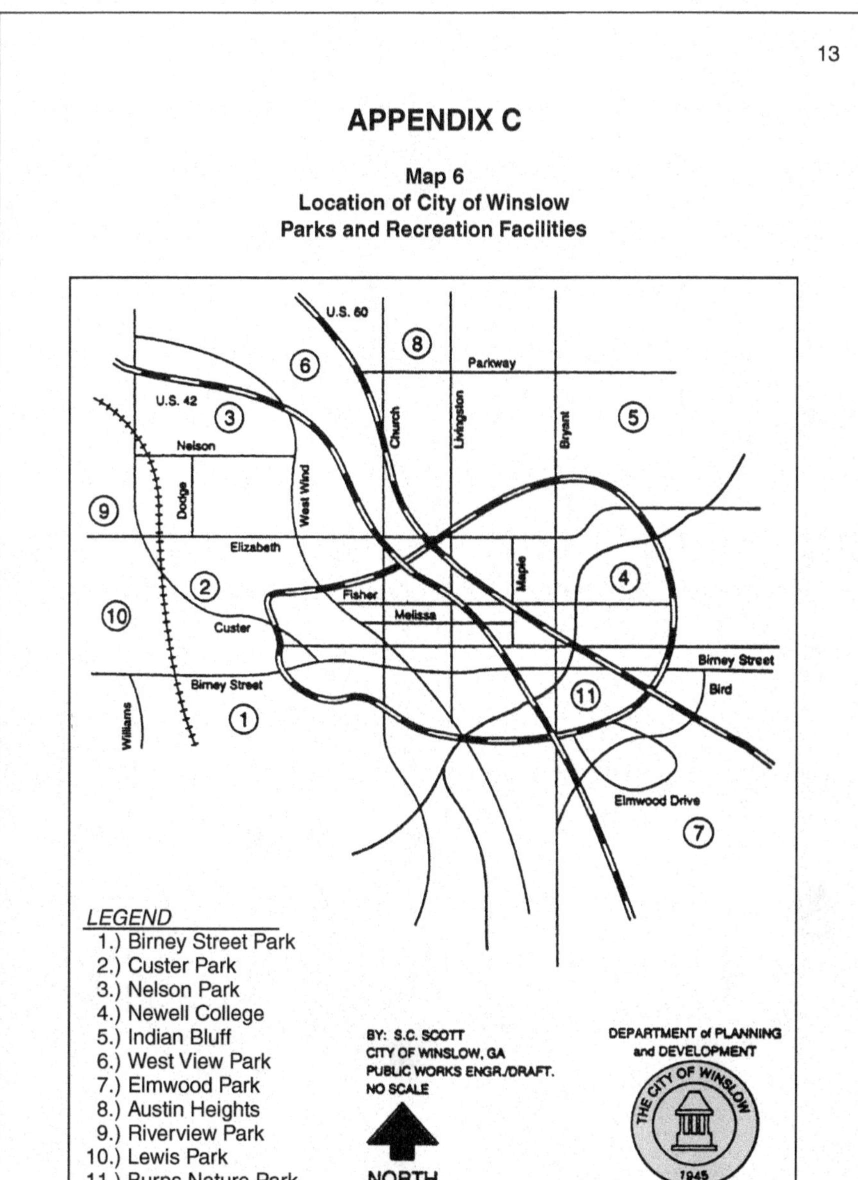

13

APPENDIX C

Map 6
Location of City of Winslow
Parks and Recreation Facilities

EXAMPLE 17 (*continued*)

4 Special Topics
Graphics and Oral Presentations

Although writing is central to your work as a technical communicator, your success also depends on your skills in two related topics—graphics and oral presentations. This chapter covers these topics in three main sections:

- **Graphics**—includes terms in graphics, reasons for using graphics, general guidelines, and specific guidelines for pie charts, bar charts, line charts, tables, and technical drawings.
- **Oral Presentations**—includes guidelines for preparation and delivery, general guidelines for speech graphics, and guidelines for overcoming nervousness.
- **PowerPoint Presentations**—includes specific guidelines for planning a PowerPoint presentation, creating PowerPoint slides, and delivering a PowerPoint presentation.

When combined with writing guidelines in Chapters 1 to 3 and the Appendix (Writing Handbook), the suggestions in this chapter provide what you will need to be a "complete technical communicator."

GRAPHICS

The availability of sophisticated graphics increases your reader's expectations that documents include them when appropriate. Therefore, technical professionals need to understand and be able to apply basic guidelines about graphics, as a complement to their writing skills. This section (1) defines some common terms in graphics, (2) explains the main reasons to use graphics, (3) gives some general graphics guidelines, and (4) lists specific guidelines for five common graphics.

Common Terms in Graphics

Terminology for graphics is not uniform in the profession. That fact can lead to some confusion. For the purposes of this chapter, some common definitions have been adopted and are listed here:

- **Graphics:** This generic term refers to any nontextual portion of documents or oral presentations. It can be used in two ways: (1) to designate the field (for example, "Graphics is an area in which he showed great interest") or (2) to name individual graphic items ("She placed three graphics in her report").
- **Illustrations, visual aids:** Used synonymously with *graphics*, these two terms also can refer to all nontextual parts of a document. The term *visual aids*, however, often is limited to the context of oral presentations.
- **Tables, figures:** These terms name two main subsets of graphics. *Tables* refers to illustrations that place numbers or words in columns or rows or both. *Figures* refers to all graphics other than tables. Examples include charts (pie, bar, line, flow, and organization), engineering drawings, maps, and photographs.
- **Charts, graphs:** A subset of *figures*, these synonymous terms refer to a type of graphic that displays data in visual form—as with bars, pie shapes, or lines on graphs. *Chart* is the term used most often in this text.

Of course, you may see other graphics terms. For example, some technical companies use the word *plates* for figures. Be sure to know the terms your readers understand and the types of graphics they use.

Reasons to Use Graphics

Before deciding whether to use a pie chart, table, or any other graphic, you need to know what graphics do for your writing. Here are four main reasons for using them.

Reason 1: Graphics Simplify Ideas

Readers may know less about the subject than you. Graphics can help them cut through technical details and grasp basic ideas. For example, a simple illustration of a laboratory instrument, such as a Bunsen burner, makes the description of a lab procedure much easier to understand. In a more complex example, Figure 4–1 uses a group of four different charts to convey one main point: A company's new Equipment Development group lags behind the company's other profit centers. A quick look at the charts tells the story of the group's difficulties much better than would several hundred words of text.

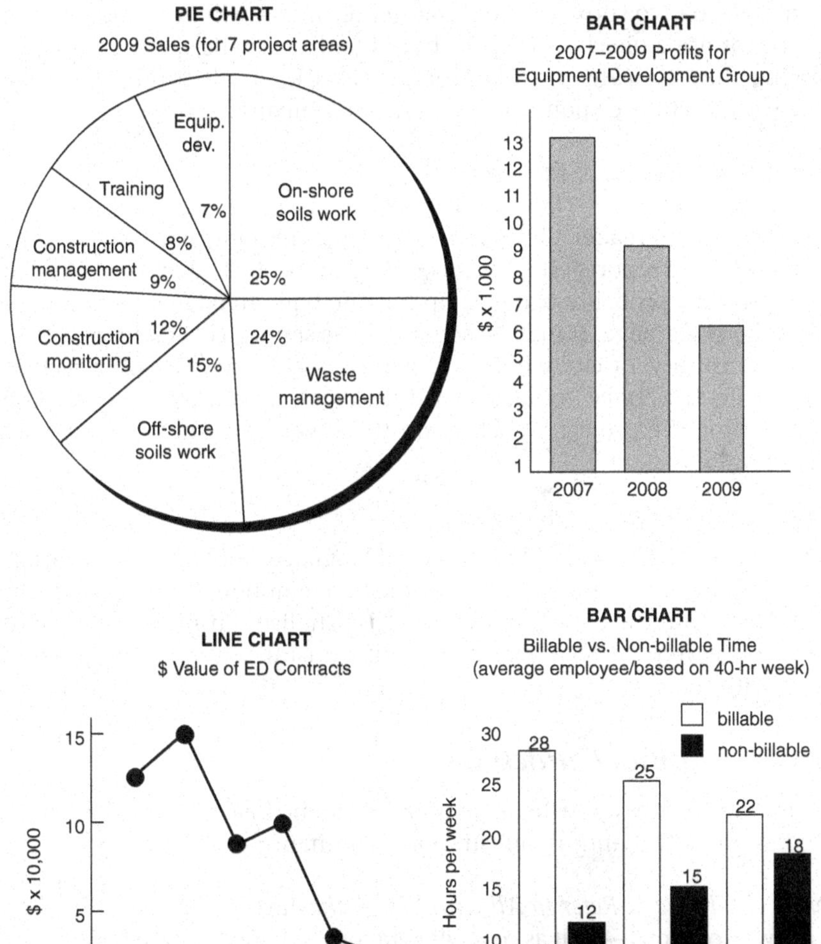

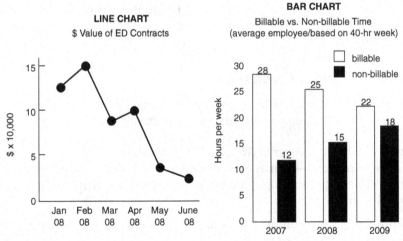

FIGURE 4–1
Graphics used to simplify ideas

Reason 2: Graphics Reinforce Ideas
When a point really needs emphasis, create a graphic. For example, you might draw a map to show where computer terminals will be located within a building, or use a pie chart to show how a budget will be spent, or include a drawing that indicates how to operate a VCR. In all three cases, the graphic would reinforce points made in the accompanying text.

Reason 3: Graphics Create Interest
Graphics are "grabbers." They can be used to entice readers into the text, just as they engage readers' interest in magazines and journals. If your customers have three reports on their desks and must quickly decide which one to read first, they probably will pick up the one with an engaging picture or chart on the cover page. It may be something as simple as (1) a map outline of the state, county, or city where you will be doing a project; (2) a picture of the product or service you are providing; or (3) a symbol of the purpose of your writing the project. Whether on the cover or in the text, graphics attract attention.

Reason 4: Graphics Are Universal
Graphics have been humankind's universal language since cave drawings. A picture, drawing, or chart makes an immediate emotional impact that can help or hurt your case. Advertisers and journalists know the power of images, and writers of technical documents must also merge the force of graphics with their text.

General Graphics Guidelines

A few basic guidelines apply to all graphics. Keep the following fundamentals in mind as you select and use illustrations to enhance your text.

Graphics Guideline 1: Refer to All Graphics in the Text
With a few exceptions—such as cover illustrations intended to grab attention—graphics should be accompanied by clear references within your text. Specifically, follow these rules:

- Include the graphic number in Arabic, not roman numerals, when you are using more than one graphic.
- Include the title, and sometimes the page number, if either is needed for clarity or emphasis.
- Incorporate the reference smoothly into the wording of your text.

Here are two ways to phrase and position a graphics reference. In Example 1, there is the additional emphasis of the graphics title, whereas in Example 2, the title is left out. Also, note that you can draw more attention to the graphic by placing the reference at the start of the sentence in a separate clause. Or you can relegate the reference to a parenthetical expression at the end or middle of the passage. Choose the option that best suits your purposes.

- **Example 1:** In the past five years, 56 businesses in the county have started in-house recycling programs. The result has been a dramatic shift in the amount of property the county has bought for new waste sites, as shown in Figure 5 ("Landfill Purchases, 1996–2001").
- **Example 2:** As shown in Figure 5, the county has purchased much less land for landfills during the past five years. This dramatic reduction results from the fact that 56 businesses have started in-house recycling programs.

Graphics Guideline 2: Think about Where to Put Graphics

In most cases, locate a graphic close to the text in which it is mentioned. This immediate reinforcement of text by an illustration gives graphics their greatest strength. Variations of this option, as well as several other possibilities, are presented here:

- **The same page as text reference:** A simple visual, such as an informal table, should go on the same page as the text reference if you think it is too small for a separate page.
- **Page opposite text reference:** A complex graphic, such as a long table, that accompanies a specific page of text can go on the page opposite the text—that is, on the opposite page of a two-page spread. Usually, this option is exercised *only* in documents that are printed on both sides of the paper throughout.
- **Page following first text reference:** Most text graphics appear on the page after the first reference. If the graphic is referred to throughout the text, it can be repeated at later points. (Note: Readers prefer to have graphics positioned exactly where they need them, rather than having to refer to another part of the document.)
- **Attachments or appendixes:** Graphics can go at the end of the document in two cases: first, if the text contains so many references to the graphic that placement in a central location, such as an appendix, would make it more accessible; and second, if the graphic contains less important supporting material that would only interrupt the text.

Graphics Guideline 3: Position Graphics Vertically When Possible

Readers prefer graphics they can view without having to turn the document sideways. However, if the table or figure cannot fit vertically on a standard 8 1/2" × 11" page, either use a foldout or place the graphic horizontally on the page. In the latter case, position the illustration so that the top is on the left margin. (In other words, the page must be turned clockwise to be viewed.)

Graphics Guideline 4: Avoid Clutter

Let simplicity be your guide. Readers go to graphics for relief from, or reinforcement of, the text. They do not want to be bombarded by visual clutter. Omit information that is not relevant to your purpose, while still making the illustration clear and self-contained. Also, use enough white space so that the readers' eyes are drawn to the graphic.

Graphics Guideline 5: Provide Titles, Notes, Keys, and Source Data

Graphics should be as self-contained and self-explanatory as possible. Moreover, they must note any borrowed information. Follow these basic rules for format and acknowledgment of sources:

- **Title:** Follow the graphic number with a short, precise title—either on the line below the number *or* on the same line after a colon (for example, Figure 3: Salary Scales).
- **Tables:** Place the number and title at the top. (As noted in Table Guideline 1 on page 124, one exception is informal tables. They have no table number or title.)
- **Figures:** Place the number and title either above or below the illustration. Either center titles or place them flush with the left margin.
- **Notes for explanation:** When introductory information for the graphic is needed, place a note directly underneath the title *or* at the bottom of the graphic.
- **Keys or legends for simplicity:** If a graphic needs many labels, consider using a legend or key, which lists the labels and corresponding symbols on the graphic. For example, a pie chart might have the letters *A, B, C, D,* and *E* printed on the pie pieces; a legend at the top, bottom, or side of the figure would list what the letters represent.
- **Source information at the bottom:** You have an ethical, and often legal, obligation to cite the person, organization, or publication from which you borrowed information for the figure. Either (1) precede the description with the word *Source* and a colon or (2) if you have edited a graphic or borrowed just part of it, introduce the citation with *Adapted from.* See Figures 2–1 and 2–5 in this book for examples of both.

Note: Besides citing the source, it is sometimes necessary to request permission to use copyrighted or proprietary information, depending on your use and the amount you are borrowing. (A prominent exception is most information provided by the federal government. Most government publications are not copyrighted.) Consult a reference librarian for details about seeking permission.

Guidelines for Pie Charts

Familiar to most readers, pie charts show relationships between the parts and the whole when just approximate information is needed. Their simple circles with clear labels can provide comforting simplicity within even the most complicated report. Yet their simplicity keeps them from being useful when you need to show detailed information. Here are specific guidelines for constructing pie charts.

Pie Chart Guideline 1: Use No More than 10 Divisions
To make pie charts work well, limit the number of pie pieces to no more than 10. In fact, the fewer the better. This approach lets the reader grasp major relationships, without having to wade through the clutter of tiny divisions that are difficult to read. Figure 4–2, for example, aims to show how a large company will staff a particular project. The reader can quickly see that project staff will come from three main offices.

Pie Chart Guideline 2: Move Clockwise from 12:00, from the Largest to the Smallest Wedge
Readers prefer pie charts oriented like a clock, with the first wedge starting at 12:00. Move from the largest to the smallest wedge to provide a convenient organizing principle.

Make exceptions to this design only for good reason. In Figure 4–2, for example, the last wedge represents a greater percentage than the previous wedge. In this way, it does not break up the sequence the writer wants to establish by grouping the three offices with the three largest individual percentages of project workers.

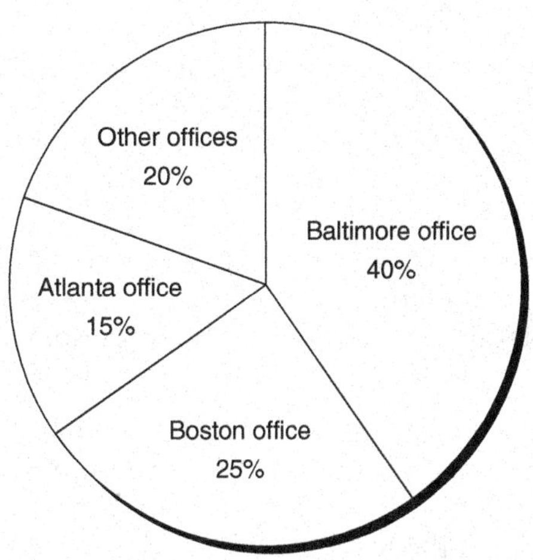

FIGURE 4–2
Pie chart with as few pieces as possible. (Chart shows workforce breakdown for a project. The company can draw most project workers from its East Coast offices.)

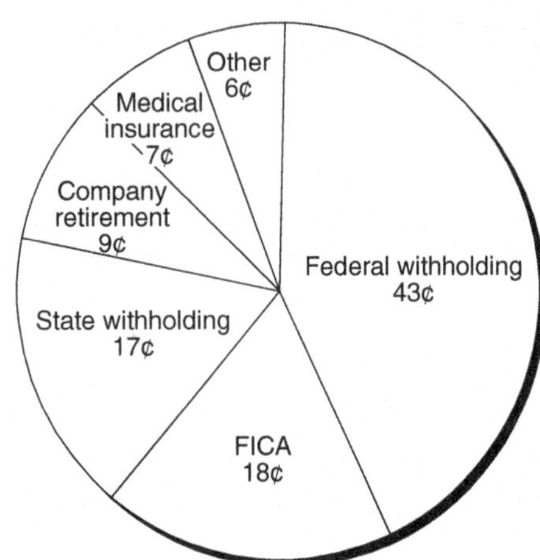

FIGURE 4–3
Pie chart showing money breakdown for average deductions from a paycheck

Pie Chart Guideline 3: Use Pie Charts Especially for Percentages and Money
Pie charts catch the reader's eye best when they represent items divisible by 100, as with percentages and dollars. Figure 4–2 shows percentages; Figure 4–3 shows money. Using the pie chart for money breakdowns is made even more appropriate by the coin-like shape of the chart.

Pie Chart Guideline 4: Be Creative, but Stay Simple
Figure 4–4 shows how you can emphasize one piece of the pie:

A. Shade a wedge.

B. Remove a wedge from the main pie.

C. Place related pie charts in a three-dimensional drawing.

Today there are graphics software packages that can create these and other variations for you, so experiment a bit. Of course, always make sure to keep your charts from becoming too detailed. Pie charts should stay simple.

Pie Chart Guideline 5: Draw and Label Carefully
The most common pie chart errors are (1) wedge sizes that do not correspond correctly to percentages or money amounts and (2) pie sizes that are too small to accommodate the information placed in them. Here are some suggestions for avoiding these mistakes:

- **Pie size:** Make sure the chart occupies enough of the page. On a standard 8 1/2″ × 11″ sheet with only one pie chart, your circle should be from 3″ to 6″ in diameter—large enough not to be dwarfed by labels and small enough to leave sufficient white space in the margins.

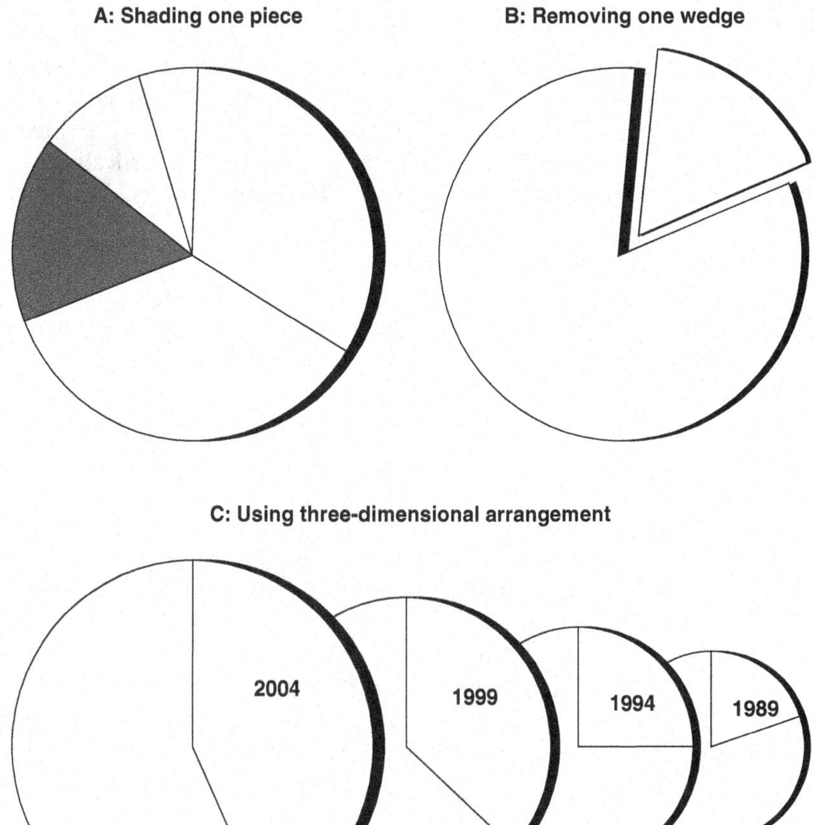

FIGURE 4–4
Techniques for emphasis in pie charts

- **Labels:** Place the wedge labels either inside the pie or outside, depending on the number of wedges, the number of wedge labels, or the length of the labels. Choose the option that produces the cleanest-looking chart.
- **Conversion of percentages:** If you are drawing the pie chart by hand, not using a computer program, use a protractor or similar device. One percent of the pie equals 3.6 degrees (3.6 × 100% = 360 degrees in a circle). With that formula as your guide, you can convert percentages or cents to degrees of a circle. Remember, however, that a pie chart does not reveal fine distinctions very well; it is best used for showing larger differences.

Guidelines for Bar Charts

Like pie charts, bar charts are easily recognized, for they are seen every day in newspapers and magazines. Unlike pie charts, however, bar charts can accommodate a good deal of technical detail. Comparisons are provided by means of two or more bars running either horizontally or vertically on the page. Follow these five guidelines to create effective bar charts.

Bar Chart Guideline 1: Use a Limited Number of Bars

Although bar charts can show more information than pie charts, both types of illustrations have their limits. Bar charts begin to break down when there are so many bars that information is not easily grasped. The maximum bar number can vary according to chart size, of course. Figure 4–5 shows several multibar charts. The impact of the charts is enhanced by the limited number of bars.

Bar Chart Guideline 2: Show Comparisons Clearly

Bar lengths should be varied enough to show comparisons quickly and clearly. Avoid using bars that are too close in length, for then readers must study the chart before understanding it. Such a chart lacks immediate visual impact.

Also, avoid the opposite tendency of using bar charts to show data that are much different in magnitude. To relate such differences, some writers resort to the dubious technique of inserting "break lines" (two parallel lines), called hash marks, on an axis to reflect breaks in scale (see Figure 4–6). Although this approach does remind readers of the breaks, it is still deceptive. For example, note that Figure 4–6 provides no *visual* demonstration of the relationship between 50 and 2,800. The reader must think about these differences before making sense of the chart. In other words, the use of hash marks runs counter to a main goal of graphics—creating an immediate and accurate visual impact.

Bar Chart Guideline 3: Keep Bar Widths Equal and Adjust Space between Bars Carefully

Although bar length varies, bar width must remain constant. As for the distance between the bars, the following are three options (along with examples in Figure 4–7):

- **Option A: Use no space** when there are close comparisons or many bars, so that differences are easier to grasp.
- **Option B: Use equal space, but less than bar width** when bar height differences are great enough to be seen in spite of the distance between bars.
- **Option C: Use variable space** when gaps between some bars are needed to reflect gaps in the data.

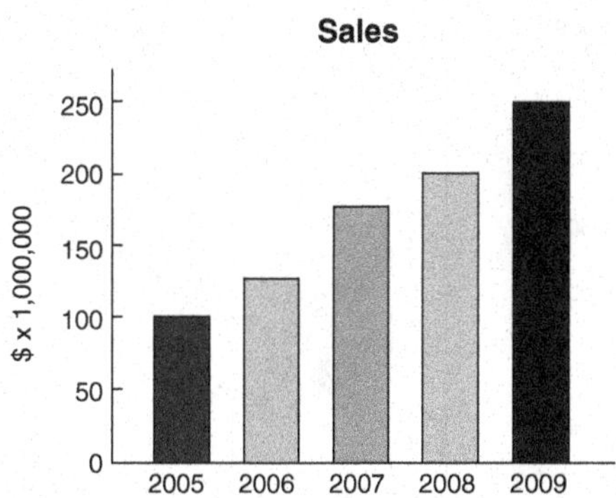

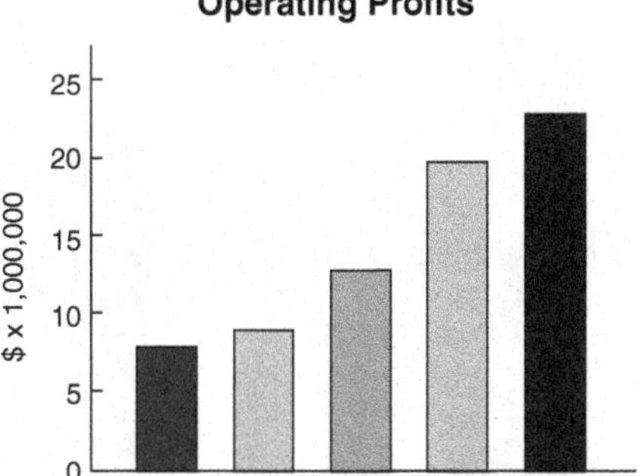

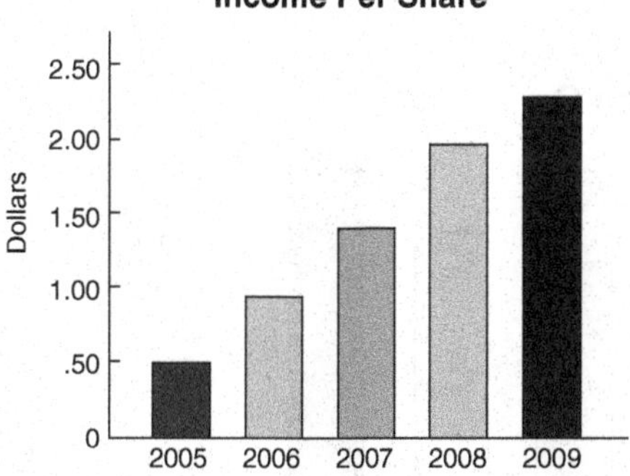

FIGURE 4–5
Bar charts

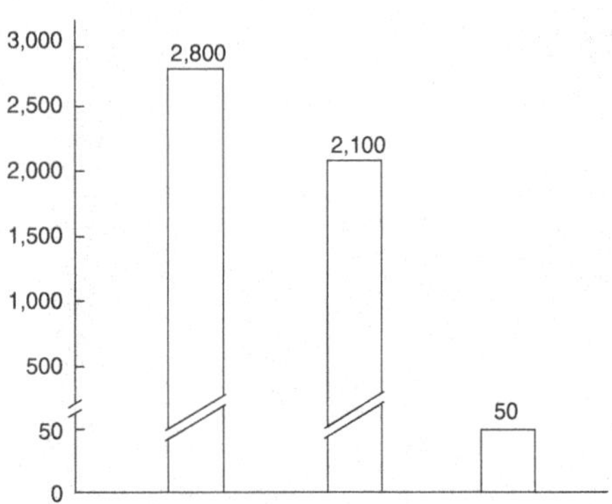

FIGURE 4–6
Hash marks on bar charts—a technique that can lead to misunderstanding

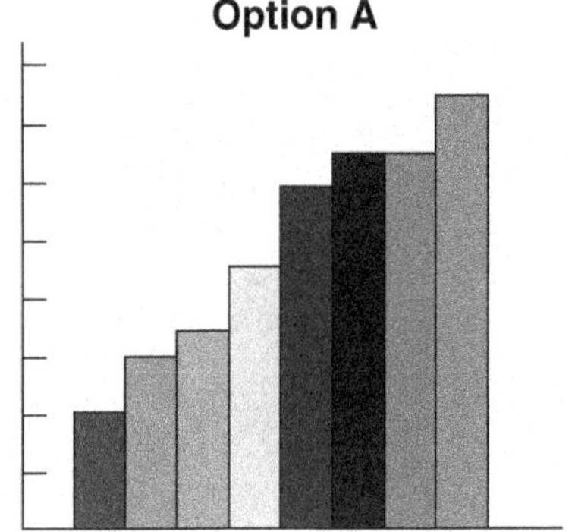

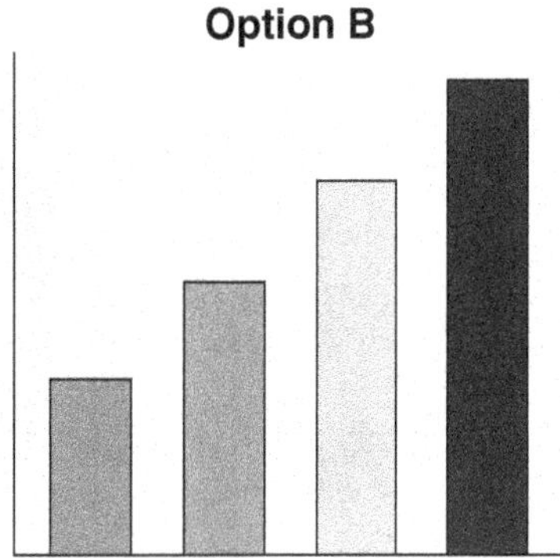

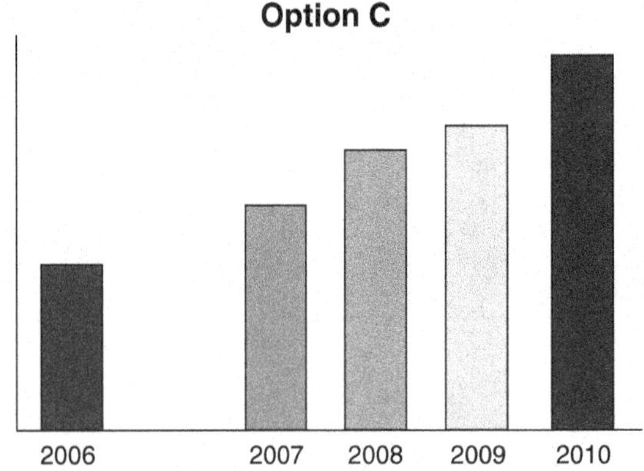

FIGURE 4–7
Bar chart variations

Bar Chart Guideline 4: Carefully Arrange the Order of Bars

The arrangement of bars is what reveals meaning to readers. Here are two common approaches:

- **Sequential:** used when the progress of the bars shows a trend—for example, a company's increasing number of environmental projects in the last five years
- **Ascending or descending order:** used when you want to make a point by the rising or falling of the bars—for example, the 2010 profits of a company's six international offices, from lowest to highest

Bar Chart Guideline 5: Be Creative

Figure 4–8 shows two bar chart variations that help display multiple trends. The *segmented bars* in Option A produce four types of information: the total sales (A + B + C) and the individual sales for A, B, and C. The *grouped bars* in Option B show the individual sales trends for D, F, and G, along with a comparison of all three by year. Note that the amounts are written on the bars to highlight comparisons.

Although these and other bar chart variations may be useful, remember to retain the basic simplicity of the chart.

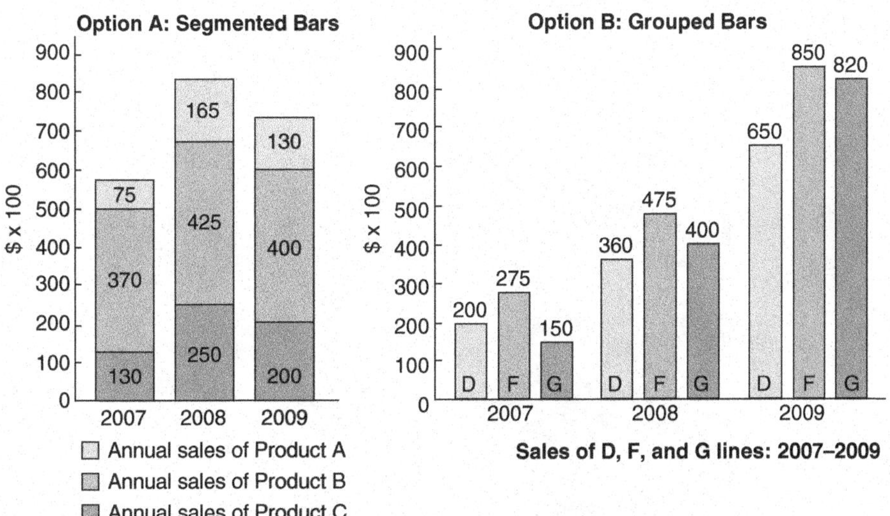

FIGURE 4–8
Bar chart variations for multiple trends

Guidelines for Line Charts

Line charts are a common graphic. Almost every newspaper contains a few charts covering topics such as stock trends, car prices, or weather. More than other graphics, line charts telegraph complex trends immediately.

They work by using vertical and horizontal axes to reflect quantities of two different variables. The vertical (or *y*) axis usually plots the dependent variable; the horizontal (or *x*) axis usually plots the independent variable. (The dependent variable is affected by changes in the independent variable.) Lines then connect points that have been plotted on the chart. When using line charts, follow these five main guidelines:

Line Chart Guideline 1: Use Line Charts for Trends

Readers are affected by the direction and angle of the chart's line(s), so take advantage of this persuasive potential. In Figure 4–9, for example, the writer wants to show the feasibility of adopting a new medical plan. Including a line chart in the study gives immediate emphasis to the most important issue— the effect the new plan would have on stabilizing the firm's medical costs.

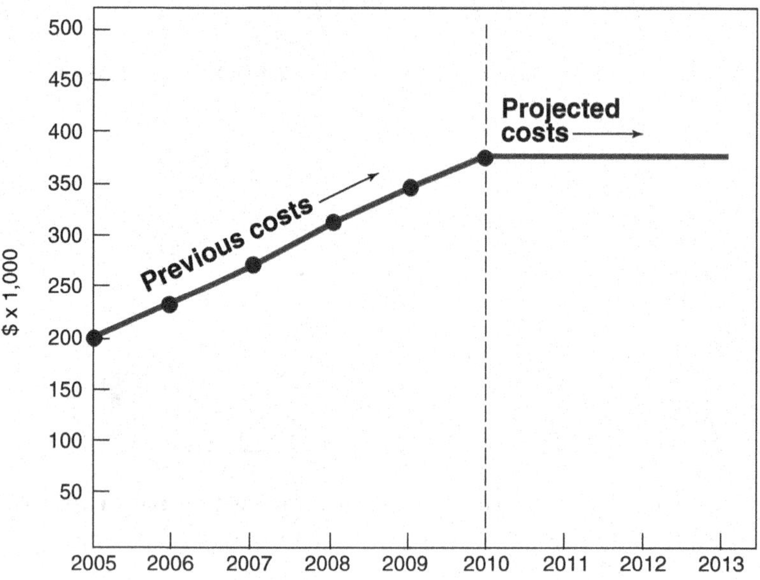

FIGURE 4–9
Line chart used to show the effect of a proposed medical plan

Line Chart Guideline 2: Locate Line Charts with Care
Given their strong impact, line charts can be especially useful as attention-grabbers. Consider placing them (1) on cover pages (to engage reader interest in the document), (2) at the beginning of sections that describe trends, and (3) in conclusions (to reinforce a major point of your document).

Line Chart Guideline 3: Strive for Accuracy and Clarity
Like bar charts, line charts can be misused or just poorly constructed. Be sure that the line or lines on the graph truly reflect the data you have used. Also, select a scale that does not mislead readers with visual gimmicks. Here are some specific suggestions to keep your line charts accurate and clear:

- Start all scales from zero to eliminate the possible confusion of breaks in amounts (see Bar Chart Guideline 2).
- Select a vertical-to-horizontal ratio for axis lengths that is pleasing to the eye (three vertical to four horizontal is common).
- Make chart lines as thick as, or thicker than, the axis lines.
- Use shading under the line when it will make the chart more readable.

Line Chart Guideline 4: Do Not Place Numbers on the Chart Itself
Line charts derive their main effect from the simplicity of lines that show trends. Avoid cluttering the chart with a lot of numbers that only detract from the visual impact.

Line Chart Guideline 5: Use Multiple Lines with Care
Like bar charts, line charts can show multiple trends. Simply add another line or two. If you place too many lines on one chart, however, you run the risk of confusing the reader with too much data. Use no more than four or five lines on a single chart (see Figure 4–10).

Guidelines for Tables

Tables present readers with raw data, usually in the form of numbers but sometimes in the form of words. Tables are classified as either informal or formal:

- **Informal tables:** limited data arranged in the form of either rows or columns
- **Formal tables:** data arranged in a grid, always with both horizontal rows and vertical columns

These five guidelines will help you design and position tables within the text of your documents.

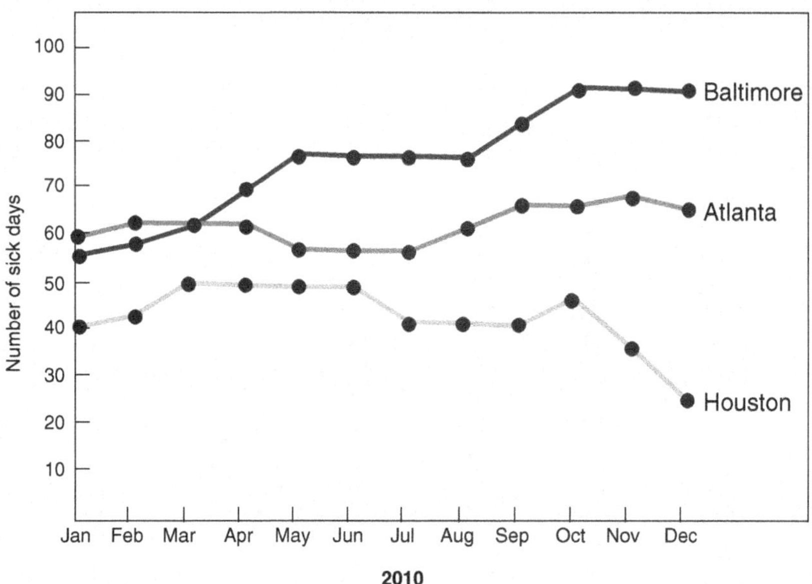

FIGURE 4–10
Line chart using multiple lines to show the number of sick days taken at four offices: 2010

Table Guideline 1: Use Informal Tables as Extensions of Text
Informal tables are usually merged with the text on a page, rather than isolated on a separate page or attachment. As such, an informal table usually has (1) no table number or title, (2) no listing in the list of illustrations in a formal report or proposal, and (3) few, if any, headings for rows or columns.

Example:
Our project in Alberta, Canada, will involve engineers, technicians, and salespeople from three offices, in these numbers:

San Francisco Office	45
St. Louis Office	34
London Office	6

Table Guideline 2: Use Formal Tables for Complex Data Separated from Text
Formal tables may appear on the page of text that includes the table reference, on the page following the first text reference, or in an attachment or appendix. In any case, you should do the following:

- Extract important data from the table and highlight them in the text
- Make every formal table as clear and visually appealing as possible

Table Guideline 3: Use Plenty of White Space

Used around and within tables, white space guides the eye through a table much better than do black lines. Avoid putting complete boxes around tables. Instead, leave one inch more of white space than you would normally leave around text.

Table Guideline 4: Follow Usual Conventions Dividing and Explaining Data

Figure 4–11 shows a typical formal table. It satisfies the overriding goal of being clear and self-contained. To achieve such an objective in your tables, follow these guidelines:

1. **Titles and numberings:** Give a title to each formal table, and place title and number above the table. Number each table if the document contains two or more tables.
2. **Headings:** Create short, clear headings for all columns and rows.
3. **Abbreviations:** Include in the headings any necessary abbreviations or symbols, such as *lb* or%. Spell out abbreviations and define terms in a key or footnote if any reader may need such assistance.
4. **Numbers:** Round off numbers when possible, for ease of reading. Also, align multidigit numbers on the right edge, or at the decimal when shown.
5. **Notes:** Place any necessary explanatory headnotes either between the title and the table (if the notes are short) or at the bottom of the table.
6. **Footnotes:** Place any necessary footnotes below the table.
7. **Sources:** Place any necessary source references below the footnotes.
8. **Caps:** Use uppercase and lowercase letters, rather than full caps.

TABLE 6: Employee Retirement Fund

Investment Type	Book Value	Market Value	% of Total Market Value
Temporary Securities	$ 434,084	$ 434,084	5.9%
Bonds	3,679,081	3,842,056	52.4
Common Stocks	2,508,146	3,039,350	41.4
Mortgages	18,063	18,063	.3
Real Estate	1,939	1,939	nil
Totals	$6,641,313	$7,335,492	100.0%

Note: This table contrasts the book value versus the market value of the Employee Retirement Fund, as of December 31, 2010.

FIGURE 4–11
Example of a formal table

Table Guideline 5: Pay Special Attention to Cost Data
Most readers prefer to have complicated financial information placed in tabular form. Given the importance of such data, edit cost tables with great care. Devote extra attention to these two issues:

- Placement of decimals in costs
- Correct totals of figures

Documents such as proposals can be considered contracts in some courts of law, so there is no room for error in relating costs.

Guidelines for Technical Drawings

Technical drawings are important tools of companies that produce or use technical products. These drawings can accompany documents such as instructions, reports, sales orders, proposals, brochures, and posters. They are preferred over photographs when specific views are more important than photographic detail. Whereas earlier all drawings used to be produced mainly by hand, now they are usually created by computer-assisted design (CAD) systems. Follow these guidelines for producing technical drawings that complement your text.

Technical Drawing Guideline 1: Choose the Right Amount of Detail
Keep drawings as simple as possible. Use only the level of detail that serves the purpose of your document and satisfies your reader's needs. For example, Figure 4–12 will be used in a brochure on maintaining home heating systems. Its intention is to focus on one part of the thermostat—the lever and attached roller. Completed on a CAD system, this drawing presents an exploded view so that the location of the arm can be seen easily.

Technical Drawing Guideline 2: Label Parts Well
A common complaint of drawings is that parts included in the illustration are not carefully or clearly labeled. Place labels on every part you want your reader to see. (Conversely, you can choose *not* to label those parts that are irrelevant to your purpose.)

When you label parts, use a typeface large enough for easy reading. Also, arrange labels so that (1) they are as easy as possible for your reader to locate and (2) they do not detract from the importance of the drawing itself. The simple labeling in Figure 4–12 fulfills these objectives.

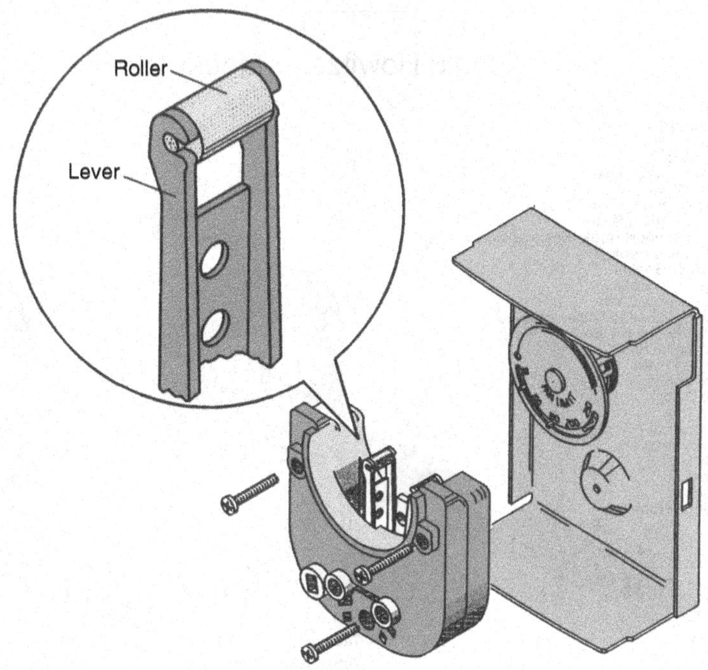

FIGURE 4–12
Technical drawing (exploded view) of home thermostat

Technical Drawing Guideline 3: Choose the Most Appropriate View
As already noted, illustrations—unlike photographs—permit you to choose the level of detail needed. In addition, drawings offer you a number of options for perspective or view:

- **Exterior view** shows surface features with either a two- or three-dimensional appearance (see Figure 4–13).
- **Cross-section view** shows a "slice" of the object so that interiors can be viewed.
- **Exploded view** shows relationship of parts to each other by "exploding" the mechanism (see Figure 4–12).
- **Cutaway view** shows inner workings of object by removing part of the exterior.

Technical Drawing Guideline 4: Use Legends When There Are Many Parts
In complex drawings, avoid cluttering the illustration with many labels. Figure 4–13, for example, places all labels in one easy-to-find spot, rather than leaving them on the drawing.

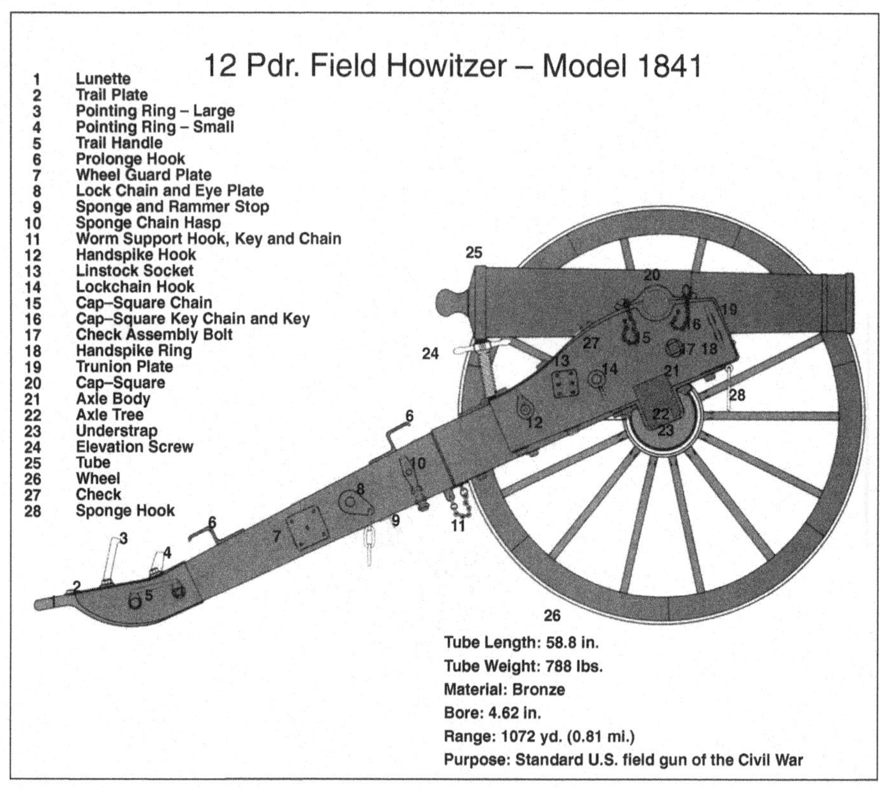

FIGURE 4–13
Technical drawing using cad system

ORAL PRESENTATIONS

Oral presentations, or speeches, are defined quite broadly. Usually, they can be classified according to criteria like these:

- **Format:** from informal question-and-answer sessions to formal speeches
- **Length:** from several-minute overviews to long sessions of an hour or more
- **Number of presenters:** from solo performances to group presentations
- **Content:** from a few highlights to detailed coverage

Throughout your career, you will speak to different-sized groups, on diverse topics, and in varied formats. The next three sections provide some guidelines for preparation and delivery, speech graphics, and overcoming nervousness. The next and final section of this chapter is devoted exclusively to a specific speech graphic, PowerPoint, because of its importance and heavy use in technical communication.

Note that before writing the text of a speech, you should use the same Planning Form this book recommends you complete before drafting documents. The form is located at the end of this book.

Guidelines for Speech Preparation and Delivery

The goal of most oral presentations is quite simple: You must present a few basic points, in a fairly brief time, to an interested but usually impatient audience. Simplicity, brevity, and interest are the keys to success. If you deliver what *you* expect when *you* hear a speech, then you will give good presentations yourself.

Speech Guideline 1: Know Your Listeners

These features are common to most listeners:

- They cannot "rewind the tape" of your presentation, in contrast to the way they can skip back and forth through the text of a report.
- They are impatient after the first few minutes, particularly if they do not know where a speech is going.
- They will daydream and often need their attention brought back to the matter at hand (expect a 30-second attention span).
- They have heard so many disappointing presentations that they might not have high expectations for yours.

To respond to these realities, you must learn as much as possible about your listeners. For example, you can (1) consider what you already know about your audience, (2) talk with colleagues who have spoken to the same group, and (3) find out which listeners make the decisions. Make sure to record what you know about your listeners on the Planning Form at the end of this book.

Most important, make sure not to talk over anyone's head. If there are several levels of technical expertise represented by the group, find the lowest common denominator and decrease the technical level of your presentation accordingly. Remember, decision-makers are often the ones without current technical experience. They may want only highlights. Later, they can review written documents for details, or they can solicit more technical information during the question-and-answer session after you speak.

Speech Guideline 2: Use the Preacher's Maxim

The well-known preacher's maxim goes like this:

> First you tell 'em what you're gonna tell 'em, then you tell 'em, and then you tell 'em what you told 'em.

Why should most speakers follow this plan? Because it gives the speech a simple three-part structure that listeners can grasp easily. Here is how your speech should be organized (note that it corresponds to the ABC Format used throughout this text for writing):

1. **Abstract (beginning of presentation):** Right at the outset, you should (1) get the listeners' interest (with an anecdote, a statistic, or other technique), (2) state the exact purpose of the speech, and (3) list the main points you will cover. Do not try the patience of your audience with an extended introduction. Use no more than a minute.

   Example: "Last year, Jones Engineering had 56% more field accidents than the year before. This morning, I'll examine a proposed safety plan that aims to solve this problem. My presentation will focus on three main benefits of the new plan: lower insurance premiums, less lost time from accidents, and better morale among the employees."

2. **Body (middle of presentation):** Here you discuss the points mentioned briefly in the introduction, in the same order that they were mentioned. Provide the kinds of obvious transitions that help your listeners stay on track.

   Example: "The final benefit of the new safety plan will be improved morale among the field-workers at all our job sites. . . ."

3. **Conclusion (end of presentation):** In the conclusion, review the main ideas covered in the body of the speech and specify actions you want to occur as a result of your presentation.

   Example: "Jones Engineering can benefit from this new safety plan in three main ways. . . . If Jones implements the new plan next month, I believe you will see a dramatic reduction in on-site accidents during the last half of the year."

This simple three-part plan for all presentations gives listeners the handle they need to understand your speech. First, there is a clear road map in the introduction so that they know what lies ahead in the rest of the speech. Second, there is an organized pattern in the body, with clear transitions between points. And third, there is a strong finish that brings the audience back full circle to the main thrust of the presentation.

Speech Guideline 3: Stick to a Few Main Points

Our short-term memory holds limited items. It follows that listeners are most attentive to speeches organized around a few major points. In fact, a good argument can be made for organizing information in groups of *threes* whenever possible. For reasons that are not totally understood, listeners seem to remember groups of three items more than they do any other size groupings—perhaps for these reasons:

- The number is simple.
- It parallels the overall three-part structure of most speeches and documents (beginning, middle, and end).

- Many good speakers have used triads (Winston Churchill's "Blood, sweat, and tears," Caesar's "I came, I saw, I conquered," etc.).

Whatever the reason, groupings of three will make your speech more memorable to the audience.

Speech Guideline 4: Put Your Outline on Cards, Paper, or Overheads

The best presentations are "extemporaneous," meaning the speaker shows great familiarity with the material but uses notes for occasional reference. Avoid the extremes of (1) reading a speech verbatim, which many listeners consider the ultimate insult, or (2) memorizing a speech, which can make your presentation seem somewhat wooden and artificial.

Ironically, you appear more natural if you refer to notes during a presentation. Such extemporaneous speaking allows you to make last-minute changes in phrasing and emphasis that may improve delivery, rather than locking you into specific phrasing that is memorized or written out word for word.

Depending on your personal preference, you may choose to write speech notes on (1) index cards, (2) a sheet or two of paper, or (3) overhead transparencies. The main advantages and disadvantages of each are listed in Figure 4–14.

Speech Guideline 5: Practice, Practice, Practice

Many speakers prepare a well-organized speech but then fail to add the essential ingredient: practice. Constant practice distinguishes superior presentations from mediocre ones. It also helps to eliminate the nervousness that most speakers feel at one time or another.

In practicing your presentation, make use of four main techniques. They are listed here, from least effective to most effective:

- **Practice before a mirror:** This old-fashioned approach allows you to hear and see yourself in action. The drawback, of course, is that it is difficult to evaluate your own performance while you are speaking. Nevertheless, such run-throughs definitely make you more comfortable with the material.
- **Use of audiotape:** Most presenters have access to a tape player, so this approach is quite practical. The portability of the machine allows you to practice almost anywhere. Although taping a presentation will not improve gestures, it will help you discover and eliminate verbal distractions such as filler words *(uhhhh, um, ya know)*.
- **Use of live audience:** Groups of your colleagues, friends, or family—simulating a real audience—can provide the kinds of responses that approximate those of a real audience. In setting up this type of practice session, however, make certain that observers understand the criteria for a good presentation and are prepared to give an honest, forthright critique.

1. ***Notes on Cards (3" × 5" or 4" × 6")***

Advantages

- Are easy to carry in a pocket or bag
- Provide a way to organize points, through ordering of cards
- Can lead to smooth delivery in that each card contains only one or two points that are easy to view
- Can be held in one hand, allowing you to move away from lectern while speaking

Disadvantages

- Keep you from viewing outline of entire speech
- Require that you flip through cards repeatedly in speech
- Can limit use of gestures with hands
- Can cause confusion if they are not in correct order

2. ***Notes on Sheets of Paper***

Advantages

- Help you quickly view outline of entire speech
- Leave your hands free to use gestures
- Are less obvious than notecards, for no flipping is needed

Disadvantages

- Tend to tie you to the lectern, where the sheets lie
- May cause slipups in delivery if you lose your place on the page

3. ***Notes on Overhead Transparencies***

Advantages

- Introduce variety to audience
- Give visual reinforcement to audience
- Can be turned on and off

Disadvantages

- Cannot be altered as easily at last minute
- Must be presented neatly and in parallel style
- Involve the usual risks that reliance on machinery always introduces into your presentation

FIGURE 4–14
Speech notes

- **Use of videotape:** This practice technique allows you to see and hear yourself as others do. Your careful review of the tape, particularly when done with another qualified observer, can help you identify and eliminate problems with posture, eye contact, vocal patterns, and gestures. At first it may be an unsettling experience, but soon you will get over the awkwardness of seeing yourself on tape.

Speech Guideline 6: Speak Vigorously and Deliberately

Vigorously means with enthusiasm; *deliberately* means with care, attention, and appropriate emphasis on words and phrases. The importance of this guideline becomes clear when you think back to how you felt during the most recent speech you heard. At the very least, you expected the speaker to show interest in the subject and to demonstrate enthusiasm. Good information is not enough. You need to arouse the interest of the listeners.

You may wonder, "How much enthusiasm is enough?" The best way to answer this question is to hear or (preferably) watch yourself on tape. Your delivery should incorporate just enough enthusiasm so that it sounds and looks a bit unnatural to you. Few, if any, listeners ever complain about a speech being too enthusiastic or a speaker being too energetic. But many, many people complain about dull speakers who fail to show that they themselves are excited about the topic. Remember, every presentation is, in a sense, "showtime."

Speech Guideline 7: Avoid Filler Words

Avoiding filler words presents a tremendous challenge to most speakers. When they think about what comes next or encounter a break in the speech, they may tend to fill the gap with filler words and phrases such as these:

uhhhhh . . .

ya know . . .

okay . . .

well . . . uh . . .

like . . .

I mean . . .

umm . . .

These gap-fillers are a bit like spelling errors in written work: Once your listeners find a few, they start looking for more and are distracted from your presentation. To eliminate such distractions, follow these three steps:

1. **Step 1: Use pauses to your advantage.** Short gaps or pauses inform the listener that you are shifting from one point to another. In signaling a transition, a pause draws attention to the point you make right after the pause. Note how listeners look at you when you pause. Do *not* fill these strategic pauses with filler words.
2. **Step 2: Practice with tape.** Tape is brutally honest: When you play it back, you will become instantly aware of fillers that occur more than once or twice. Keep a tally sheet of the fillers you use and their frequency. Your goal will be to reduce this frequency with every practice session.

3. **Step 3: Ask for help from others.** After working with recorders in Step 2, give your speech to an individual who has been instructed to stop you after each filler. This technique gives immediate reinforcement.

Speech Guideline 8: Use Rhetorical Questions

Enthusiasm, of course, is your best delivery technique for capturing the attention of the audience. Another technique is the use of rhetorical questions at pivotal points in your presentation.

Rhetorical questions are those you ask to get listeners thinking about a topic, not those that you would expect them to answer out loud. They prod listeners to think about your point and set up an expectation that important information will follow. Also, they break the monotony of standard declarative sentence patterns. For example, here is a rhetorical question used by a computer salesperson in proposing a purchase:

> I've discussed the three main advantages that a centralized word-processing center would provide your office staff. But is this an approach that you can afford at this point in the company's growth?

Then the speaker would follow the question with remarks supporting the position that the system is affordable.

What-if scenarios provide another way to introduce rhetorical questions. They gain the listeners' attention by having them envision a situation that might occur. For example, a safety engineer could use this kind of rhetorical question in proposing asbestos-removal services to a regional bank:

> What if you repossessed a building that contained dangerous levels of asbestos?
>
> Do you think that your bank would then be liable for removing all the asbestos?

Again, the question pattern heightens listener interest.

Rhetorical questions do not come naturally. You must make a conscious effort to insert them at points when it is most important to gain or redirect the attention of the audience. Three particularly effective uses follow:

1. **As a grabber at the beginning of a speech:** "Have you ever wondered how you might improve the productivity of your word-processing staff?"
2. **As a transition between major points:** "We've seen that centralized word processing can improve the speed of report production, but will it require any additions to your staff?"
3. **As an attention-getter right before your conclusion:** "Now that we've examined the features of centralized word processing, what's the next step you should make?"

Speech Guideline 9: Maintain Eye Contact

Your main goal—always—is to keep listeners interested in what you are saying. This goal requires that you maintain control, using whatever techniques you can to direct the attention of the audience. Frequent eye contact is one good strategy.

The simple truth is that listeners pay closer attention to what you are saying when you look at them. Think how you react when a speaker makes constant eye contact with you. If you are like most people, you feel as if the speaker is speaking to you personally, even if there are 100 people in the audience. Also, you tend to feel more obligated to listen when you know that the speaker's eyes will be meeting yours throughout the presentation. Here are some ways you can make eye contact a natural part of your own strategy for effective oral presentations:

- **With audiences of about 30 or less:** Make regular eye contact with everyone in the room. Be particularly careful not to ignore members of the audience who are seated to your far right and far left (see Figure 4–15). Many speakers tend to focus on the listeners within Section B. Instead, make wide sweeps so that listeners in Sections A and C get equal attention.
- **With large audiences:** There may be too many people or a room too large for you to make individual eye contact with all listeners. In this case, focus on just a few people in all three sections of the audience noted in Figure 4–15. This approach gives the appearance that you are making eye contact with the entire audience.
- **With any size audience:** Occasionally, look away from the audience—either to your notes or toward a part of the room where there are no faces looking back. In this way, you avoid the appearance of staring too intensely at your audience. Also, such breaks give you the chance to collect your thoughts or check your notes.

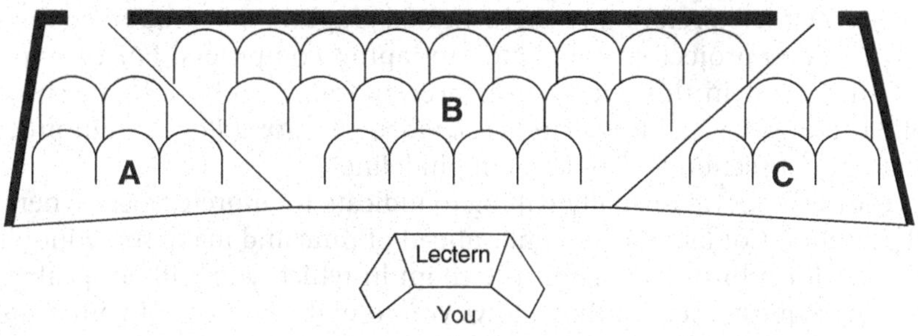

FIGURE 4–15
Audience Sections

Speech Guideline 10: Use Appropriate Gestures and Posture
Speaking is only one part of giving a speech; others are adopting appropriate posture and using gestures that will reinforce what you are saying. Note that good speakers are much more than "talking heads" before a lectern. Instead, they do the following:

- Use their hands and fingers to emphasize major points
- Stand straight, without leaning on or gripping the lectern
- Step out from behind the lectern on occasion, to decrease the distance to the audience
- Point toward visuals on screens or charts, without losing eye contact with the audience

The audience will judge you by what you say *and* what they see, a fact that again makes videotaping a crucial part of your preparation. With work on this facet of your presentation, you can avoid problems like keeping your hands constantly in your pockets, rustling change (remove pocket change and keys beforehand), tapping a pencil, scratching nervously, slouching over a lectern, and shifting from foot to foot.

General Guidelines for Speech Graphics

More than ever before, listeners expect good graphics during oral presentations. Much like gestures, graphics transform the words of your presentation into true communication with the audience. The following 10 guidelines will help you use graphics to enhance each speech. Then the next section will provide guidelines for a common form of speech graphic: PowerPoint slide shows.

Speech Graphics Guideline 1: Discover Listener Preferences
Some professionals prefer simple speech graphics, such as a conventional flip chart. Others prefer more sophisticated graphics that require equipment such as video projectors connected to laptop computers. For example, if your instructor in this course uses presentation graphics, he or she may make use of overhead transparencies, video clips, or a PowerPoint program (see the next section for PowerPoint guidelines).

Your listeners are usually willing to indicate their preferences when you call on them. Contact the audience ahead of time and make some inquiries. Also, ask for information about the room in which you will be speaking. If possible, request a setting that allows you to make best use of your graphics choice. If you have no control over the setting, then choose graphics that best fit the constraints. Details about lighting, wall space, and chair configuration can greatly influence your selection.

Speech Graphics Guideline 2: Think about Graphics Early

Graphics done as an afterthought usually look tacked on. Plan graphics while you prepare the text, so that the final presentation will seem fluid. This guideline holds true especially if you rely on specialists to prepare your visuals. These professionals need some lead time to do their best work. Also, they can often provide helpful insights about how visuals will enhance the presentation—*if* you consult them early enough and *if* you make them a part of your presentation team.

The goal is to use graphics of which you can be proud. Never put yourself in the position of having to apologize for the quality of your graphic material. If an illustration is not up to the quality your audience would expect, do *not* use it.

Speech Graphics Guideline 3: Keep the Message Simple

Listeners may be suspicious of slick visual effects that appear to be more important than the speech itself. Many prefer the simplicity of overhead transparencies and flip charts. However, even if you may prefer to use PowerPoint slides, video, or other sophisticated graphics, remember that graphics should support the speech, not draw attention to themselves.

Speech Graphics Guideline 4: Make Any Wording Brief and Visible

Some basic design guidelines apply whether you are using posters, overhead transparencies, or computer-aided graphics.

- Use few words, emphasizing just one idea on each frame.
- Use much white space, perhaps as much as 60% to 70% per frame.
- Use "landscape" format more often than "portrait," especially since it is the preferred default setting for most presentation software.
- Use sans serif large print, from 14 to 18 point minimum for text to 48 point for titles.

Your goal should be to create graphics that are easily seen from anywhere in the room and that complement—but do *not* overpower—your presentation.

Speech Graphics Guideline 5: Use Colors Carefully

Colors can add flair to visuals. Follow these simple guidelines to make colors work for you:

- Have a good reason for using color (such as the need to highlight three different bars on a graph with three distinct colors).
- Use only dark, easily seen colors for text, and be sure that a color you choose contrasts enough with its background (for example, yellow on white would not work well).

- Use no more than three or four colors in each graphic (to avoid a confused effect).
- For variety, consider using white on a black or dark green background.

Speech Graphics Guideline 6: Leave Up Graphics Long Enough
Because graphics reinforce text, they should be shown only while you address the particular point at hand. For example, reveal a graph just as you are saying, "As you can see from the graph, the projected revenue reaches a peak in 2008." Then pause and leave up the graph a bit longer for the audience to absorb your point.

How long is *too* long? A graphic outlives its usefulness when it remains in sight after you have moved on to another topic. Listeners will continue to study it and ignore what you are now saying. If you use a graphic once and plan to return to it, take it down after its first use and show it again later.

Speech Graphics Guideline 7: Avoid Handouts
Because timing is so important in your use of speech graphics, handouts are usually not appropriate. Readers will move through a handout at their own pace, rather than at the pace the speaker might prefer. Thus, handouts cause you to lose the attention of your audience. Use them only if (1) no other visual will do, (2) your listener has requested them, or (3) you distribute them as reference material *after* you have finished talking.

Speech Graphics Guideline 8: Maintain Eye Contact While Using Graphics
Do not stare at your visuals while you speak. Maintain control of listeners' responses by looking back and forth from the visual to faces in the audience. To point to the graphic aid, use the hand closest to the visual rather than the opposite hand. Using the opposite hand would cause you to cross over your torso, forcing you to turn away from the audience.

Speech Graphics Guideline 9: Include All Graphics in Your Practice Sessions
Dry runs before the actual presentation should include every graphic you plan to use, in its final form. Running through a final practice without graphics would be much like doing a dress rehearsal for a play without costumes and props—you would be leaving out parts that require the greatest degree of timing and orchestration. Practicing with graphics helps you improve the smoothness of your delivery and the effectiveness of your transitions in the speech.

Speech Graphics Guideline 10: Use Your Own Equipment
Murphy's Law always seems to apply when you use another person's audiovisual equipment: Whatever can go wrong, will. For example, a new bulb

burns out, there is no extra bulb in the equipment drawer, an extension cord is too short, the screen does not stay down, or the client's computer doesn't read your disk. Many speakers have experienced these problems and others. Even if the equipment works, it often operates differently from what you are used to. The only sure way to put the odds in your favor is to carry your own equipment and set it up in advance.

However, most of us have to rely on someone else's equipment at least sometimes. Here are a few ways to ward off disaster:

- Find out exactly who will be responsible for providing the equipment and contact that person in advance.
- Have some easy-to-carry backup supplies with you: an extension cord, an overhead projector bulb, felt-tip markers, and chalk, for example.
- Bring handout versions of some or all of your visuals to use as a last resort.

In short, you want to avoid putting yourself in the position of having to apologize. Plan well.

Guidelines for Overcoming Nervousness

The problem of nervousness deserves special mention because it is so common. Virtually everyone who gives speeches feels some degree of nervousness before "the event." An instinctive fight-or-flight response kicks in for the many people who have an absolute dread of presentations. As the cliché goes, do not try to eliminate "butterflies" before a presentation—just get them to fly in formation. It is best to acknowledge that a certain degree of nervousness will always remain. Then go about the business of getting it to work for you. Here are a few suggestions.

No Nerves Guideline 1: Know Your Speech

The most obvious suggestion is also the most important one. If you prepare your speech well, your command of the material will help to conquer any queasiness you feel, particularly at the beginning of the speech when nervousness is usually at its peak. Be so sure of the material that your listeners will overlook any initial discomfort you may feel.

No Nerves Guideline 2: Prepare Yourself Physically

Your physical well-being before the speech can have a direct bearing on anxiety. More than ever before, most cultures understand the essential connection between mental and physical well-being. This connection suggests you should take these precautions before your presentation.

- **Avoid caffeine or alcohol for at least several hours before you speak.** You do not need the additional jitters brought on by caffeine or the false sense of ease brought on by alcohol.

- **Eat a light, well-balanced meal within a few hours of speaking.** However, do not overdo it—particularly if a meal comes right before your speech. If you are convinced that any eating will increase your anxiety, wait to eat until after speaking.
- **Practice deep-breathing exercises before you speak.** Inhale and exhale slowly, making your body slow down to a pace you can control. If you can control your breathing, you can probably keep the butterflies flying in formation.
- **Exercise normally the same day of the presentation.** A good walk will help invigorate you and reduce nervousness. However, do not wear yourself out by exercising more than you would normally.

No Nerves Guideline 3: Picture Yourself Giving a Great Presentation
Many speakers become nervous because their imaginations are working overtime. They envision the kinds of failure that almost never occur. Instead, speakers should be constantly bombarding their psyches with images of success, not failure. Mentally take yourself through the following steps of the presentation:

- Arriving at the room
- Feeling comfortable at your chair
- Getting encouraging looks from your audience
- Giving an attention-getting introduction
- Presenting your supporting points with clarity and smoothness
- Ending with an effective wrap-up
- Fielding questions with confidence

Sometimes called imaging, this technique helps to program success into your thinking and to control negative feelings that pass through the minds of even the best speakers.

No Nerves Guideline 4: Arrange the Room as You Want
To control your anxiety, assert some control over the physical environment as well. You need everything going for you if you are to feel at ease. Make sure that chairs are arranged to your satisfaction, that the lectern is positioned to your taste, that the lighting is adequate, and so on. These features of the setting can almost always be adjusted if you make the effort to ask. Again, it is a matter of your asserting control to increase your overall confidence.

No Nerves Guideline 5: Have a Glass of Water Nearby
Extreme thirst and a dry throat are physical symptoms of nervousness that can affect delivery. There is nothing to worry about as long as you have water available. Think about this need ahead of time so that you do not have to interrupt your presentation to pour a glass of water.

No Nerves Guideline 6: Engage in Casual Banter before the Speech
If you have the opportunity, chat with members of the audience before the speech. This ice-breaking technique will reduce your nervousness and help start your relationship with the audience.

No Nerves Guideline 7: Remember That You Are the Expert
As a final "psyching up" exercise before you speak, remind yourself that you have been invited to speak on a topic about which you have knowledge. Your listeners want to hear what you have to say and are eager for you to provide useful information to them. So tell yourself, "I'm the expert here!"

No Nerves Guideline 8: Do Not Admit Nervousness to the Audience
No matter how anxious you may feel, never admit it to others. First of all, you do not want listeners to feel sorry for you—that is not an emotion that will lead to a positive critique of your speech. Second, nervousness is almost never apparent to the audience. Your heart may be pounding, your knees may be shaking, and your throat may be dry, but few, if any, members of the audience can see these symptoms. Why draw attention to the problem by admitting to it? Third, you can best defeat initial anxiety by simply pushing on.

No Nerves Guideline 9: Slow Down
Some speakers who feel nervous tend to speed through their presentations. If you have prepared well and practiced the speech on tape, you are not likely to let this happen. Having heard yourself on tape, you will be better able to sense that the pace is too quick. As you speak, constantly remind yourself to maintain an appropriate pace. If you have had this problem before, you might even write "Slow down!" in the margin of your notes.

No Nerves Guideline 10: Join a Speaking Organization
The previous nine guidelines will help reduce your anxiety about a particular speech. To help solve the problem over the long term, however, consider joining an organization like Toastmasters International, which promotes the speaking skills of all its members. Like some other speech organizations, Toastmasters has chapters that meet at many companies and campuses. These meetings provide an excellent, supportive environment in which all members can refine their speaking skills.

POWERPOINT PRESENTATIONS

Since PowerPoint technology arrived on the scene decades ago, speakers have had a fascinating tool for informing and persuading audiences. It has become one of the most commonly used graphic aids in business, industry, education, and government. Like all technical tools, however, it can be abused—and most certainly has been. This section provides a few guidelines for using PowerPoint slides to enhance an oral presentation.

Effective use of PowerPoint format requires you to follow guidelines included in other sections of this book as well. For example, you can find suggestions in Chapter 1 for audience analysis, in Chapter 2 for design, and earlier in this chapter for presentations and speech graphics in general. To give you a one-stop reference for PowerPoint use, this section combines suggestions from other parts of this book with guidelines specifically related to PowerPoint presentations. The resulting guidelines that follow are organized into three sections: (1) Planning a PowerPoint Presentation, (2) Formatting PowerPoint Slides, and (3) Delivering a PowerPoint Presentation.

Planning a PowerPoint Presentation

As with all forms of technical communication, you need to spend as much time planning your slides as you do actually creating or drafting them. If you strictly adhere to a process that includes adequate planning, your drafting stage will move smoothly. Here are a few suggestions:

PowerPoint Planning Guideline 1: Use and Review the Planning Form

This section offers general guidelines that apply to most speeches, but remember that the needs of your specific listeners come first. The preferences of your "real" audience, combined with the purpose of the document, drive any strategy you choose to organize a speech and the PowerPoint slides that accompany it. Use the Planning Form at the end of this book to record information about the purpose, audience, and structure of a speech. It includes reference to the graphics preferences of your audience.

For example, careful analysis of the needs of your listeners might lead you to conclude that they want to know why the quality of your product can justify its higher cost than competing products. Thus, your proposal presentation might begin with several PowerPoint slides on what you've learned about the client's needs, followed by slides on related features of your product. Only later will you show a slide on price options because you want viewers to be "sold" before you mention money. Yet an oral report, as opposed to a proposal, might begin with several "bottom line" PowerPoint slides that summarize the results that you know your audience wants to see first.

In other words, always respond to the needs of the readers that you have listed on the Planning Form. The form guides the organization and design of PowerPoint slides as much as it guides the organization and design of the text of your presentation.

PowerPoint Planning Guideline 2: Outline the Entire Speech Before You Create Slides

The last section of the Planning Form recommends you attach a topic outline to the completed form. Make sure to complete the outline BEFORE you begin the process of creating PowerPoint slides. Your presentation outline should guide the development of a PowerPoint show, not vice versa. Slides are a tool, not an end in themselves. Once you have the outline completed, then locate opportunities to insert slides into the presentation. Each point at which you decide to insert a slide should be used to reinforce a main point you intend to make in presentation, catch the attention of listeners, or advance their attention from one part of the presentation to the next. In other words, think strategically about the use of slides so that they enhance your presentation.

PowerPoint Planning Guideline 3: Make a List of All Slides Before You Create Them

Your slide list can include some or all of the following information: (a) title, (b) purpose of the slide, (c) reference to a point in the speech where the slide will be used, and (d) possible design ideas. The list will give you the "big picture" perspective of the slide show you intend to create. As you look at it, you may think of other opportunities for inserting additional slides and find slides you wish to delete. Thus, it will help you realize how diverse slides should fit together into an organic whole that supports the speech.

PowerPoint Planning Guideline 4: Keep Slides as Simple and Brief as Possible

As you move from planning to formatting, remember the KISS guideline mentioned in Chapter 1: Keep it Short and Simple. All viewers, no matter how technical their background, prefer simplicity. They expect that slides will make the narrative of your speech easier—not harder—to understand. Indeed, have you ever heard someone claim a presentation was too clear and simple? Instead, you've likely heard people observe, or you have observed yourself, that complex PowerPoint slides confused rather than clarified a presentation. Therefore, at the planning stage—before you even begin designing slides—be thinking about the simplicity and brevity with which you can express ideas in PowerPoint format.

Formating PowerPoint Slides

As already noted, you draft PowerPoint slides after you have prepared an outline (or draft) of your presentation and a list of proposed slides. With these items at hand, you can focus all your attention on selecting the best format and design to achieve your goals for each slide. The following are guidelines for the drafting process:

PowerPoint Format Guideline 1: Use the Same General Format for All Slides PowerPoint slides should reinforce your presentation, not draw attention to themselves. This goal is best achieved when all slides have the same general format, a strategy that gives readers a predictable mental map into which they place information as they view your presentation.

There are various formats and styles that you can glean from PowerPoint manuals or that you can develop on your own. For example, you may choose to place a short phrase or title at the top of every slide, followed by several bullets or a graphic (see Figure 4–16 and 4–17). Or you may decide to reserve slides just for graphics (see Figure 4–18). Whatever style you select, here are some basic rules to follow:

- Use no more than three to five bullets
- Avoid second- or third-level bullet breakdowns

By avoiding absestos contamination, you can

- Prevent health problems
- Satisfy regulatory requirements
- Give yourself peace of mind

FIGURE 4–16
Powerpoint slide with title and bullet points

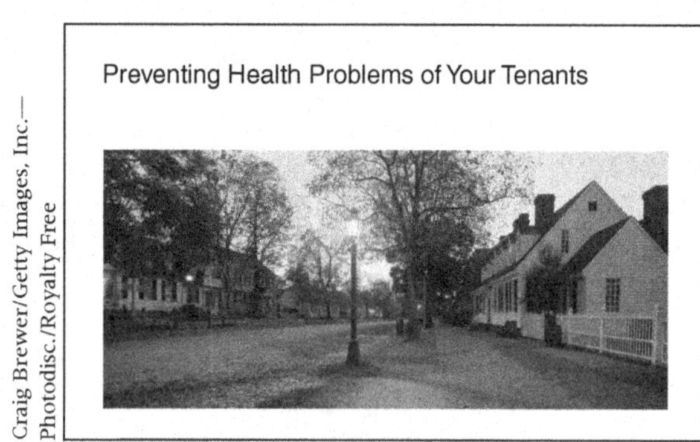

Craig Brewer/Getty Images, Inc.—Photodisc./Royalty Free

FIGURE 4–17
PowerPoint slide with title and graphics

David A. Ponton/ Creative Eye/MIRA.com

FIGURE 4–18
PowerPoint slide just with graphic

- Avoid using all capitals because they are hard to read
- Left justify bullets for easier reading

It is worth noting one particular technique that is especially useful when your speech includes a large number of slides and/or when you intend to leave a copy of your slides with the audience. This option requires that you create titles for all slides, with each title appearing at the top of its respective slide. Then, when all these titles are viewed together, they will reflect the structure of the entire speech—in a type of outline. Some listeners may want a hard copy of the PowerPoint slides, with titles, so they can more easily recollect the substance of your talk. If you decide to prepare hard copies of slides, however, do not hand them out until after your speech. You don't want to lose the attention of your audience during the speech.

PowerPoint Format Guideline 2: Use Few Words
One common PowerPoint mistake is to include too much verbiage, an error that leads to the audience reading slides rather than focusing on the presentation. PowerPoint text should distill rather than repeat words you deliver in the speech. Besides focusing attention where it should be—on you the speaker—using a few words in slides allows you to use a larger, more visible type (see Figure 4–19).

It's *your* asbestos!

FIGURE 4–19
PowerPoint slide just with brief phrase

One way to achieve the goal of brevity and simplicity on your slides is to always keep the following rule in mind when you are designing a PowerPoint presentation: Include only one main idea on each slide. Your idea might be embodied in a graphic, in one phrase, or in several bullet points. But it will always be just one main idea.

PowerPoint Format Guideline 3: Consider Font and Color Choice Very Carefully

Speech Graphics Guidelines #4 and #5 (see pages 137 to 138) provide information that applies to all speech graphics, including PowerPoint slides. It's worth including similar cautions in this section because the dizzying array of choices in PowerPoint technology does not necessarily lead to better presentations. Simply because many choices abound doesn't mean they have to be used. Simplicity, clarity, and, of course, visibility are the best virtues.

To achieve them, (a) keep colors fairly standard throughout the slide show, for example by using the same color background, (b) avoid garish color combinations, (c) make sure colors you use are visible from all parts of the room, (d) use the same font(s) throughout, and (e) use sans serif fonts with bold and visible lines, unless you have good reason to do otherwise.

PowerPoint Format Guideline 4: Don't "Dump" Data on to Slides

Perhaps the most off-putting PowerPoint mistake is to dump data from reports on to slides. Listeners have difficulty reading and understanding slides with excessive data, even when you don't use PowerPoint slides. It is preferable to include just major pieces of data in an oral presentation, which also ensures you will use a large font that is visible.

If you must include a good deal of data in PowerPoint format because the audience expects it, use multiple slides so that the data are more visible and easier to digest. Also, break up your discussion of figures with information that is not focused on data, giving readers a visual break. Finally, you can keep the attention of your audience during a discussion of data by revealing it in stages, using PowerPoint animation features that help you build messages as new information is introduced onto the screen.

Delivering a PowerPoint Presentation

Delivering a PowerPoint speech will go well if you follow the general guidelines mentioned earlier in this chapter and in this section. Plus, if you follow the two main guidelines that follow—and remember to practice, practice, and then practice some more—you will achieve the ultimate reward of a satisfied audience.

PowerPoint Delivery Guideline 1: Keep the Attention on You, not on the Slides

As already mentioned, you want the listener to be focused on you and your presentation, not on the PowerPoint slide show as an end in itself. There's always the temptation to dazzle an audience with complex graphics. Avoid this temptation at all costs. If all the listeners wanted were graphics, you could have sent them a DVD. They want more—they want to see a human being giving a speech that speaks to their needs, not a slide show with a speaker who seems secondary to the slides. Here are a few strategies for keeping you, the speaker, at the center of attention.

- Delay showing your first slide until you have established a "connection" with the audience, thus setting a tone that slides are there to support you
- Maintain constant eye contact with the audience, even when slides are being used
- Use a remote control device to avoid the distraction of reaching for the computer to change slides
- Keep a slide up long enough to be fully understood
- Cover a slide when it has served its purpose, if you are not ready to slow the next slide, or insert "blanks" into the presentation sequence
- Use animation features with care

On the last point, animation allows you to reveal wording in stages, such as with bullet points, so you can retain the attention of listeners. Make sure the animation feature you choose doesn't distract the audience, as can happen with an annoying visual or sound effect. If you would prefer not to use animation, the best technique for ensuring the audience doesn't read points before you get to them is to use only one point per slide. This technique also permits you to select a larger and more visible font size.

PowerPoint Delivery Guideline 2: Recheck Equipment and the Facility before the Presentation

If you've seen a few PowerPoint presentations, you've probably witnessed the variety of technical glitches that can accompany them. Users often encounter "surprises" such as the following: (a) failure of a laptop to boot properly, (b) failure of PowerPoint slides to be in sync with audio, if external media is being used, (c) too much distance between the screen and the speaker's position, causing the speaker to lose the attention of the audience, and (d) too much light in the room such that PowerPoint slides are difficult to see.

To be sure, some of these problems are generic to all speech graphics and thus are addressed by general guidelines in the previous section, especially Speech Graphic Guideline #10 that suggests using your own equipment. However, because speakers who use PowerPoint format tend to depend on it for supporting their presentation even more than speakers who use other graphics, you should apply an even higher level of scrutiny when using PowerPoint technology. If you remember that Murphy's Law may be at work (that is, everything that can go wrong, will), you'll do the following:

- Check and recheck all the equipment you will be using
- Do a "dress rehearsal" in the same room where you'll be speaking
- Locate a technical expert you can talk to personally about any equipment or rooms you cannot check yourself before the speech
- Have a technical assistant in the room or nearby who can assist with technical problems during the speech

PowerPoint presentations offer you and your audience immense rewards if you prepare carefully and deliver effectively. If successful, you can land a great contract, earn the respect of your colleagues and supervisors, and of course gain an excellent grade if you're in school.

The following chapters are taken from:
Strategies for Business and Technical Writing, Seventh Edition
by Kevin J. Harty

5 Evaluating and Testing as You Revise

Linda Flower and John Ackerman

Both Linda Flower, a member of the faculty at Carnegie Mellon University, and John Ackerman, a member of the faculty at the University of Utah, are nationally recognized authorities on the teaching of writing.

IMAGINING A READER'S RESPONSE

Even if you have a model or text to work from, as a writer you will work hard to construct a text: generating and discarding ideas, trying to figure out your point, sketching out alternative organizations, and then trying to signal that point and structure to your reader. But the story does not end there because your various readers have to work equally hard to construct a meaning based on your text. That is, readers want to construct *in their own minds* a coherent text, with a hierarchical organization (like an issue tree) based on key points. And they need to see a purpose for reading. Readers want to know *Why read this? What is the point?* and *How is all of this connected?*—and they want to find answers as quickly as possible.

Readers begin to predict the structure of a text and its meaning as soon as they face a page. They will look for cues that the text might offer about point, purpose, and structure, but if they do not find them, they will go ahead and construct their own version of the text *and assume that is what you intended.* It may be helpful to imagine your readers as needing to *write* your text for themselves. Thus, their own goals and interests will strongly influence what they look for in a text and the meaning they make out of it. Your goal, then, as a writer is to do the best job you can to make sure a reader's process through your text and his or her understanding matches or comes close to what you intended.

Once your ideas are down in a draft of some form, **revision** lets you anticipate how readers will respond and adjust the text to get the response you hope for. **Local revision** involves editing, correcting spelling and grammar, and making local improvements in wording or sentence style. **Global revision** involves looking at the big picture, but that does not mean throwing the draft out and starting again, and it may not even take a lot of time. Global revision, however, does mean looking at the text as a whole—thinking globally about the major rhetorical decisions and plans you made—now that the draft is complete. Global revisions alter the focus, organization, argument, or detail to improve the overall text.

Revision begins with a tricky reading process, a close reading of your own text. You know from your own experience in school that readers can read for different purposes: to skim a text to prepare for class discussion and then to read more carefully for an examination. In business, because writing usually augments a transaction between people, readers look for information but they also look for how well a piece of writing is adapted to their needs. The key to your success as a reviser is your ability to read your own writing critically for different features and purposes. At the simplest level, revision is *re-vision*—the process of stepping back from one's text and seeing it anew. . . .

STRATEGY 1: LOOK FOR WRITER-BASED PROSE

Why is it that even experienced writers typically choose to draft and revise rather than write a final text in one pass? Suppose you put time into planning your paper; you followed a good model; you thought about your reader as you chose what to say. Why should your first draft not do the job? One reason is because first drafts often contain large sections of **writer-based prose.** Writer-based prose appears when writers are essentially talking to themselves, talking through a problem, exploring their own knowledge, or trying to get their ideas out. In fact, producing writer-based prose is often a smart problem-solving strategy. Instead of getting blocked or spending hours staring at a blank page trying to write a perfect text the first time through, writers can literally walk through their own memory, talking out on paper what they know. Other concerns, including what the reader needs to hear, are put on temporary hold. Writer-based prose is, in fact, a very effective strategy for searching your memory and for dealing with difficult topics or lots of information. Writer-based prose may also be the best a writer can do in a new situation. A writer facing an unfamiliar task may produce writer-based prose, uncertain of what readers expect.

Whether it is a strategy or consequence, the downside of this strategy is that the text it produces is typically focused on the writer's thinking—not the readers' questions or needs—and it often comes out organized as a narrative or a river of connections. A number of studies of writers new to organizations demonstrate the reasoning behind writer-based prose and its ill-effect. New employees write consciously and unconsciously to report their discovery process or to survey all they know. And their readers impatiently wade through the river looking for the specific ideas and information they need.

. . . [Figure 5–1] is the first draft of a progress report written by four students in an organizational psychology course who were doing a consulting

Draft 1

Group Progress Report

(1) Work began on our project with the initial group decision to evaluate the Oskaloosa Brewing Company. Oskaloosa Brewing Company is a regionally located brewery manufacturing several different types of beer, notably River City and Brough Cream Ale. This beer is marketed under various names in Pennsylvania and other neighboring states. As a group, we decided to analyze this organization because two of our group members had had frequent customer contact with the sales department. Also, we were aware that Oskaloosa Brewing had been losing money for the past five years, and we felt we might be able to find some obvious problems in its organizational structure.

(2) Our first meeting, held February 17th, was with the head of the sales department, Jim Tucker. Generally, he gave us an outline of the organization, from president to worker, and discussed the various departments that we might ultimately decide to analyze. The two that seemed the most promising and more applicable to the project were the sales and production departments. After a few group meetings and discussions with the personnel manager, Susan Harris, and our advisor, Professor Charns, we felt it best suited our needs and Oskaloosa Brewing's needs to evaluate their bottling department.

(3) During the next week we had a discussion with the superintendent of production, Henry Holt, and made plans for interviewing the supervisors and line workers. Also, we had a tour of the bottling department that gave us a first-hand look at the production process. Before beginning our interviewing, our group met several times to formulate appropriate questions to use in interviewing, for both the supervisors and the workers. We also had a meeting with Professor Charns to discuss this matter.

(4) The next step was the actual interviewing process. During the weeks of March 14–18 and March 21–25, our group met several times at Oskaloosa Brewing and interviewed ten supervisors and twelve workers. Finally, during this past week, we have had several group meetings to discuss our findings and the potential problem areas within the bottling department. Also, we have spent time organizing the writing of our progress report.

1 of 2

FIGURE 5–1
The Oskaloosa Brewing Progress Memo, Draft 1

(5) The bottling and packaging division is located in a separate building, adjacent to the brewery, where the beer is actually manufactured. From the brewery the beer is piped into one of five lines (four bottling lines and one canning line) in the bottling house, where the bottles are filled, crowned, pasteurized, labeled, packaged in cases, and either shipped out or stored in the warehouse. The head of this operation, and others, is production manager Phil Smith. Next in line under him in direct control of the bottling house is the superintendent of bottling and packaging, Henry Holt. In addition, there are a total of ten supervisors who report directly to Henry Holt and who oversee the daily operations and coordinate and direct the twenty to thirty union workers who operate the lines.

(6) During production, each supervisor fills out a data sheet to explain what was actually produced during each hour. This form also includes the exact time when a breakdown occurred, what it was caused by, and when production was resumed. Some supervisors' positions are production-staff-oriented. One takes care of supplying the raw material (bottles, caps, labels, and boxes) for production. Another is responsible for the union workers' assignments each day.

These workers are not all permanently assigned to a production-line position. Workers called "floaters" are used, filling in for a sick worker or helping out after a breakdown.

(7) The union employees are generally older than 35, some in their late fifties. Most have been with the company many years and are accustomed to having more workers per a slower moving line. . . .

2 of 2

FIGURE 5–1 (*continued*)

project with a local organization, the Oskaloosa Brewing Company. As a reader, put yourself first in the position of Professor Charns. He is reading the report to answer three questions: As analysts, what assumptions and decisions did these students make in setting up their study? Why did they make them? And where are they in the project now? Then take on the role of the client, the company vice president who follows their progress and wants to know: O.K. What is the problem (i.e., how did they define it)? And what did they conclude? Would this draft answer these questions for either of its intended readers?

Put yourself in the shoes of the professor. What would you look for in a progress report? According to Charns, he used this report to evaluate the group's progress: Were they on schedule; were they on task; did he need to intervene? However, he didn't need a blow-by-blow story to do that. As an evaluator he wanted to see whether they knew how to analyze an organization: Were they making good decisions (that is, decisions they could justify in this report); had they made any discoveries about this company? His needs as a reader, then, reflected his dual role as a teacher (supervisor) and an evaluator.

When we showed this draft to a manager (with comparable experience and responsibility to the Oskaloosa VP), we got a very different response. Here was a reader looking quickly for the information she wanted and building an image of the writers' business savvy based on their text. Here is part of her response as she read and thought aloud (the student text she reads is underlined):

> Work began on our project with the initial group decision to evaluate . . . OK. Our project What project is this? I must have a dozen "projects" I keep tabs on. And who is this group? This beer is marketed . . . blah, blah, I'm tempted to skim. This must be a student project. But why am I reading about the fact somebody bought a lot of beer for their frat? Maybe the next paragraph.
>
> Our first meeting . . . Ok, they saw Jim and Susan, . . . looked at bottling, . . . wrote their paper. And now they are telling me where my packaging division is located! This is like a shaggy plant tour story. They are just wasting my time. And I suppose I should say that I am also forming an image of them as rather naive, sort of bumbling around the plant, interrupting my staff with questions. I mean, what are they after? Do they have any idea of what they are doing?

Now put yourself in the shoes of the professor. What would you look for in a progress report? How would you evaluate this group as decision makers? Have they learned anything about analyzing organizations? How would you evaluate their progress at this point? Have they made any discoveries, or are they just going through the steps?

Fortunately, this is not the draft the writers turned in to their professor or the company manager. The revised draft [as shown in Figure 5–2] was written after a short conference with a writing instructor who instead of offering advice, asked the writers to predict what each of their readers would be looking for. It took ten minutes to step back from their draft and to rethink it from the perspective of their professor and the Oskaloosa manager. They found that they needed global revision—a revision that kept the substance of their writer-based first draft, but transformed it into reader-based text. As you compare these two drafts, notice the narrative and survey organization in the first draft and the "I did it" focus that are often a tip-off to writer-based prose, and how they improved the second draft.

How would you characterize the differences between drafts one and two? One clear difference is the use of a conventional memo/report format to focus the reader's attention. But beyond the visual display of information, the writers moved away from narrative organization, an "I" focus, and a survey form or "textbook" pattern of organization. Watch for these three patterns as you revise.

Draft 2

MEMORANDUM

TO: Professor Martin Charns

FROM: Nancy Lowenberg, Todd Scott, Rosemary Nisson, Larry Vollen

DATE: March 31, 1987

RE: Progress Report: The Oskaloosa Brewing Company

Why Oskaloosa Brewing?

Oskaloosa Brewing Company is a regionally located brewery manufacturing several different types of beer, notably River City and Brough Cream Ale. As a group, we decided to analyze this organization because two of our group members have frequent contact with the sales department. Also, we were aware that Oskaloosa Brewing had been losing money for the past five years and we felt we might be able to find some obvious problems in its organizational structure.

Initial Steps: Where to Concentrate?

After several interviews with top management and a group discussion, we felt it best suited our needs, and Oskaloosa Brewing's needs, to evaluate the production department. Our first meeting, held February 17, was with the head of the sales department, Jim Tucker. He gave us an outline of the organization and described the two major departments, sales and production. He indicated that there were more obvious problems in the production department, a belief also suggested by Susan Harris, the personnel manager.

Next Step

The next step involved a familiarization with the plant and its employees. First, we toured the plant to gain an understanding of the brewing and bottling processes. Next, during the weeks of March 14–18 and March 21–25, we interviewed ten supervisors and twelve workers. Finally, during the past week we had group meetings to exchange information and discuss potential problems.

The Production Process

Knowledge of the actual production process is imperative in understanding the effects of various problems on efficient production. Therefore, we have included a brief summary of this process.

The bottling and packaging division is located in a separate building, adjacent to the brewery, where the beer is actually manufactured. From the brewery the beer is piped into one of five lines (four bottling lines and one canning line) in the bottling house, where the bottles are filled, crowned, pasteurized, labeled, packaged in cases, and either shipped out or stored in the warehouse.

FIGURE 5–2
The Oskaloosa Brewing Progress Memo, Draft 2

Problems

Through extensive interviews with supervisors and union employees, we have recognized four apparent problems within the bottling house operations. The first is that the employees' goals do not match those of the company. . . . This is especially apparent in the union employees, whose loyalty lies with the union instead of the company. This attitude is well-founded, as the union ensures them of job security and benefits. . . .

FIGURE 5–2 (*continued*)

Narrative Organization

The first four paragraphs of the first draft are organized as a narrative, starting with the phrase "Work began. . . ." We are given a story of the writers' discovery process. Notice how all of the facts are presented in terms of when they were discovered, not in terms of their implications or logical connections. The writers want to tell us what happened and when; the reader, on the other hand, wants to ask "why?" and "so what?"

A narrative organization is tempting to write because it is a prefabricated order and easy to generate. All of us walk around with stories in our head, and chronology is a common rhetorical move. Instead of creating a **hierarchical** organization among ideas or worrying about a reader, the writer can simply remember his or her own discovery process and write a story. Remember that in a hierarchical structure, such as an issue tree, the ideas at the top of the structure work as the organizing concepts that include other ideas. The alternative is often a string of ideas simply linked by association or by the order in which the writer thought about them. Papers that start out, "In studying the reasons for the current decline in our return customers, ..." are often a dead giveaway. They tell us we are going to watch the writer's mind at work and follow him or her through the process of thinking out conclusions. Following one's own associations makes the text easier to write. But another reason new employees are tempted to write narrative reports is that they were often rewarded for narratives at some point in their career *as students*. They fail to realize that in business the reader is someone who expects to *use* this text (not check off whether or not they did the assignment).

A narrative pattern, of course, has the virtue of any form of drama—it keeps you in suspense by withholding closure. But this drama is an effective strategy only if the audience is willing to wait that long for the point. Most professional and academic readers are impatient, and they tend to interpret such narrative, step-by-step structures either as wandering and confused (Is there a point?) or as a form of hedging. Narrative structures may be read as veiled attempts to hide what really happened or the writers' actual position. Although a progress report naturally involves narrative, how has Draft 2 been able to *use* the narrative to answer readers' questions?

The "I" Focus

The second feature of Draft 1 is that it is a discovery story starring the writers. Its drama, such as it is, is squarely focused on the writer: "I did/I thought/I felt. . . ." Of the fourteen sentences in the first three paragraphs, ten are grammatically focused on the writer's thoughts and actions rather than on the issues. For example: "Work began . . . ," "We decided . . . ," Also, "we were aware . . . and we felt. . . ." Generally speaking, the reader is more interested in issues and ideas than in the fact that the writer thought them.

In pointing out the "I" focus in Draft 1, we are not saying that writers cannot refer to themselves or begin a sentence with "I," as many learned in school. Sometimes a specific reference to oneself is exactly the information a reader needs, and a reader may respond to the honesty and directness. Use "I" or "we" to make a claim or when it is an important piece of information, not just as a convenient way to start a sentence. In Draft 2, the students are clearly present as people doing the research, but the focus is on the information the reader wants to hear.

Survey Form or Textbook Organization

In the fifth paragraph of Draft 1 the writers begin to organize their material in a new way. Instead of a narrative, we are given a survey of what the writers observed. Here, the raw facts of the bottling process dictated the organization of the paragraph. Yet the client-reader already knows this, and the professor probably does not care. In the language of computer science we could say the writers are performing a "memory dump": printing out information in the exact form in which they stored it in memory. Notice how in the revised version the writers try to use their observations to understand production problems.

The problem with a survey or "textbook" pattern is that it ignores the reader's need for a different organization of the information. Suppose, for example, you are writing to model airplane builders about wind resistance. The information you need comes out of a physics text, but that text is organized around the field of physics; it starts with subatomic particles and works up from there. To meet the needs of your reader, you have to adapt that knowledge, not lift it intact from the text. Sometimes writers can simply survey their knowledge, but generally the writer's main task is to use knowledge rather than reprint it.

To sum up, in Draft 2 of the Oskaloosa report, the writers made a real attempt to write for their readers. Among other things, the report is now organized around major questions readers might have, it uses headings to display the overall organization of the report, and it makes better use of topic sentences that tell the reader what each paragraph contains and why to read it. Most important, it focuses more on the crucial information the reader wants to obtain.

Obviously this version could still be improved. But it shows the writers attempting to transform writer-based prose into reader-based prose and change their narrative and survey pattern into a more issue-centered top-to-bottom organization.

STRATEGY 2: TEST YOUR TEXT FOR A READER-BASED STRUCTURE

Reading your text for writer-based prose lets you spot places where you were still exploring ideas or talking to yourself—places that probably call for some sort of global or structural revision to make this text a reader-based document. But that does not tell you how to revise. **Reader-based prose** foregrounds and makes explicit the information a reader needs or expects to find. Reader-based prose tries to anticipate and support an active reader, one who probably will use your writing for some specific end. What do you want your reader to see, think, or do? How will your reader respond? One important approach to global revision is to look at your text as a conversation with the reader in which you set up some initial agreements and expectations and then fulfill your promises. We offer three ways to test for a reader-based structure: *testing your drafts against your initial plans, using clues that reveal this plan to a reader,* and *keeping the promises you made in your writing.*

Does Your Text Reflect Your Plans?

Texts have a way of running off by themselves. The more text you produce, the more convinced you are that your prose is complete, readable, even entertaining. This is natural given the commitment it takes to write anything, but because texts often drift away from your intentions, you need a way to keep your text honest or to realize that you have come up with a better approach. So instead of reading your text "as written" and just going with the flow, start by setting up an image of your purpose and plans in your mind's eye, then test your text against that image. Can you find any evidence of your plans in the text?

To get a good image of your plan, return to . . . your planning notes to review your plans consciously. In your mind or on paper, restate the plans *to do* and *say* that you produced prior to your current draft, and find the exact places in your text where your writing satisfies (or departs from) your plans to reach a reader. You could set the mental exercise up as a checklist [Figure 5–3].

Holding your draft up against the backdrop of your own plans can help you notice how well the two fit together. Did you have important goals, or good points in your notes that have just not appeared in your text yet? Did you simply forget ideas? Or did you find—as many writers do—that the act of writing was itself an inventive, generative process? Your plans may have changed as a result of writing. If that happened, what should you do? At this point, inexperienced writers often abandon their old plans and follow wherever the text seems to be taking them. However, experienced writers make another move. They go back into planning and look for possible ways to consolidate their new ideas with other old plans. They try to build a new plan that makes use of the good parts of both ideas. They use this round of planning to guide their global revisions consciously.

This strategy is obviously one you will use more than once—a kind of in-process evaluation that lets you keep checking in with your goals for writing and checking your text against the big picture of what you want it to do.

My plans for writing, to do and say were...

The important Goals and Purposes I gave myself...
My Key Points...
How I wanted my Reader to respond (and what other responses I anticipated)...
My choice of Text Conventions...
How I planned to make all of this work together...

As a checklist, I could evaluate my writing this way:

Plans *to do* and *say*	Draft	Text Reference
Goals...	✓	~~~~~~~~~~~~~~~~~~~~~~
Key points...	✓	~~~~~~~~~~~~~~~~~~~~~~~~
Intended Response...	✓	~~~~~~~~~~~~~~~~~~~~
Text Conventions, Models...	✓	~~~~~~~~~~~~~~~~~~~~~~~~
Making it all work together...	????	*oops, gotta work on this!!!*

FIGURE 5–3
Checking Your Text Against Your Plans

Cues That Reveal Your Plans to Your Reader

Maybe you are satisfied that you have indeed defined a real and shared problem for your reader, and compared some alternative ways to respond to it, supported them with examples, while proposing your favored course of action. But will the reader recognize all of those rhetorical moves? It is possible that you "talked about" this information, but did not make your good rhetorical plan to define, compare, support and propose fully apparent or explicit.

In most pieces of writing there are two conversations going on. One is the information that the reader needs or expects to find: the recommendations that you want to make, the results of your study, the idea you are proposing, the specifics of a solution. As we shall see, this conversation is held together, usually, by a strong chain of topics and an appropriate rhetorical pattern. But the second conversation is explicitly between the writer and the reader, announcing what the reader will find, in what order, and reminding the reader of where he or she is in the text.

This second conversation is often called **metadiscourse.** *Meta-* is a Greek prefix that means "along with" or "among," and the basic strategy is to include explicit statements and cues to the reader that announce and reinforce your intentions along with your content. There are two main ways writers give such cues. One is to talk directly to the reader, inserting metacomments that preview what will come, remind, predict, or summarize. This lets the writer step back, make the plan of the text more visible, and direct traffic, by telling the reader, "In the next section I will argue that. . . ." The other kind of cues work more like traffic signals—they are the conventional words and phrases that signal transitions, or logic, or the structure of ideas. Readers often expect to find these metacomments and signalling cues in some standard places. Some common places to insert cues to the reader include:

Title, title page

Table of contents

Abstract

Introduction or first paragraphs

Headings

The beginning and end of paragraphs (i.e., topic sentences)

Entire paragraphs in between long sections

So review your text first to see if you have used enough cues to make your plan clear, and second to see if you have included cues in places readers expect to see some guidance on what to look for and how to read this document [Figure 5–4].

Cues that signal your plan and guide the reader:

<u>Cues that lead the reader forward</u>

To show addition:		*To show time:*	
Again	Moreover,	At length	And then
And	Nor,	Immediately thereafter,	Later,
And then,	Too,	Soon,	Previously,
Besides	Next,	After a few hours,	Formerly,
Equally important,	First, second, etc.	Afterwards,	First, second, etc.
Finally	Lastly,	Finally,	Next, etc.
Further,	What's more,	Then	
Furthermore,			

<u>Cues that make the reader stop and compare</u>

But	Notwithstanding,	Although
Yet,	On the other hand,	Although this is true,
And yet,	On the contrary,	While this is true,
However,	After all,	Conversely,
Still	For all that,	Simultaneously,
Nevertheless,	In contrast,	Meanwhile
Nonetheless,	At the same time,	In the meantime,

<u>Cues that develop and summarize</u>

To give examples:	*To emphasize:*	*To repeat:*	*To signal a relationship:*
For instance,	Obviously,	In brief,	Finally
For example,	In fact,	In short,	Because
To demonstrate,	As a matter of fact,	As I have said,	Yet
To illustrate,	Indeed,	As I have noted,	For instance,
As an illustration,	In any case,	In other words,	
	In any event,	That is,	

To introduce conclusions:	*To summarize:*
Hence,	In brief,
Therefore,	On the whole,
Accordingly,	Summing up,
Consequently,	To conclude,
Thus,	In conclusion,
As a result,	

FIGURE 5–4
Giving Cues to the Reader

Metacomment cues that announce and reinforce your intentions

To ask a question about your topic or the argument unfolding:

What series of events led to event? . . .
To answer that question . . .

To preview what will come:

In the next section, we will see how this formula applies . . .
The third paragraph will reveal how . . .

To summarize what has been said thus far:

In the preceding pages, I've described . . .
Thus far, I have argued . . .

To comment on your writing and thinking as it unfolds:

I haven't mentioned yet that . . .
I'm talking about . . .
My main point is . . .

FIGURE 5–4 (*continued*)

There is an endless variety of sentences and phrases that can be invented and inserted to announce and reinforce your main ideas and the progression that you want your reader to follow. To show you the power of metadiscourse and how it plays out in a text, here is an excerpt from a shareowner's letter with the metadiscourse highlighted [Figure 5–5]. We offer the original paragraph numbers with the cues underlined and the rhetorical purpose of the cues as we read them. . . .

Did You Keep Your Promises?

Your text started out with the best of intentions—a strong rhetorical plan and cues that keep your reader on track. The next test is to see if you followed through on the promises that you made. Read your text as if you were outlining its key points and promises and then look back to see if you have delivered the necessary detail. For instance:

- Your problem/purpose statement promises four main points and an extended example: Does each paragraph keep that promise? By referring back

Chairman's Letter

	Rhetorical Purpose/Cues	
1		Often the greatest opportunities ....
4	ties to history	Our strong 1984 results speak for themselves ......
5		Pacific Telesis Group earned $829 million ....
6	forces question	What happened? How did the corporation that many observers predicted would be the biggest loser in the AT&T breakup turn out to be one of the biggest winners?
7	links date with solution	To answer that question, you have to go back to 1980, when we developed ....
8	signals logic	Our employees mobilized to make it work. And work it did. More specifically: ....
8c	signals order & emphasis	Third, and very important, we've built a relationship with the California Public Utilities Commission ....
	previews, emphasizes	a subject I'll return to later on in this letter. ....
		The Future of Your Investment
34	previews	A corporation, particularly one as new as ours, must operate with a clearly articulated and widely understood vision of its future ....
37	summarizes	In the preceding pages I've described to you our strategies for deploying technology, marketing technology, and diversifying into new lines ....
38	summarizes, emphasizes	I've talked about our determination ....
	signals logic, emphasis uses authority	But there is another very significant factor I haven't mentioned. I'm talking about the people who work for the Pacific Telesis Group

FIGURE 5–5
Metadiscourse in the Chairman's Letter

to your announced plan and delivering four main (i.e., well-developed) points in the same order that you promised?

- Your topic sentence in the seventh paragraph promises the two key instances that support a legal precedent: Does the paragraph deliver them in the order and detail necessary?

6 Gobbledygook
Stuart Chase

Stuart Chase worked for many years as a consultant to various government agencies; his other books include The Tyranny of Words (1938) and Democracy Under Pressure (1945).

[Editor's note: Chase's essay first appeared in 1953, and so the author uses the "generic he," the standard for pronoun usage at the time. Today, as the guidelines from the University of Wisconsin reprinted later in this section of *Strategies* make clear, such usage should be avoided. Chase's discussion and advice are, nonetheless, still invaluable to writers today.]

Said Franklin Roosevelt, in one of his early presidential speeches: "I see one-third of a nation ill-housed, ill-clad, ill-nourished." Translated into standard bureaucratic prose his statement would read:

> It is evident that a substantial number of persons within the Continental boundaries of the United States have inadequate financial resources with which to purchase the products of agricultural communities and industrial establishments. It would appear that for a considerable segment of the population, possibly as much as 33.3333* of the total, there are inadequate housing facilities, and an equally significant proportion is deprived of the proper types of clothing and nutriment.
>
> *Not carried beyond four places.

This rousing satire on gobbledygook—or talk among the bureaucrats—is adapted from a report[1] prepared by the Federal Security Agency in an attempt to break out of the verbal squirrel cage. "Gobbledygook" was coined by an exasperated Congressman, Maury Maverick of Texas, and means using two, or three, or ten words in the place of one, or using a five-syllable word where a single syllable would suffice. Maverick was censuring the forbidding prose of executive departments in Washington, but the term has now spread to windy and pretentious language in general.

"Gobbledygook" itself is a good example of the way a language grows. There was no word for the event before Maverick's invention; one had to say: "You know, that terrible, involved, polysyllabic language those government people use down in Washington." Now one word takes the place of a dozen.

[1]This and succeeding quotations from FSA report by special permission of the author, Milton Hall.

A British member of Parliament, A. P. Herbert, also exasperated with bureaucratic jargon, translated Nelson's immortal phrase, "England expects every man to do his duty":

> England anticipates that, as regards the current emergency, personnel will face up to the issues, and exercise appropriately the functions allocated to their respective occupational groups.

A New Zealand official made the following report after surveying a plot of ground for an athletic field:[2]

> It is obvious from the difference in elevation with relation to the short depth of the property that the contour is such as to preclude any reasonable developmental potential for active recreation.

Seems the plot was too steep.

An office manager sent this memo to his chief:

> Verbal contact with Mr. Blank regarding the attached notification of promotion has elicited the attached representation intimating that he prefers to decline the assignment.

Seems Mr. Blank didn't want the job.

> A doctor testified at an English trial that one of the parties was suffering from "circumorbital haematoma."

Seems the party had a black eye.

In August 1952 the U.S. Department of Agriculture put out a pamphlet entitled:

> "Cultural and Pathogenic Variability in Single-Condial and Hyphaltip Isolates of Hemlin-Thosporium Turcicum Pass."

Seems it was about corn leaf disease.

On reaching the top of the Finsteraarhorn in 1845, M. Dollfus-Ausset, when he got his breath, exclaimed:

> The soul communes in the infinite with those icy peaks which seem to have their roots in the bowels of eternity.

Seems he enjoyed the view.

A government department announced:

> Voucherable expenditures necessary to provide adequate dental treatment required as adjunct to medical treatment being rendered a pay patient in

[2]This item and the next two are from the piece on gobbledygook by W. E. Farbstein, *New York Times*, March 29, 1953.

> in-patient status may be incurred as required at the expense of the Public Health Service.

Seems you can charge your dentist bill to the Public Health Service. Or can you?

LEGAL TALK

Gobbledygook not only flourishes in government bureaus but grows wild and lush in the law, the universities, and sometimes among the literati. Mr. Micawber was a master of gobbledygook, which he hoped would improve his fortunes. It is almost always found in offices too big for face-to-face talk. Gobbledygook can be defined as squandering words, packing a message with excess baggage and so introducing semantic "noise." Or it can be scrambling words in a message so that meaning does not come through. The directions on cans, bottles, and packages for putting the contents to use are often a good illustration. Gobbledygook must not be confused with double talk, however, for the intentions of the sender are usually honest.

I offer you a round fruit and say, "Have an orange." Not so an expert in legal phraseology, as parodied by editors of *Labor:*

> I hereby give and convey to you, all and singular, my estate and interests, right, title, claim and advantages of and in said orange, together with all rind, juice, pulp and pits, and all rights and advantages therein . . . anything hereinbefore or hereinafter or in any other deed or deeds, instrument or instruments of whatever nature or kind whatsoever, to the contrary, in any wise, notwithstanding.

The state of Ohio, after five years of work, has redrafted its legal code in modern English, eliminating 4,500 sections and doubtless a blizzard of "whereases" and "hereinafters." Legal terms of necessity must be closely tied to their referents, but the early solons tried to do this the hard way, by adding synonyms. They hoped to trap the physical event in a net of words, but instead they created a mumbo-jumbo beyond the power of the layman, and even many a lawyer, to translate. Legal talk is studded with tautologies, such as "cease and desist," "give and convey," "irrelevant, incompetent, and immaterial." Furthermore, legal jargon is a dead language; it is not spoken and it is not growing. An official of one of the big insurance companies calls their branch of it "bafflegab." Here is a sample from his collection.[3]

[3]Interview with Clifford B. Reeves by Sylvia F. Porter, *New York Evening Post,* March 14, 1952.

> One-half to his mother, if living, if not to his father, and one-half to his mother-in-law, if living, if not to his mother, if living, if not to his father. Thereafter payment is to be made in a single sum to his brothers. On the one-half payable to his mother, if living, if not to his father, he does not bring in his mother-in-law as the next payee to receive, although on the one-half to his mother-in-law, he does bring in the mother or father.

You apply for an insurance policy, pass the tests, and instead of a straightforward "here is your policy," you receive something like this:

> This policy is issued in consideration of the application therefore, copy of which application is attached hereto and made part hereof, and of the payment for said insurance on the life of the above-named insured.

ACADEMIC TALK

The pedagogues may be less repetitious than the lawyers, but many use even longer words. It is a symbol of their calling to prefer Greek and Latin derivatives to Anglo-Saxon. Thus instead of saying: "I like short clear words," many a professor would think it more seemly to say: "I prefer an abbreviated phraseology, distinguished for its lucidity." Your professor is sometimes right, the longer word may carry the meaning better—but not because it is long. Allen Upward in his book *The New Word* warmly advocates Anglo-Saxon English as against what he calls "Mediterranean" English, with its polysyllables built up like a skyscraper.

Professional pedagogy, still alternating between the Middle Ages and modern science, can produce what Henshaw Ward once called the most repellent prose known to man. It takes an iron will to read as much as a page of it. Here is a sample of what is known in some quarters as "pedageese":

> Realization has grown that the curriculum or the experiences of learners change and improve only as those who are most directly involved examine their goals, improve their understandings and increase their skill in performing the tasks necessary to reach newly defined goals. This places the focus upon teacher, lay citizen and learner as partners in curricular improvement and as the individuals who must change, if there is to be curriculum change.

I think there is an idea concealed here somewhere. I think it means: "If we are going to change the curriculum, teacher, parent, and student must all help." The reader is invited to get out his semantic decoder and check on my translation. Observe there is no technical language in this gem of pedageese, beyond possibly the word "curriculum." It is just a simple idea heavily oververbalized.

In another kind of academic talk the author may display his learning to conceal a lack of ideas. A bright instructor, for instance, in need of prestige may select a common sense proposition for the subject of a learned monograph—say, "Modern cities are hard to live in"—and adorn it with imposing polysyllables: "Urban existence in the perpendicular declivities of megalopolis . . ." et cetera. He coins some new terms to transfix the reader—"megadecibel" or "stratocosmopolis"—and works them vigorously. He is careful to add a page or two of differential equations to show the "scatter." And then he publishes, with 147 footnotes and a bibliography to knock your eye out. If the authorities are dozing, it can be worth an associate professorship.

While we are on the campus, however, we must not forget that the technical language of the natural sciences and some terms in the social sciences, forbidding as they may sound to the layman, are quite necessary. Without them, specialists could not communicate what they find. Trouble arises when experts expect the uninitiated to understand the words; when they tell the jury, for instance, that the defendant is suffering from "circumorbital haematoma."

Here are two authentic quotations. Which was written by a distinguished modern author, and which by a patient in a mental hospital? You will find the answer at the end of [this selection].

1. Have just been to supper. Did not knowing what the woodchuck sent me here. How when the blue blue blue on the said anyone can do it that tries. Such is the presidential candidate.
2. No history of a family to close with those and close. Never shall he be alone to be alone to be alone to be alone to be alone to lend a hand and leave it left and wasted.

REDUCING THE GOBBLE

As government and business offices grow larger, the need for doing something about gobbledygook increases. Fortunately the biggest office in the world is working hard to reduce it. The Federal Security Agency in Washington,[4] with nearly 100 million clients on its books, began analyzing its communication lines some years ago, with gratifying results. Surveys find trouble in three main areas: correspondence with clients about their social security problems, office memos, official reports.

Clarity and brevity, as well as common humanity, are urgently needed in this vast establishment which deals with disability, old age, and unemployment.

[4]Now the Department of Health and Human Services.

The surveys found instead many cases of long-windedness, foggy meanings, clichés, and singsong phrases, and gross neglect of the reader's point of view. Rather than talking to a real person, the writer was talking to himself. "We often write like a man walking on stilts."

Here is a typical case of long-windedness:

> *Gobbledygook as found:* "We are wondering if sufficient time has passed so that you are in a position to indicate whether favorable action may now be taken on our recommendation for the reclassification of Mrs. Blank, junior clerk-stenographer, CAF 2, to assistant clerk-stenographer, CAF 3?"
>
> *Suggested improvement:* "Have you yet been able to act on our recommendation to reclassify Mrs. Blank?"

Another case:

> Although the Central Efficiency Rating Committee recognizes that there are many desirable changes that could be made in the present efficiency rating system in order to make it more realistic and more workable than it now is, this committee is of the opinion that no further change should be made in the present system during the current year. Because of conditions prevailing throughout the country and the resultant turnover in personnel, and difficulty in administering the Federal programs, further mechanical improvement in the present rating system would require staff retraining and other administrative expense which would seem best withheld until the official termination of hostilities, and until restoration of regular operations.

The FSA invites us to squeeze the gobbledygook out of this statement. Here is my attempt:

> The Central Efficiency Rating Committee recognizes that desirable changes could be made in the present system. We believe, however, that no change should be attempted until the war is over.

This cuts the statement from 111 to 30 words, about one-quarter of the original, but perhaps the reader can do still better. What of importance have I left out?

Sometimes in a book which I am reading for information—not for literary pleasure—I run a pencil through the surplus words. Often I can cut a section to half its length with an improvement in clarity. Magazines like *The Reader's Digest* have reduced this process to an art. Are long-windedness and obscurity a cultural lag from the days when writing was reserved for priests and cloistered scholars? The more words and the deeper the mystery, the greater their prestige and the firmer the hold on their jobs. And the better the candidate's chance today to have his doctoral thesis accepted.

The FSA surveys found that a great deal of writing was obscure although not necessarily prolix. Here is a letter sent to more than 100,000 inquirers, a classic example of murky prose. To clarify it, one needs to *add* words, not cut them:

In order to be fully insured, an individual must have earned $50 or more in covered employment for as many quarters of coverage as half the calendar quarters elapsing between 1936 and the quarter in which he reaches age 65 or dies, whichever first occurs.

Probably no one without the technical jargon of the office could translate this; nevertheless, it was sent out to drive clients mad for seven years. One poor fellow wrote back: "I am no longer in covered employment. I have an outside job now."

Many words and phrases in officialese seem to come out automatically, as if from lower centers of the brain. In this standardized prose people never *get* jobs, they "secure employment"; *before* and *after* become "prior to" and "subsequent to"; one does not *do,* one "performs"; nobody *knows* a thing, he is "fully cognizant"; one never *says,* he "indicates." A great favorite at present is "implement."

Some charming boners occur in this talking-in-one's-sleep. For instance:

The problem of extending coverage to all employees, regardless of size, is not as simple as surface appearances indicate.

Though the proportions of all males and females in ages 16–45 are essentially the same . . .

Dairy cattle, usually and commonly embraced in dairying . . .

In its manual to employees, the FSA suggests the following:

Instead of	**Use**
give consideration to	consider
make inquiry regarding	inquire
is of the opinion	believes
comes into conflict with	conflicts
information which is of a confidential nature	confidential information

Professional or office gobbledygook often arises from using the passive rather than the active voice. Instead of looking you in the eye, as it were, and writing "This act requires . . .," the office worker looks out of the window and writes: "It is required by this statute that . . ." When the bureau chief says, "We expect Congress to cut your budget," the message is only too clear; but usually he says, "It is expected that the departmental budget estimates will be reduced by Congress."

GOBBLED: "All letters prepared for the signature of the Administrator will be single spaced."
UNGOBBLED: "Single space all letters for the Administrator." (Thus cutting 13 words to 7.)

Only People Can Read

The FSA surveys pick up the point . . . that human communication involves a listener as well as a speaker. Only people can read, though a lot of writing seems to be addressed to beings in outer space. To whom are you talking? The sender of the officialese message often forgets the chap on the other end of the line.

A woman with two small children wrote the FSA asking what she should do about payments, as her husband had lost his memory. "If he never gets able to work," she said, "and stays in an institution would I be able to draw any benefits? . . . I don't know how I am going to live and raise my children since he is disable to work. Please give me some information. . . ."

To this human appeal, she received a shattering blast of gobbledygook, beginning, "State unemployment compensation laws do not provide any benefits for sick or disabled individuals . . . in order to qualify an individual must have a certain number of quarters of coverage . . ." et cetera, et cetera. Certainly if the writer had been thinking about the poor woman he would not have dragged in unessential material about old-age insurance. If he had pictured a mother without means to care for her children, he would have told her where she might get help—from the local office which handles aid to dependent children, for instance.

Gobbledygook of this kind would largely evaporate if we thought of our messages as two way—in the above case, if we pictured ourselves talking on the doorstep of a shabby house to a woman with two children tugging at her skirts, who in her distress does not know which way to turn.

Results of the Survey

The FSA survey showed that office documents could be cut 20 to 50 percent, with an improvement in clarity and a great saving to taxpayers in paper and payrolls.

A handbook was prepared and distributed to key officials.[5] They read it, thought about it, and presently began calling section meetings to discuss gobbledygook. More booklets were ordered, and the local output of documents began to improve. A Correspondence Review Section was established as a kind of laboratory to test murky messages. A supervisor could send up samples for analysis and suggestions. The handbook is now used for training new members; and many employees keep it on their desks along with the dictionary. Outside the Bureau some 25,000 copies have been sold (at 20 cents each) to individuals, governments, business firms, all over the world.

[5]By Milton Hall.

It is now used officially in the Veterans Administration and in the Department of Agriculture.

The handbook makes clear the enormous amount of gobbledygook which automatically spreads in any large office, together with ways and means to keep it under control. I would guess that at least half of all the words circulating around the bureaus of the world are "irrelevant, incompetent, and immaterial"—to use a favorite legalism; or are just plain "unnecessary"—to ungobble it.

My favorite story of removing the gobble from gobbledygook concerns the Bureau of Standards at Washington. I have told it before but perhaps the reader will forgive the repetition. A New York plumber wrote the Bureau that he had found hydrochloric acid fine for cleaning drains, and was it harmless? Washington replied: "The efficacy of hydrochloric acid is indisputable, but the chlorine residue is incompatible with metallic permanence."

The plumber wrote back that he was mighty glad the Bureau agreed with him. The Bureau replied with a note of alarm: "We cannot assume responsibility for the production of toxic and noxious residues with hydrochloric acid, and suggest that you use an alternate procedure." The plumber was happy to learn that the Bureau still agreed with him.

Whereupon Washington exploded: "Don't use hydrochloric acid; it eats hell out of the pipes!"[6]

[6]Note: The second quotation on page 61 comes from Gertrude Stein's *Lucy Church Amiably.*

7 "What Do You Mean You Don't Like My Style?"

John S. Fielden

When he wrote this essay for the Harvard Business Review, John S. Fielden was Professor of Management Communications at the University of Alabama. With his colleague Ronald Dulek, he coauthored a series of books on effective business writing.

In large corporations all over the country, people are playing a game of paddleball—with drafts of letters instead of balls. Volley after volley goes back and forth between those who sign the letters and those who actually write them. It's a game nobody likes, but it continues, and we pay for it. The workday has no extra time for such unproductiveness. What causes this round robin of revision?

Typos? Factual misstatements? Poor format? No. *Style* does. Ask yourself how often you hear statements like these:

- "It takes new assistants about a year to learn my style. Until they do, I have no choice but to bounce letters back for revision. I won't sign a letter if it doesn't sound like me."
- "I find it difficult, almost impossible, to write letters for my boss's signature. The boss's style is different from mine."

In companies where managers primarily write their own letters, confusion about style also reigns. Someone sends out a letter and hears later that the reaction was not at all the one desired. It is reported that the reader doesn't like the writer's "tone." A colleague looks over a copy of the letter and says, "No wonder the reader doesn't like this letter. You shouldn't have said things the way you did. You used the wrong style for a letter like this." "Style?" the writer says. "What's wrong with my style?" "I don't know" is the response. "I just don't like the way you said things."

Everybody talks about style, but almost nobody understands the meaning of the word in the business environment. And this lack of understanding hurts both those who write letters for another's signature and those who write for themselves. Neither knows where to turn for help. Strunk and

White's marvelous book *The Elements of Style* devotes only a few pages to a discussion of style, and that concerns only literary style.[1] Books like the Chicago *Manual of Style*[2] seem to define style as all the technical points they cover, from abbreviations and capitalizations to footnotes and bibliographies. And dictionary definitions are usually too vague to be helpful.

Even such a general definition as this offers scant help, although perhaps it comes closest to how business people use the word:

> Style is "the way something is said or done, as distinguished from its substance."[3]

Managers signing drafts written by subordinates, and the subordinates themselves, already know that they have trouble agreeing on "the way things should be said." What, for instance, is meant by "way"? In trying to find that way, both managers and subordinates are chasing a will-o'-the-wisp. There *is* no magical way, no perfect, universal way of writing things that will fend off criticism of style. There is no one style of writing in business that is appropriate in all situations and for all readers, even though managers and subordinates usually talk and behave as if there were.

But why all the confusion? Isn't style really the way we say things? Certainly it is. Then writing style must be made up of the particular words we select to express our ideas and the types of sentences and paragraphs we put together to convey those ideas. What else could it be? Writing has no tone of voice or body gesture to impart additional meanings. In written communication, tone comes from what a reader reads into the words and sentences used.

Words express more than *denotations,* the definitions found in dictionaries. They also carry *connotations.* In the feelings and images associated with each word lies the capacity a writing style has for producing an emotional reaction in a reader. And in that capacity lies the tone of a piece of writing. Style is largely a matter of tone. The writer uses a style; the reader infers a communication's tone. Tone comes from what a reader reads into the words and sentences a writer uses.

In the business environment, tone is especially important. Business writing is not literary writing. Literary artists use unique styles to "express" themselves to a general audience. Business people write to particular persons in particular situations, not so much to express themselves as to accomplish particular purposes, "to get a job done." If a reader doesn't like a novelist's tone, nothing much can happen to the writer short of failing to sell some books. In the business situation, however, an offensive style may not only prevent a sale but may also turn away a customer, work against a promotion, or even cost you a job.

---

[1]William Strunk, Jr. and E.B. White, *The Elements of Style* (New York: Macmillan, 1979).

[2]*Manual of Style* (Chicago: University of Chicago Press, 1969).

[3]*The American Heritage Dictionary of the English Language* (Boston: American Heritage and Houghton Mifflin, 1969).

While style can be distinguished from substance, it cannot be divorced from substance. In business writing, style cannot be divorced from the circumstances under which something is written or from the likes, dislikes, position, and power of the reader.

> **A workable definition of style** in business writing would be something like this:
> Style is that choice of words, sentences, and paragraph format which by virtue of being appropriate to the situation and to the power positions of both writer and reader produces the desired reaction and result.

WHICH STYLE IS YOURS?

Let's take a case and see what we can learn from it. Assume that you are an executive in a very large information-processing company. You receive the following letter:

Mr.(Ms.) Leslie J. Cash
XYZ Corporation
Main Street
Anytown, U.S.A.

Dear Leslie:

As you know, I respect your professional opinion highly. The advice your people have given us at ABC Corporation as we have moved into a comprehensive information system over the past three years has been very helpful. I'm writing to you now, however, in my role as chairman of the executive committee of the trustees of our hospital. We at Community General Hospital have decided to establish a skilled volunteer data processing evaluation team to assess proposals to automate our hospital's information flow.

I have suggested your name to my committee. I know you could get real satisfaction from helping your community as a member of this evaluation team. Please say yes. I look forward to being able to count on your advice. Let me hear from you soon.

Frank J. Scalpel
Chairman
Executive Committee
Community General Hospital
Anytown, U.S.A.

If you accepted the appointment mentioned in this letter, you would have a conflict of interest. You are an executive at XYZ, Inc. You know that XYZ will submit a proposal to install a comprehensive information system for the hospital. Mr. Scalpel is the vice president of finance at ABC Corp., a very good customer of yours. You know him well since you have worked with him on community programs as well as in the business world.

I can think of four typical responses to Scalpel's letter. Each says essentially the same thing, but each is written in a different business style:

Response 1

Mr. Frank J. Scalpel
Chairman, Executive Committee
Community General Hospital
Anytown, U.S.A.

Dear Frank,

As you realize, this litigious age often makes it necessary for large companies to take stringent measures not only to avoid conflicts of interest on the part of their employees but also to preclude even the very suggestion of conflict. And, since my company intends to submit a proposal with reference to automating the hospital's information flow, it would not appear seemly for me to be part of an evaluation team assessing competitors' proposals. Even if I were to excuse myself from consideration of the XYZ proposal, I would still be vulnerable to charges that I gave short shrift to competitors' offerings.

If there is any other way that I can serve the committee that will not raise this conflict-of-interest specter, you know that I would find it pleasurable to be of service, as always.

Sincerely,

Response 2

Dear Frank,

Your comments relative to your respect for my professional opinion are most appreciated. Moreover, your invitation to serve on the hospital's data processing evaluation team is received with gratitude, albeit with some concern.

Response 2 (*continued*)

The evaluation team must be composed of persons free of alliance with any of the vendors submitting proposals. For that reason, it is felt that my services on the team could be construed as a conflict of interest.

Perhaps help can be given in some other way. Again, please be assured that your invitation has been appreciated.

Sincerely,

Response 3

Dear Frank,

Thank you for suggesting my name as a possible member of your data processing evaluation team. I wish I could serve, but I cannot.

XYZ intends, naturally, to submit a proposal to automate the hospital's information flow. You can see the position of conflict I would be in if I were on the evaluation team.

Just let me know of any other way I can be of help. You know I would be more than willing. Thanks again for the invitation.

Cordially,

Response 4

Dear Frank,

Thanks for the kind words and the invitation. Sure wish I could say yes. Can't, though. XYZ intends to submit a sure-fire proposal on automating the hospital's information. Shouldn't be judge and advocate at the same time!

Any other way I can help, Frank—just ask. Thanks again.

Cordially,

What Do You think of these Letters?

Which letter has the style you like best? Check off the response you prefer.

Response	1	2	3	4
	❑	❑	❑	❑

Which letter has the style resembling the one you customarily use? Again, check off your choice.

Response	1	2	3	4
	❑	❑	❑	❑

Which terms best describe the style of each letter? Check the appropriate boxes.

Response 1	❑ Colorful	❑ Passive	❑ Personal
	❑ Dull	❑ Forceful	❑ Impersonal
Response 2	❑ Colorful	❑ Passive	❑ Personal
	❑ Dull	❑ Forceful	❑ Impersonal
Response 3	❑ Colorful	❑ Passive	❑ Personal
	❑ Dull	❑ Forceful	❑ Impersonal
Response 4	❑ Colorful	❑ Passive	❑ Personal
	❑ Dull	❑ Forceful	❑ Impersonal

Let's Compare Reactions

Now that you've given your reactions, let's compare them with some of mine.

Response 1 seems cold, impersonal, complex. Most business people would, I think, react somewhat negatively to this style because it seems to push the reader away from the writer. Its word choice has a cerebral quality that, while flattering to the reader's intelligence, also parades the writer's.

Response 2 is fairly cool, quite impersonal, and somewhat complex. Readers' reactions will probably be neither strongly positive nor strongly negative. This style of writing is "blah" because it is heavily passive. Instead of saying "I appreciate your comments," it says "Your comments are most appreciated"; instead of "I think that my services could be construed as a conflict of interest," it says "It is felt that my services could be construed. . . ." The use of the passive voice subordinates writers modestly to the back of sentences or causes them to disappear.

This is the impersonal, passive style of writing that many with engineering, mathematics, or scientific backgrounds feel most comfortable using. It is harmless, but it is certainly not colorful; nor is it forceful or interesting.

Response 3 illustrates the style of writing that most high-level executives use. It is simple; it is personal; it is warm without being syrupy; it is forceful, like a firm handshake. Almost everybody in business likes this style, although lower-level managers often find themselves afraid to write so forthrightly (and, as a result, often find themselves retreating into the styles of responses 1 and 2—the style of 1 to make themselves look "smart" to superiors and the style of 2 to appear unbossy and fairly impersonal). Persons who find response 2 congenial may feel a bit dubious about the appropriateness of response 3. (Although I have no way of proving this judgment, I would guess that more readers in high positions—perhaps more owner-managers—would like response 3 than would readers who are still in lower positions.)

Response 4 goes beyond being forceful; it is annoyingly self-confident and breezy. It is colorful and conversational to an extreme, and it is so intensely personal and warm that many business people would be offended, even if they were very close acquaintances of Frank Scalpel's. "It sounds like an advertising person's chitchat," some would probably say.

STRATEGY IS PART OF STYLE

As you compared your responses with mine, did you say, "What difference does it make which style *I* like or which most resembles *my* customary style? What matters is which style will go over best with Mr. Scalpel in this situation"? If you did, we're getting somewhere.

Earlier, when we defined business writing style, some may have wanted to add, "And that style should sound like me." This was left out for a good reason. Circumstances not only alter cases; they alter the "you" that it is wise for your style to project. Sometimes it's wise to be forceful; at other times it's suicidal. Sometimes being sprightly and colorful is appropriate; at other times it's ludicrous. There are times to be personal and times to be impersonal.

Not understanding this matter of style and tone is why the big corporation game of paddleball between managers and subordinates goes on and on. The subordinate tries to imitate the boss's style, but in actuality—unless the boss is extremely insensitive—he or she has no single style for all circumstances and for all readers. What usually happens is that after several tries, the subordinate writes a letter that the boss signs. "Aha!" the subordinate says. "So that's what the boss wants!" And then the subordinate tries to use that style for all situations and readers. Later, the superior begins rejecting drafts written in the very style he or she professed liking before. Both parties throw up their hands.

This volleying is foolish and wasteful. Both superior and subordinate have to recognize that in business writing, style cannot be considered apart from the given situation or from the person to whom the writing is directed. Expert writers select the style that fits a particular reader and the type of writing situation with which they are faced. In business, people often face the following writing situations:

Positive situations.
Saying yes or conveying good news.

Situations where some action is asked of the reader.
Giving orders or persuading someone to do as requested.

Information-conveying situations.
Giving the price of ten widgets, for example.

Negative situations.
Saying no or relaying bad news.

In each of these situations, the choice of style is of strategic importance.

In positive situations, a writer can relax on all fronts. Readers are usually so pleased to hear the good news that they pay little attention to anything else. Yet it is possible for someone to communicate good news in such a cold, impersonal, roundabout, and almost begrudging way that the reader becomes upset.

Action-request situations involve a form of bargaining. In a situation where the writer holds all the power, he or she can use a forceful commanding style. When the writer holds no power over the reader, though, actions have to be asked for and the reader persuaded, not ordered. In such cases, a forceful style will not be suitable at all.

In information-conveying situations, getting the message across forcefully and straightforwardly is best. Such situations are not usually charged emotionally.

In negative situations, diplomacy becomes very important. The right style depends on the relative positions of the person saying no and the person being told no.

For instance, if you were Leslie Cash, the person in the example at the beginning of the article whom Frank Scalpel was inviting to serve on a hospital's evaluation team, you would be in a situation of having to say no to a very important customer of your company. You would also be in a doubly sensitive situation because it is unlikely that Mr. Scalpel would fail to recognize that he is asking you to enter a conflict-of-interest situation. He is probably asking you *anyway*. Therefore, you would not only have to tell him no, but you would have to avoid telling him that he has asked you to do something that is highly unethical. In this instance, you would be faced with communicating two negative messages at once or else not giving Scalpel any sensible reason for refusing to serve.

SUIT YOUR STYLE TO THE SITUATION

Now that we've thought about the strategic implications of style, let's go back to look at each of the responses to Scalpel's request and ask ourselves which is best.

Do we *want* to be personal and warm? Usually yes. But in this situation? Do we want to communicate clearly and directly and forcefully? Usually yes. But here? Do we want to appear as if we're brushing aside the conflict, as the third response does? Or do we want to approach that issue long-windedly, as in the first response, or passively, as in the second? What is the strategically appropriate style?

In the abstract, we have no way of knowing which of these responses will go over best with Mr. Scalpel. The choice is a matter of judgment in a concrete situation. Judging the situation accurately is what separates successful from unsuccessful executive communicators.

Looking at the situation with strategy in mind, we note that in the first response, the writer draws back from being close, knowing that it is necessary to reject not only one but two of the reader's requests. By using legalistic phraseology and Latinate vocabulary, the writer lowers the personal nature of the communication and transforms it into a formal statement. It gives an abstract, textbooklike response that removes the tone of personal rejection.

The very fact that response 1 is difficult to read and dull in impact may be a strategic asset in this type of negative situation. But if in this situation a subordinate presented response 1 to you for your signature, would it be appropriate for you to reject it because it is not written in the style *you* happen to *like* best in the abstract—say, the style of response 3?

Now let's look at response 2. Again, we see that a lack of personal warmth may be quite appropriate to the situation at hand. Almost immediately, the letter draws back into impersonality. And by using the passive constantly, the writer avoids the need to say "I must say no." Furthermore, the term *construed* reinforces the passive in the second paragraph. This term is a very weak but possibly a strategically wise way of implying that *some* persons (*other* people, not the writer) could interpret Scalpel's request as an invitation to participate in an improper action. Now we can see that, instead of seeming dull and lacking in personal warmth as it did in the abstract, response 2 may be the type of letter we would be wise to send out, that is, when we have taken the whole situation into careful consideration and not just our personal likes and dislikes.

The third response, and to even greater extent the fourth, have styles that are strategically inappropriate for this situation. In fact, Scalpel might well regard the colorful style of the fourth response as highly offensive.

Both responses directly and forcefully point out the obvious conflict, but by being so direct each runs the risk of subtly offending him. (The third response is "you can see the position of conflict I'd be in if I were on the evaluation team," and the fourth is "Shouldn't be judge and advocate at the same time!") We could make a pretty strong argument that the direct, forceful, candid style of the third response and the breezy, warm, colorful, intensely personal "advertising" style of the fourth response may both prove ineffectual in a delicate, negative situation such as this.

WHAT EFFECT DO YOU WANT?

At this point, readers may say, "All right. I'm convinced. I need to adjust my style to what is appropriate in each situation. And I also need to give directions to others to let them know how to adjust their styles. But I haven't the foggiest notion of how to do either!" Some suggestions for varying your writing style follow. I am not implying that a communication must be written in one style only. A letter to be read aloud at a colleague's retirement party, for instance, may call not only for a warm, personal style but for colorfulness as well. A long analytic report may require a passive, impersonal style, but the persuasive cover letter may call for recommendations being presented in a very forceful style.

For a Forceful Style

This style is usually appropriate only in situations where the writer has the power, such as in action requests in the form of orders or when you are saying no firmly but politely to a subordinate.

- Use the active voice. Have your sentences do something to people and to objects, not just lie there having things done to them; have them give orders:
  "Correct this error immediately" (you-understood is the subject) instead of "A correction should be made" (which leaves the reader wondering, made by whom).
- Step up front and be counted:
  "I have decided not to recommend you for promotion" instead of "Unfortunately, a positive recommendation for your promotion is not forthcoming."
- Do not beat around the bush or act like a politician. If something needs to be said, say it directly.
- Write most of your sentences in subject-verb-object order. Do not weaken them by putting namby-pamby phrases before the subject:

"I have decided to fund your project" instead of "After much deliberation and weighing of the pros and cons, I have decided to fund your project."

- Do not weaken sentences by relegating the point or the action to a subordinate clause:
  If your point is that your company has won a contract, say "Acme won the contract, although the bidding was intense and highly competitive," not "Although Acme won the contract, the bidding was intense and highly competitive."
- Adopt a tone of confidence and surety about what you say by avoiding weasel words like:
  "Possibly," "maybe," "perhaps."
  "It could be concluded that. . . ."
  "Some might conclude that. . . ."

For a Passive Style

This style is often appropriate in negative situations and in situations where the writer is in a lower position than the reader.

- Avoid the imperative—never give an order:
  Say "A more effective and time-conserving presentation of ideas should be devised before our next meeting" as opposed to "Do a better job of presenting your ideas at our next meeting. Respect my time and get right to the point."
- Use the passive voice heavily because it subordinates the subject to the end of the sentence or buries the subject entirely. The passive is especially handy when you are in a low-power position and need to convey negative information to a reader who is in a higher position (an important customer, for instance):
  Say "Valuable resources are being wasted" instead of "Valuable resources are being wasted by your company" or, even worse, "You are wasting valuable resources."
- Avoid taking responsibility for negative statements by attributing them to faceless, impersonal "others":
  Say "It is more than possible that several objections to your proposed plans might be raised by some observers" or "Several objections might be raised by those hostile to your plans" instead of "I have several objections to your plans."
- Use weasel words, especially if the reader is in a high-power position and will not like what you are saying.
- Use long sentences and heavy paragraphs to slow down the reader's comprehension of sensitive or negative information.

For a Personal Style

This style is usually appropriate in good-news and persuasive action-request situations.

- Use the active voice, which puts you, as the writer, at the front of sentences:
  "Thank you very much for your comments" or "I appreciated your comments" instead of "Your comments were very much appreciated by me" or the even more impersonal "Your comments were very much appreciated."
- Use persons' names (first names, when appropriate) instead of referring to them by title:
  "Bill James attended the meeting" instead of "Acme's director attended the meeting."
- Use personal pronouns—especially "you" and "I"—when you are saying positive things:
  "I so much appreciate the work you've done" as opposed to "The work you've done is appreciated."
- Use short sentences that capture the rhythm of ordinary conversation:
  "I discussed your proposal with Frank. He's all for it!" as opposed to "This is to inform you that your proposal was taken up at Friday's meeting and that it was regarded with favor."
- Use contractions ("can't," "won't," "shouldn't") to sound informal and conversational.
- Direct questions to the reader:
  "Just ask yourself, how would your company like to save $10,000?"
- Interject positive personal thoughts and references that will make the reader know that this letter is really to him or her and not some type of form letter sent to just anyone.

For an Impersonal Style

This style is usually appropriate in negative and information-conveying situations. It's always appropriate in technical and scientific writing and usually when you are writing to technical readers.

- Avoid using persons' names, especially first names. Refer to people, if at all, by title or job description:
  "I would like to know what you think of this plan" instead of "What do you think of this, Herb?"
  "Our vice president of finance" or "the finance department," not "Ms. Jones."
- Avoid using personal pronouns, especially "you" and "I" ("we" may be all right because the corporate we is faceless and impersonal):

"The logistics are difficult, and the idea may not work" instead of "I think you have planned things so that the logistics are difficult and your idea may not work." "We wonder if the idea will work" rather than "I don't think the idea will work."

- Use the passive voice to make yourself conveniently disappear when desirable:
  "An error in the calculations has been made" instead of "I think your calculations are wrong."
- Make some of your sentences complex and some paragraphs long, avoid the brisk, direct, simple-sentence style of conversation.

For a Colorful Style

Sometimes a lively style is appropriate in good-news situations. It is most commonly found in the highly persuasive writing of advertisements and sales letters.

- Insert some adjectives and adverbs:
  Instead of "This proposal will save corporate resources," write "This (hard-hitting) (productivity-building) (money-saving) proposal will (easily) (surely) (quickly) (immediately) save our (hard-earned) (increasingly scarce) (carefully guarded) corporate resources."
- If appropriate, use a metaphor (A is B) or a simile (A is like B) to make a point: "Truly this program is a *miracle* of logical design." "Our solution strikes at the very *root* of Acme's problems." "This program is like *magic* in its ability to. . . ."

For a Less Colorful Style

By avoiding adjectives, adverbs, metaphors, and figures of speech, you can make your style less colorful. Such a style is appropriate for ordinary business writing and also results from:

- Blending the impersonal style with the passive style.
- Employing words that remove any semblance of wit, liveliness, and vigor from the writing.

Please bear in mind that these six styles are not mutually exclusive. There is some overlap. A passive style is usually far more impersonal than personal and also not very colorful. A forceful style is likely to be more personal than impersonal, and a colorful style is likely to be fairly forceful. Nevertheless, these styles are distinct enough to justify talking about them. If we fail to make such distinctions, style becomes a catchall term that means nothing specific. Even if not precise, these distinctions enable us to talk about style and its elements and to learn to write appropriately for each situation.

DISCUSS NEEDS FIRST

What conclusions can we draw from this discussion? Simply that, whether you write your own letters or have to manage the writing of subordinates, to be an effective communicator, you must realize that:

1. Each style has an impact on the reader.
2. Style communicates to readers almost as much as the content of a message.
3. Style cannot be isolated from a situation.
4. Generalizing about which style is the best in all situations is impossible.
5. Style must be altered to suit the circumstances.
6. Style must be discussed sensibly in the work situation.

These conclusions will be of obvious help to managers who write their own letters. But what help will these conclusions be to managers who direct assistants in the writing of letters? In many instances, writing assignments go directly to subordinates for handling. Often, manager and assistant have no chance to discuss style strategy together. In such cases, rather than merely submitting a response for a signature, the subordinate would be wise to append a note: e.g., "This is a very sensitive situation, I think. Therefore, I deliberately drew back into a largely impersonal and passive style." At least, the boss will not jump to the conclusion that the assistant has written a letter of low impact by accident.

When they do route writing assignments to assistants, superiors could save much valuable time and prevent mutual distress if they told the subordinates what style seemed strategically wise in each situation. Playing guessing games also wastes money.

And if, as is often the case, neither superior nor subordinate has a clear sense of what style is best, the two can agree to draft a response in one style first, and if that doesn't sound right, to adjust the style appropriately.

Those who write their own letters can try drafting several responses to tough but important situations, each in a different style. It's wise to sleep on them and then decide which sounds best.

Whether you write for yourself or for someone else, it is extremely unlikely that in difficult situations a first draft will be signed by you or anyone else. Only the amateur expects writing perfection on the first try. By learning to control your style and to engineer the tone of your communications, you can make your writing effective.

SUCH STUFF AS STYLE IS MADE ON

To Frank A. Nichols, Secretary,
Concord Free Trade Club

Hartford, March 1885
Dear Sir:

I am in receipt of your favor of the 24th inst., conveying the gratifying intelligence that I have been made an honorary member of the Free Trade Club of Concord, Massachusetts, and I desire to express to the Club, through you, my grateful sense of the high compliment thus paid me.

It does look as if Massachusetts were in a fair way to embarrass me with kindnesses this year. In the first place a Massachusetts Judge has just decided in open court that a Boston publisher may sell not only his own property in a free and unfettered way, but may also as freely sell property which does not belong to him but to me—property which he has not bought and which I have not sold. Under this ruling I am now advertising that judge's homestead for sale; and if I make as good a sum out of it as I expect I shall go on and sell the rest of his property.

In the next place, a committee of the public library of your town has condemned and excommunicated my last book [*Adventures of Huckleberry Finn*], and doubled its sale. This generous action of theirs must necessarily benefit me in one or two additional ways. For instance, it will deter other libraries from buying the book and you are doubtless aware that one book in a public library prevents the sale of a sure ten and a possible hundred of its mates. And secondly it will cause the purchasers of the book to read it, out of curiosity, instead of merely intending to do so after the usual way of the world and library committees; and then they will discover, to my great advantage and their own indignant disappointment, that there is nothing objectionable in the book, after all.

And finally, the Free Trade Club of Concord comes forward and adds to the splendid burden of obligations already conferred upon me by the Commonwealth of Massachusetts, an honorary membership which is more worth than all the rest since it endorses me as worthy to associate with certain gentlemen whom even the moral icebergs of the Concord library committee are bound to respect.

May the great Commonwealth of Massachusetts endure forever, is the heartfelt prayer of one who, long a recipient of her mere general good will, is proud to realize that he is at last become her pet. . . .

Your obliged servant
S. L. Clemens

To the gas company

Hartford, February 1, 1891
Dear Sirs:

Some day you will move me almost to the verge of irritation by your chuckle-headed Goddamned fashion of shutting your Goddamned gas off without giving any notice to your Goddamned parishioners. Several times you have come within an ace of smothering half of this household in their beds and blowing up the other half by this idiotic, not to say criminal, custom of yours. And it has happened again to-day. Haven't you a telephone?

Ys
S. L. Clemens

8 International Communication and Language

Gwyneth Olofsson

Gwyneth Olofsson owns Communico, an international training and consulting firm based in Sweden.

English has become the *lingua franca* of the business world, and people from Amsterdam to Zanzibar use it every day as a "tool of the trade." They also spend a lot of time and money trying to eliminate their language mistakes, not realizing that the fewer they make the more dangerous the errors are likely to become, because people aren't expecting them. Furthermore, just because someone has mastered the grammar and vocabulary of a language and pronounces it better than some native speakers does not mean he or she *uses* it in the same way.

Communication is not only about what the words mean in the dictionary, it's also about how you string them together. There is, after all, a certain difference between "Do that job tomorrow," "I'd appreciate it if you did that job tomorrow," and "Do that job tomorrow or I'll have your guts for garters," even if all three phrases are designed to achieve the same end. Those of us who are native English speakers have a responsibility not to use expressions that are likely to confuse non-native speakers (e.g., "Have you cottoned on, or do I have to spell that out to you?"). We also have to ensure that when "born" English speakers encounter a communication style that seems brusque, unfriendly, or arrogant in someone whose native language is not English, they will not assume that this is a true reflection of this person's personality or intention. It may well be that the speaker hasn't mastered the many nuances of words and body language that a native speaker interprets without even thinking about it. So in an unfamiliar culture, newcomers may find themselves wondering if the downcast eyes that accompany a statement are a sign of modesty or dishonesty.

Recently I ran an intercultural simulation, one part of which involved a group of ten British participants "learning" to be members of a fictitious culture. This made-up culture valued touch, and as part of the exercise participants were encouraged to touch each other at every opportunity, especially when communicating with each other. The simulation was a nightmare for everyone involved. The older male members of the group in particular found it extremely difficult to touch their colleagues at all. It wasn't surprising. Their physical contact with non-family members over the last forty years had been limited to a handshake with customers and a quick elbow in the ribs from strangers on a crowded subway, so to learn to communicate with colleagues in a tactile way that is the norm for millions of people in Latin America or Africa was just too much of a challenge.

Communication is about your facial expression, gestures, and actions. This was brought home to me a few years ago when a young family moved in to the next farm. My Swedish husband was born and brought up on a farm located on an island off the Swedish coast, and the new family had moved there from an outlying island and had two young children, as we did.

The four kids started to play together one day and were having a wonderful time when it started to rain. I went out and asked them, in Swedish, if they wanted to come into the house to play. The two new children looked at me and said nothing, then suddenly turned tail and ran as fast as they could in the direction of their home.

I couldn't make any sense of this, but when I went in and told my husband what had happened he showed no surprise. Without looking up from his newspaper he said, "They've gone home to ask their mother if they can come in." I was amazed. How did he know? He'd never even met them. But sure enough, in a couple of minutes there was a knock at the door and there they stood. Thinking about it, there were two things that surprised me. The first was that the two children hadn't said a word when I'd asked them a question, and the second was that my husband had understood the whole situation without even having seen what had happened.

The explanation was, of course, that he and the two children shared the same cultural roots. He had grown up, as they had, in a community where everyone knew everyone else; a homogenous community where people understood what their neighbors would do before they did it. If you grow up in a society like this you don't need to spell things out. Communication takes place without words because the situation is familiar and is governed by a set of unwritten rules that everyone understands.

If, on the other hand, you look at a country with an entirely different profile, like the U.S., for example, a relatively new country where enormous numbers of people immigrated from other cultures, communication patterns developed quite differently. With high levels of mobility as thousands of people headed west across the continent, individuals were forced to get to know one another quickly and establish their own rules as they went along. It's clear that in such a situation good communication skills were vital, because you couldn't expect the people you met to share your background or assumptions, so your communications with your peers had to be clear, unambiguous, and explicit. This explains why today many people in the U.S. have a very different communication style than the natives of the small island off the west coast of Sweden—and many other places where people have known each other all their lives.

Moral

The way we communicate, and what we do or do not say, may be entirely mystifying to people from other cultures, even though we believe we have made ourselves perfectly clear.

WHAT TO SAY AND HOW TO SAY IT

Even those of us who pride ourselves on being direct don't always say what we mean. If English speakers were to phone a colleague's secretary and ask "Is David in?" we would be surprised if she answered, "Yes" and put the phone down. We assume she would answer the question we *didn't* ask, "May I speak to David?"

Different cultures have different attitudes to directness. I remember a time several years ago when I was in England and having problems with my car. I drove to a garage, parked the car in front, and went inside to report the problem. There was a long line, and as I waited a truck driver came in and addressed the woman waiting behind me in a broad Newcastle accent. "Thanks for moving your car, pet. The other wife just walked away and blocked me in."

In fact, "the other wife" was me. I hadn't seen the truck arrive behind me, and by leaving my car where I did had managed to block his exit. We're talking here about a Newcastle-upon-Tyne truck driver, with tattoos, beer belly, and shaven head, wearing a T-shirt with a picture of a man, not unlike himself, strangling a big snake. But because of the way he had been brought up, this poor guy could not bring himself to speak to me directly and tell me I was blocking his exit, but had to speak to the woman behind me to give him a pretext to tell the world of my stupidity. I mean, it wasn't as if he looked like he was afraid of conflict or had spent his formative years at Eton with Prince William learning how to conduct himself correctly in court circles. But somewhere in his cultural softwiring he'd learned that in certain situations, and addressing a certain type of person (e.g., a middle-aged woman, as opposed to a young man), he should use an indirect communication style.

Your own personal communication style will be affected by many factors. Obviously, the culture you come from plays a large part, as does your own native language. Even climate may have a role to play in how we express ourselves. One interesting (although not entirely serious) observation on this theme was made by the English writer Ford Madox Ford who wrote, "You cannot be dumb [silent] when you live with a person, unless you are an inhabitant of the North of England or the State of Maine." As someone with roots in the North of England I don't know if I can agree wholeheartedly with his conclusion that the colder the climate, the more taciturn the people. However, he's not alone in his conclusion: in both Italy and France the people of the south regard those in the cooler north as reserved and antisocial.

Other considerations affect both what we say and how we say it. For example, the CEO of a large corporation might mutter to a few friends over a drink at the club. "Well, guys, we really made a balls up of the last year's sales, didn't we?" However, he probably wouldn't make the same comment at the annual general meeting (although it might wake up the shareholders). He is more likely to say, "Due to circumstances beyond our control, our sales performance in the last year was disappointing." No matter where we come from, we all know that how we speak depends on the audience we are speaking to.

And speaking of audiences, if you gave a presentation and asked for questions, would you be pleased or worried if there weren't any? Would you take the silence to mean that you had made your point so clearly that everyone understood everything or as a warning sign that trouble was brewing? Would you assume that the audience had found your talk so boring they'd all dropped off to sleep? Or would [you] expect questions to emerge later during the informality of the coffee break? It depends, among other things, on whether the audience was comfortable with silence and whether they came from a culture where asking questions in public is about losing face. Or perhaps they all came from the State of Maine or the North of England. . . .

Letters 1–2

Many of us ask questions if we don't understand something. However, in some cultures this is not a step to be taken lightly.

Asking Questions — *Letter 1*

From the U.S. about ***Mexico***

The company is introducing a complicated new process in one of its workshops in Mexico. We know it's difficult, and we have a training and support package we can offer if needed. I strongly suspect that they're having prob-

> lems down there, but we haven't received a single request for advice or support. Why not?

As you know the process is a complicated one, why don't you provide the support package automatically instead of waiting for a request? Admitting you need help can be a difficult thing to do no matter what culture you come from. Questions of prestige and fear of losing face can mean that people are unwilling to expose themselves to possible criticism. Also, if in your culture you have learned that good employees know all the answers, you may well hesitate to tell your bosses that you don't! This problem can be compounded if headquarters is located abroad, especially in a country that is bigger or richer than your own; this can make national sensitivities even worse.

He Asked What? *Letter 2*

From Canada about ***China***

> I enjoyed my trip to China, but I was very surprised by some questions business acquaintances I hardly knew asked me. Two questions they asked me during a meal were how much my watch cost and how old my wife was. (I'm just glad she wasn't there to hear it!)

It's odd what different cultures regard as acceptable questions. In France and many other European countries, they regard the North American exchange of personal information (Do you have any children? What do you do in your free time?) as rather intrusive, though the French will quite happily discuss matters of religion, which are regarded as taboo by, for example, many people from the Middle East. Canadians and North Americans, of course, simply see such inquiries as a friendly way of building a relationship, and they expect to answer the same questions themselves. At the same time, North Americans usually find questions about money and age too personal to ask business acquaintances. However, for many Chinese, whether in China or elsewhere in Asia, and for people in the Middle East these questions form part of ordinary conversation and are just one way of getting to know you better. Indeed, such questions are seen as a natural way to show you're interested in your new acquaintance. People in countries as far apart as China, India, and Mexico might even think it rather unfriendly if people they met did *not* show any interest in their personal concerns.

Letters 3–4

The way people communicate with each other at work is affected by the structure of the organization they work for and by the expectations of fellow employees.

Communication Stop — *Letter 3*

From Sweden about ***Germany***

> I work for a multinational company and am involved in a project that requires a lot of technical input. I contacted a German colleague I'd met at a conference for a little help. When I spoke to him on the phone he was quite pleased to help us, but the next day my manager got an e-mail from the German guy's boss saying that my colleague was too busy to help me.

I think the problem here is that you didn't use the "correct" channels of communication, according to the German company, anyway. In Germany, and indeed in the majority of European and American companies, the manager wants to be informed of what his or her department members are doing, as it's an important part of his or her role to co-ordinate their efforts. What you should have done first was to contact the manager and ask if you could approach your German colleague for some assistance. Not doing so might be interpreted by his or her manager as very rude, and even a bit underhanded.

I understand that you come from a country, Sweden, where it's the norm to delegate an enormous amount of power to non-managerial staff and give them a high degree of independence, especially if they are technical specialists. However, this is certainly not the case in most countries, which tend to be much more hierarchical. Indeed, most managers from the U.K. to the United Arab Emirates, by way of the U.S., would want to be informed of such an approach to a subordinate.

I suggest your manager make a formal request to his German counterpart asking if you may contact the specialist. You should include a description of the kind of questions to be tackled, and a description of the benefits your project will make to the company. And be *very* polite. After all, you are asking the manager for a favor—to be allowed to use the valuable time of one of the department's members.

Communication Breakdown — *Letter 4*

From New Zealand about ***France***

> We're having real problems with our French subsidiary. We want a couple of departments in the French head office to collaborate in preparing a program for some visiting customers who want to see production operations. Naturally, this will involve consultation with the factory staff to see what is practicable. However, arrangements seem to be at a standstill. We can't understand what the problem can be.

What you have asked your French managers to do is to communicate in ways they may not be used to. First, you are asking your managers to operate across departmental boundaries; hence, it's not clear who is responsible for what. Second, they are being asked to communicate across hierarchical boundaries, because the managers will not be able to arrange a trip to see production facilities without some collaboration and discussion with the factory personnel.

The French, as well as Latin American and Southern European business cultures, tend to have very clear hierarchies where each person's responsibilities are spelled out. The same applies to cultures with a Confucian heritage like Japan, China, and South Korea, where respect is awarded to age, education, and rank in the company. The French also have rather compartmentalized communication patterns, and information is not freely shared as a matter of course, but tends to remain the property of those higher up the ladder. "Knowledge is power" is the name of the game, and one likely to hinder interdepartmental collaboration. Your culture (which is more tolerant of uncertainty) is more like that of the Scandinavians, the British, and Irish in your belief in a free flow of information, but many other cultures find this difficult to deal with. You are more likely to get a positive result if you give *one* of the managers responsibility for arranging the visit, and instruct him or her to involve the factory in the plans.

Letters 5–6

You may like to have things out in the open, or prefer to leave them unsaid.

A Major Error — *Letter 5*

From Mexico about ***Germany***

> We have a new German manager who is making himself extremely unpopular here. He has introduced a new quality control system that is complicated and takes time to learn. Inevitably mistakes are made. However, when he finds an error, he seems to delight in pointing this out to the person involved in front of everyone. Several people are already thinking of handing in their notices.

Your new manager is certainly not trying to offend people intentionally. In his own direct way, a way shared by U.S. Americans who also believe that it is better to "tell it like it is," he might even be trying to help by identifying the problem. He obviously does not understand that Mexicans regard this very direct approach as fault-finding, confrontational, and aggressive. Mexicans, like most Central and South Americans and East Asians, are skilled at avoiding confrontations and situations that involve a loss of face, but this is still something your new manager has to learn. Until he does, try not to take his criticism personally.

No No *Letter 6*

From the U.S. about ***Indonesia***

> I found it very difficult working in Indonesia because I couldn't get a straight answer to a straight question, and this often led to misunderstandings. As far as I could see, they often said yes when they meant no. Why?

Most Indonesians find it hard to give a straightforward *no* to a request. If you ask for something to be done that is difficult or even impossible your Indonesian colleague, instead of saying *no* or *sorry,* may say instead that he will try. Also, a promise to do something that keeps getting postponed can be another indirect way of refusing a request. There is no intention to deceive, but simply a wish to avoid situations leading to open disagreement or disappointment that would cause you to lose face. And bear in mind that people from cultures with this indirect communication style are perfectly well understood by each other. They are simply tuned in to "reading between the lines" in a way you are not.

This communication pattern is not confined to Indonesia. In countries as far away from Indonesia as Pakistan, India, and Japan the word *no* is regarded as impolite and is rarely heard in a business context. In Mexico and South America, too, politeness and diplomacy are valued as useful ways of avoiding conflict.

But bear in mind that speakers of English can be indirect sometimes too. If invited to a party they don't want to attend, the vast majority of English speakers will say they have a cold rather than admit that they're planning to spend the evening in front of the TV. This is just another variation on the "white lie" theme, and as such is remarkably similar to the indirect response you mentioned in your question.

Letters 7–9

It's easy to create the wrong impression if you choose an inappropriate communication style—and what is inappropriate is in the ear of the listener.

Aggressive *Letter 7*

From Sweden about ***France***

> I find it extremely difficult to discuss business with the French. It is impossible to talk about things with them calmly and sensibly. They are very critical of any ideas that they have not originated themselves, but take any criticism of their own plans personally and get angry.

If you come from a country like Sweden, where open conflict is frowned on, you may find the French debating style very aggressive. For the French, a love of words is combined with a liking for verbal combat, and they are used to organizing their case logically and presenting their arguments with force and conviction, not necessarily because they believe in them, but because they consider that it is through argument and counter-argument that you will eventually arrive at the truth or the best solution to a problem. And if you don't, the debate has been an enjoyable chance to flex your intellectual muscles anyway!

However, the bad feelings that may result from such spectacular clashes will usually quickly be forgotten, which is also hard for people from more low-key cultures to understand. Of course, the French are not alone in their love of discussion. Greeks, Israelis, Argentineans, and Poles all enjoy a good debate too, and North Americans and Australians are no shrinking violets when it comes to putting their points forward. For the French and Australians in particular, debate is a way of taking the measure of a new acquaintance.

In your particular case, at a meeting with the French you should emphasize the most important points of your argument and repeat them patiently. Don't get tied up with details or try to score debating points. Instead, focus on the most important points you want to achieve and keep the meeting focused on them. Be very well prepared, and if in a corner, be ready to use a weapon to which the French have no defense—silence.

Patronizing Pommie — *Letter 8*

From Australia about the **U.K.**

> We have a new boss from the U.K. with one of the most affected upper-class English accents I have ever heard. Every time he opens his mouth I can just see him at the Queen's garden party in a tuxedo and top hat. I just can't take him seriously, and I wonder how he expects to communicate with the other guys in the company.

For historical reasons an upper-class English accent in Australia is associated with money and power, and the use and misuse of both. Australia is a proud new multiethnic country and many Aussies find reminders of their colonial past, that includes the accent of the former ruling class, embarrassing and even painful.

But it's true that this particular type of British accent (RP, which is short for Received Pronunciation) is linked to a certain powerful social group in a way that different U.S. regional accents are not. It also continues to be an accent that dominates the boardrooms of many companies. Even in England itself people with strong regional accents may associate RP with snobbery and privilege, which is why younger members of the upper classes try to tone it down a bit. But give your boss a chance. It would be unfair to judge how well he's likely to do his job on the basis of his vowel sounds!

Just Making Conversation *Letter 9*

From BRITAIN about ***JAPAN***

> I met several Japanese businesspeople who visited Britain recently, and I tried to be pleasant and help them relax. I told a few jokes that seemed to go down well, but I later heard that they hadn't been appreciated. Yet at the time everyone laughed!

Your mistake was to treat your visitors as if they were from your own country. I'm sure this was done from the best of motives, but it is a mistake to assume that every culture shares the same kind of humor. Just because your Japanese visitors laughed didn't necessarily mean that they found your joke funny—people from different cultures tend to laugh at different things. Research about what people of different nationalities find funny concluded that the Irish, British, Australians, and New Zealanders thought that jokes involving word play were funniest. Canadians and U.S. Americans preferred jokes where there was a sense of superiority—either because a person looked stupid or was made to look stupid by another person. Many European countries, like France, Denmark, and Belgium, liked rather surreal jokes and jokes about serious topics like death and illness.

You don't say whether you told your jokes during a business meeting or after work in the pub. However, in many countries humor is confined to non-work situations, and joking in an important meeting, for example, is seen as a sign that you are not treating the subject (or the individual) with respect. This would certainly apply to Germany and Finland as well as Japan, where humor when business matters were being discussed would be regarded as inappropriate. And of course it might well be that your visitors didn't understand your English but did not want to lose face by showing it, because even if you are fluent in a foreign language, jokes are always the last things you understand.

Finally, you need to know that people from East Asian countries as widely apart as Japan, South Korea, and Thailand may laugh if embarrassed or nervous as well as when they're happy.

Letters 10–11

Rudeness may be what the listener hears, rather than what the speaker intends.

Rude, or Just Informal? *Letter 10*

From DENMARK about ***DENMARK***

> In Denmark we tend to communicate in an informal way and consequently leave out titles like "Mr." or "Dr." We also like to communicate directly rather than "beating about the bush." But I know this isn't the case in other cultures and wondered just how rude we are perceived to be.

It depends where you're going and who you're meeting. In Northern Europe, Australia, and the U.S., communication styles are quite relaxed and informal, and people take pride in talking to both manual workers and top managers in more or less the same way. They also tend to be rather pragmatic in their understanding of what language is for—generally it's to get things done. So they say clearly what they mean so the message comes over loud and clear. This group won't regard your informal and direct style as at all rude.

In other cultures, however, what you say may be secondary to how you say it, and the British, along with the Arabs and people from many Asian cultures, put a lot of weight on how the message is delivered. Words are regarded as an important way of establishing and building relationships, not simply a tool for getting things done. If your "tone" is wrong and you are perceived as rude, people from these cultures can take offense, and, for example, not using the right titles for an individual can be regarded as a sign of disrespect.

As a general rule, it's better to err on the side of formality when communicating with people of other nationalities, even if you've worked together for quite some time. Words define your relationship with an individual, and if you want to ensure that the relationship is one of mutual respect, your communication style must reflect that.

Let Me Finish! *Letter 11*

From SOUTH AFRICA about ***ITALY***

> I travel often in Italy and in other Mediterranean countries, and I find it very irritating to be constantly interrupted. What can I do to stop this?

The short answer is—not a lot. What you as a South African would call a rude interruption, nationals from Southern European countries may regard as perfectly acceptable. They may instead see an interruption as an expression of interest and involvement in what the speaker is saying and in his or her ideas. In short, in countries such as Italy, if you wait for a pause in the conversation in order to present your own point of view, you'll never open your mouth! You'll find that the nationals of these countries interrupt each other too, so don't take it personally. This is because silence does not have an important role in the communication patterns of most Latin countries. Indeed, the tempo of conversation may simply be too fast to allow for a pause between speakers.

If you are interrupted in the middle of a presentation, don't show annoyance but say that you'll deal with the points raised at the end of your talk; don't let yourself be thrown off track. If the interruption occurs in the middle of an informal meeting, accept that this is regarded as a legitimate way of raising relevant points and practice your debating skills.

Letters 12–13

When to remain silent is a decision we make almost unconsciously when operating in our own culture. But in another culture this decision may be interpreted in a way we don't expect.

Stuck Dumb — *Letter 12*

From POLAND about **SOUTH KOREA**

> During my recent trips to South Korea I have built up a good relationship with an engineer of about my own age who works in my own area of expertise. He speaks good English, and we have had a number of informal meetings where we've made tentative decisions about some technical developments. However, when his boss is present he hardly ever opens his mouth, even though this manager has to use an interpreter and does not have a technical background.

It is quite usual in South Korea, and neighboring Japan, that a younger employee will be quiet in front of older managers as a sign of respect. It would be regarded as immodest to display his superior knowledge of English or the technical matter at hand in front of his boss. This manager will not be directly involved in the technical side of things, but will want to know a little about you personally and see you "in action" so he can come to some conclusion about whether you and the company you represent are likely to make good working partners.

Small Talk Versus Silence — *Letter 13*

From FINLAND about the **U.K.**

> We hear a lot about the importance of "small talk" when doing business with the British. But if you don't have anything particular to say, why should you keep on talking? Surely it makes more sense to keep your mouth shut.

In cultures where conversation is an art form, as in France and Italy, a firmly shut mouth may be equated with a firmly shut mind. You may be regarded as rude if you are not prepared to make an effort to get to know your counterparts on a personal rather than simply on a business level. However, you are not the only one to find this need for "small talk" difficult. In addition to Finns, Swedes and Norwegians also have a problem with it. In your cultures silence is accepted as a part of conversation in a way it is not in many others (although the Japanese are more like you in their acceptance of silence). To many Europeans and Americans, general social conversation is a prelude to more serious discussions and is regarded as a way of getting to know your colleague before you get down to brass tacks.

If you are stuck about what to talk about, non-controversial topics are best to start with. In 1758, Samuel Johnson wrote, "It is commonly observed that when two Englishmen meet, their first talk is of the weather." Some things just don't change, and not only the English find this subject a useful "icebreaker" with strangers. Other useful subjects are the journey to the meeting, sports, and questions about your visitor's hometown or area, but the real secret is to relax and allow yourself to show you are interested in your partner and what he or she has to say. Feel free to ask questions, as long as they don't get *too* personal. People usually enjoy talking about themselves. Neither should you be afraid to talk about yourself and your own interests. Conversation is like dancing the tango (surprisingly, perhaps, this is very popular in Finland) in that it needs practice. It also requires sensitivity to what your "partner" is feeling and anticipation of the next move.

Letter 14

Giving presentations at home can be bad enough, but speaking to people of other cultures can be even harder.

Political Correctness — *Letter 14*

From AUSTRALIA about the ***U.S.***

I've just returned from the U.S. where I gave a number of lectures on a technical matter. During one of my talks I used the expression "to call a spade a spade." One of my listeners raised his hand and said that he found the expression offensive—he had taken it as a racist comment! Is this political correctness run wild?

To put it bluntly, yes it is. The expression "to call a spade a spade" simply means to describe something truthfully and honestly. However, in the U.S.

spade is a derogatory term for a black person; it comes from the expression "as black as the ace of spades." Your listener obviously confused the two.

When you speak in public on any subject, it is simple good manners to ensure that what you say does not unintentionally offend any particular group, hurt their feelings, or show them disrespect, especially if this group has been given a hard time by society at large over the years; women, black people, homosexuals, and handicapped people are some groups that spring to mind. It's obvious that people belonging to these groups are just as deserving of consideration and courtesy as the traditional top dogs—white heterosexual able-bodied males.

However, this respect for the dignity of others should not stop you from getting your own message across. The term *political correctness* has unfortunately come to be associated with a "holier than thou" attitude, and some North Americans use it to beat less politically correct fellow citizens over the head. Luckily, it is primarily a North American phenomenon, but one that the rest of us should be aware of when we have contact with Canadians or U.S. Americans.

IN A NUTSHELL: WHAT TO SAY AND HOW TO SAY IT

Global Business Standards

Good small talk topics:

Weather is always safe, although boring, especially in countries that don't have a lot!

Sports are usually safe too, unless the city or country has suffered a spectacular defeat in the national sport recently.

The art and cultural history of the country is usually safe (but watch out for any historical discussion that can lead to a political debate.)

Global Warnings

No swearing in your own or any other language.

Keep humor to a minimum until you are sure your partners/guests laugh at the same things as you.

Don't comment negatively about another culture—especially on religion, politics, or sexual matters. (Occasionally requests for information on the first two may be interpreted favorably, but be careful.)

- **Argentina:** People like to express opinions and love to debate. Voices may be louder than elsewhere in South America. (See Letters 4, 5, 6, 7, 11, and 13.)
- **Australia:** People enjoy talking and debating. There is an informal style of communication that is not based on hierarchy. (See Letters 7, 8, 9, 10, and 14.)
- **Austria:** Communication within companies is inhibited by departmental and hierarchical boundaries. There is a direct yet formal communication style. May be an adversarial approach to debate among peers. (See Letter 3.)
- **Belgium:** Communication within companies is inhibited by departmental and hierarchical boundaries. French speakers' adversarial style in discussions may appear very negative or aggressive. Flemish speakers are more low-key. (See Letters 3 and 9.)
- **Brazil:** Relatively personal questions (in more reserved cultures) about income, age, and so on are acceptable. Emotions are expressed openly. (See Letters 4, 5, 6, 11, and 13.)
- **Canada:** There are different communication styles depending on whether you are in English- or French-speaking Canada. (See U.K. and France.) (See Letters 2, 7, 9, and 14.)
- **China:** Personal questions about income, age, and so on are acceptable. Ordinary conversations can be loud and may sound unintentionally rude or angry. (See Letters 2, 4, and 5.)
- **Denmark:** Informal communication style is the norm. (See Letters 4, 9, and 10.)
- **Finland:** Small talk is not usual. Silence is accepted. The verbal style is very quiet and restrained. (See Letters 4, 9, and 10.)
- **France:** Communication within companies is inhibited by departmental and hierarchical boundaries. Adversarial style in discussions may appear to outsiders to be very negative or aggressive. (See Letters 2, 3, 4, 7, and 9.)
- **Germany:** Communication within companies may be inhibited by departmental and hierarchical boundaries. There is a direct yet formal communication style. Adversarial style in discussions may appear very negative or aggressive. Negative messages are given directly; tact is not a priority. (See Letters 3, 5, and 9.)
- **Hong Kong:** Personal questions about income, age, and so on are acceptable. Ordinary conversations can be loud, and may sound unintentionally rude or angry. (See Letters 2, 4, and 5.)
- **India:** Personal questions about income, age, and so on are acceptable. In these "high context" cultures a straight *no* is regarded as rude. Explanations and communication styles may be indirect. (See Letters 2 and 6.)
- **Indonesia:** Quiet, calm polite conversation style is the norm. This is also appreciated in others. (See Letters 2, 5, and 6.)

- **Italy:** Overlapping conversational style is the norm. Interruptions are not regarded negatively. Emotions are expressed openly. (See Letters 3, 4, 11, and 13.)
- **Japan:** Deference to senior and older colleagues (when present) may inhibit Japanese from communicating. Self-consciousness about their English may be another inhibiting factor. There is an oblique and indirect communication style and modesty is important. A straight *no* is regarded as rude. (See Letters 4, 5, 6, 9, 12, and 13.)
- **Mexico:** There is an indirect communication style. Direct confrontation is avoided. It's important to "save face." (See Letters 1, 2, 4, 5, 6, 11, and 13.)
- **Netherlands:** People have a rather blunt and straightforward speaking style and are quite informal.
- **Norway:** There is an informal and direct communication style. Silence is an accepted part of communication. (See Letters 4, 10, and 13.)
- **Poland:** People enjoy debate and discussions. Politeness and formality are quite important. (See Letter 7.)
- **Russia:** The first response to any question is usually *no*, but persistence is often rewarded. It is important for Russians not to lose face in discussions. They may show disagreement or anger quite openly.
- **Saudi Arabia:** Ordinary conversations can be loud and may sound unintentionally rude or angry to outsiders. Emotions are expressed openly. (See Letters 2 and 10.)
- **South Africa:** Lots of sports analogies (from rugby, cricket, etc.) used. Different ethnic groups use different communication styles. (See Letter 11.)
- **South Korea:** When getting to know you, people may ask personal questions, but they are not intending to be rude. (See Letters 5, 9, and 12.)
- **Spain:** A straight *no* is regarded as rude. Explanations and communication styles may be indirect. (See Letters 3, 4, 11, and 13.)
- **Sweden:** Communication across hierarchical boundaries is common. Written communication in English may sound brusque, even rude, because of first language interference. Silence is an accepted part of communication. (See Letters 3, 4, 7, 10, and 13.)
- **Switzerland:** Humor has little place in business. German speakers will not make small talk, but French and Italian speakers will.
- **Taiwan:** See China.
- **Thailand:** There is a very tactful communication style, and heated debates are not popular. (See Letters 5 and 9.)
- **Turkey:** People may be reluctant to say *no*. It is more important to be polite than to be accurate or clear. (See Letters 3 and 4.)
- **U.K.:** Small talk is an important social skill. Humor is used widely to defuse tension and to create positive social contacts. People are judged according to how they use language. An oblique style, including understatement or irony, may be used. (See Letters 3, 4, 8, 9, 10, and 13.)

- **U.S.:** Political correctness (and good manners) means that you should be very careful how you express yourself. This applies to all references to gender, age, race, religion, or sexual orientation. Communication is generally direct and explicit. (See Letters 1, 2, 3, 5, 6, 7, 9, 10, and 14.)
- **Venezuela:** People like to debate but rarely admit they are wrong or do not know something. (See Letters 4, 5, 6, 11, and 13.)

A GLOBAL LANGUAGE?

There are over 400 million speakers of English as a first language in the world, with about the same number of people using it as a second language. However, over 700 million people speak one of the many dialects of Chinese. The world also contains almost 300 million Spanish speakers, and about 180 million speakers of Hindi and Arabic, respectively. (And undoubtedly included in these figures are a good few thousand gifted people who speak *all* these languages.)

However, English speakers can take comfort from statistics that say 75 percent of the world's mail, telexes, and cables are in English, that it is the medium for 80 percent of the information stored on the world's computers, and that it is the language of over half the world's technical and scientific periodicals. In fact, it can be said with justice that English is on the way to becoming the first truly global language.

The need for a language in which people from Siberia to Santiago can communicate directly with each other has long been acknowledged, and the establishment of artificial languages such as Esperanto has tried unsuccessfully to fulfill this need. Now, due to a series of accidents of history, it looks as if English is likely to step into the breach. But if a language is "global," it is no longer the exclusive property of its native speakers. Indeed, it is claimed that there is a European variety of English, sometimes called *Euro-English*, which is already evolving, and some people believe that it will eventually become the European language of business. It even has an official name: English as a lingua franca in Europe (ELFE). This version of English regards as acceptable some "mistakes" that most teachers of the language spend their careers trying to eradicate. For example, "He goes to work every day at 8:00 o'clock" would be accepted as correct, as the meaning of the sentence remains clear.

Some academics believe that this modified version of English, which would turn increasingly to continental Europe rather than to the U.S. or the U.K. for its standards of correctness and appropriateness, is the future. Whether that is true remains to be seen, but whatever happens, the message is clear: English is a useful tool for international communication, but it is no longer the exclusive property of people who speak it as a first language.

And what about this privileged group: Those of us who by an accident of birth have learned to speak the global language of business and industry without effort? Can we just rest on our laurels in the knowledge that our customers, suppliers, and even our employers will communicate with us in *our* native language, rather than in *theirs?*

That might be a mistake. I know of at least one international company of management consultants that will not employ anyone who does not speak at least one foreign language fluently. The reason given is that each language gives you a new perspective on the world, and if you are going to work with people not from your own culture you need to be able to shift away from your "native" perceptions from time to time, because language affects how you think.

Letters 15–16

It's inevitable that when speaking English as a foreign language you will make mistakes, and these mistakes can take many forms.

Rude Writers — *Letter 15*

From SPAIN about **SWEDEN**

> In the office where I work we have often had visitors from Sweden, and we've been very impressed both by their English and by their pleasant and friendly manners. However, we have received some letters from these very same people lately and have been amazed by the poor standard of their English and by the tone of the letters, which we find rather arrogant.

You'll be wiser to trust your first impressions. There's a major difference between how we speak and how we write, and whether we're using our native language or someone else's. For example, Swedish children learn English from about the age of eight and quickly become fluent and accurate speakers, but there isn't the same emphasis on written skills (the reverse is true in Japan and South Korea, where writing is prioritized).

When they write in their own language, Swedes are often very informal and rather blunt; this reflects their egalitarian approach to their fellow citizens. When they transpose this style into written English they can unintentionally sound very rude, especially as there isn't a Swedish equivalent for *please* as there is, for example, in Spanish (*por favor*).

It is often difficult to establish the right "tone" in written communication when body language and tone of voice are missing from the communication equation. I have noticed when people from French-, Arabic-, and Spanish-speaking countries write to me, although the grammar and vocabulary may be less than perfect, the tone is extremely polite and rather more formal than letters and e-mails from the U.S. or the U.K. This is because the writers are imitating the more formal and courteous written styles of their own languages and transposing them to English.

Misunderstandings such as you describe, which arise from the tone of a letter or written material, are often the result of "first language interference" and can be hard to identify and correct. It's easier if you make the wrong impression during a face-to-face encounter, because then you get immediate feedback from your listener's body language or facial expression.

The moral is that when writing in any language you should be more formal than when you're speaking, and most importantly, ensure that the tone of the letter is polite and friendly. This is hard to do in a foreign language, but it is even more important than getting the grammar or vocabulary right. If you feel that you cannot judge the tone of your letter yourself, try to get a native speaker to read it before sending it off to ensure that you're not going to offend anyone by appearing less charming than you actually are!

Thin Skin — *Letter 16*

From the NETHERLANDS about ***FRANCE***

> I made a mistake the other day when a French visitor used a wrong word when he was speaking English. He told a group of us when we arrived at this office to "Please sit down, and I'll enjoy you in a minute." We Dutch laughed a little about this, and thought he would too, for we know him well and have always worked well together. However, he was extremely offended. We are sorry for our tactlessness but also surprised at his sensitivity.

His reaction is not hard to account for. There is a lot of prestige involved in how well you speak a foreign language, and if the corporate language is English but it isn't your native language, you can feel threatened if you are concerned that your English isn't up to standard. And when people feel threatened, they can become both defensive and aggressive. Speaking a foreign language means that, like it or not, you have to give a public display of how well you command one of the most important tools of your profession, and that can be a nerve-wracking experience.

The standard of English in the Netherlands and in Northern Europe is extremely high, and this fact may have made your French colleague's reaction worse. Until relatively recently the French have not taken English-language learning seriously (although they have not been as bad as the British and Americans about learning foreign languages). He may have been able to accept a native speaker's superiority, but to have another non-native speaker laughing at his errors was humiliating.

Letters 17–18

There are many countries with more than one national language and most nations have linguistic minorities. To forget these facts is to show an unacceptable degree of ignorance of the culture you are dealing with.

One Country—Two Languages *Letter 17*

From BRAZIL about ***CANADA***

I'll be going to Quebec soon but speak only English. How important is it to be able to speak French as well?

I'd take at least a few lessons in French if you intend to do a lot of business in Canada, for this is one country where English is not regarded simply as an efficient tool for international business communication. Instead, it's regarded by some of its French-speaking citizens as a symbol of the oppression by the English-speaking majority of the French-speaking minority.

Canada is divided into ten different provinces, and they have both French and English as their official languages. Today you will find both languages on maps, tourist brochures, and product labels. Historically there has been friction between the French-speaking Québécois and the English-speaking people who have surrounded them for centuries. The Québécois have seen French speakers in other provinces become assimilated into the English-speaking culture, and they take great pains to preserve their language and culture so the same thing doesn't happen to them. So if Quebec is your destination I suggest learning as much French as possible before departure, both as a goodwill gesture and as a survival measure in case you meet some of the Québécois who can't or won't speak English. But be warned: The French they speak in Canada is not the same as that spoken in France, and even some of the English you hear in Québec may be unfamiliar, as many French words have been incorporated into the English they speak there.

One Country—Several Languages *Letter 18*

From AUSTRALIA about ***BELGIUM***

I will probably be traveling to Belgium in the near future. I speak elementary French and my native language is English. Will that be enough?

A lot depends on where in Belgium you are going, for despite its small size and population of around 10 million, there are two completely different languages spoken. In Flanders, the northern part of the country, the people speak Flemish, which is a variation of Dutch, and all employers in Flanders are required by law to use Flemish in the workplace.

In Wallonia, the southern part of the country, they speak French, as do many of the inhabitants of Brussels. For Belgians, which language they speak is very much a part of their national identity. The situation in the country is made even more complicated because many Walloons cannot speak Flemish and some Flemish people are reluctant to speak French! However, in the capital about a quarter of the residents are non-Belgian, so there English is increasingly accepted. Be grateful that English is your native language, because it can be regarded as a sort of "neutral territory" outside the political and historical issues that otherwise make the language question in Belgium such a hot potato.

Letters 19–20

There are many different "Englishes," two of which are described here.

British versus U.S. English *Letter 19*

*From FRANCE about the **U.S.***

> I've recently come back from the U.S. where I attended a conference. One lecture dealt with different human resources issues, and I was surprised to hear the term *attrition* used in this context. The only time I've heard it before is in war of *attrition,* meaning a war involving total destruction of the enemy. When I got home I checked in my English dictionary and found *attrition* means "the state of wearing away." I'm none the wiser!

I'm not surprised. This is an excellent example of what George Bernard Shaw meant when he wrote "England and America are two countries separated by the same language." I imagine you learned British English rather than American, and there is a little area where the two don't correspond. Don't be alarmed: *Attrition* doesn't refer to a particularly drastic (and permanent) way of getting rid of unwanted staff! It's a human resources term describing the process by which people leave their jobs at a company when they move to another position, retire, decide to study, and so on and are not replaced. The term for the same phenomenon in England is *natural wastage* (which most Americans think sounds like some sort of sewerage system).

Don't blame your dictionary. Apart from the British-English and American-English differences, the English language is in a constant state of change and dictionaries cannot possibly keep up with all developments.

"International English" for Presentations *Letter 20*

From the U.S. about ***the Rest of the World***

> I'm used to giving presentations in the U.S., but I will soon be going abroad for the first time. I'll be presenting information in a number of different countries where I guess most people do not speak English as their first language. Are there any changes I should make to my presentations to adapt them?

Speaking to non-native English speakers certainly requires extra thought, although in certain parts of Asia, for example, Singapore and Hong Kong, which are former British colonies, people may speak English as a first language.

To give a clear message speak slowly and clearly and pause often. In addition, use a tape recorder or ask someone not from your own hometown to establish whether you have a strong accent and if you do, try to tone it down. It's important to be confident and believe in what you are presenting, but make sure you don't come over as too loud (aggressive) or too relaxed (casual). In the more restrained cultures of Eastern Asia or Northern Europe you could appear to be trying to dominate your audience.

To give non-English native speakers a chance to absorb the key facts, repeat your main points in different ways. Try not to use sports metaphors. Violent metaphors are also inappropriate, especially in cultures that value gentle and controlled behavior, so don't use phrases like "bite the bullet," "twist your arm," or "ride roughshod over someone."

If you want your listeners to understand you, avoid the latest buzzwords, idioms, and slang. The use of initials and abbreviations can also be confusing, so use the full form instead. Two more things: don't use even the mildest swear words, and be careful in your use of humor.

It would also be wise to avoid using hand gestures to illustrate a point as they may not be interpreted the same way internationally. One example would be the way a Mexican speaker brought a presentation to a speedy halt in the U.K. by indicating the number two by two raised fingers with the back of his hand facing the audience. He had inadvertently told his British audience to f*** off.

What you *should* do is to make sure that you take plenty of visual material, as this can remove the need for words, and clarify points for people whose native language is not English. Another idea is to distribute written information (in English or the home language) before the meeting so participants have time to read it and translate it if necessary. Remember that it is hard work listening to a foreign language, so keep your presentation shorter than you would at home and make sure you have lots of breaks. This also gives people the chance to ask you questions, something they may not wish to do in front of a large audience if their English is shaky, or if they feel such questions would entail a loss of face by revealing they haven't followed everything you have said.

And a final word of advice: If you don't already speak a foreign language, start to learn one. It will give you an insight into what your Asian colleagues are up against.

Letter 21

Native speakers of English have an enormous business advantage, but they should not misuse it, or they will cause resentment.

Sensitive Speakers Sought — *Letter 21*

*From MEXICO about the **U.K.**, the **U.S.**, **Australia**, etc.*

> Why can't native English-speakers show a little more sensitivity in their dealings with non-English speakers? They often use their superiority in the language to dominate meetings, and if there are two or more present they speak far too fast and use words and expressions we are not familiar with.

Your question is a useful reminder to everyone who has English as his or her first language. People who speak no foreign languages themselves, and this includes many British and American people, often forget what a strain it is listening to a foreign tongue, and when speaking to foreigners they make no concessions when it comes to their choice of words. Not only that, they forget that their listeners may have learned to speak British RP (Received Pronunciation) or Network Standard American English at school and are not used to strong regional accents. Ironically, it's when non-native speakers speak really good English that the worst problems arise, for it's then that Aussies, Kiwis, or Brits forget they're talking to a foreigner and speak in exactly the same way they would to someone from back home, while their poor listeners struggle to keep up.

One of the most important things for native speakers to remember is to listen. Don't treat a person's silence as a sign for you to continue to speak, but wait. Your colleague has to formulate his or her ideas in a foreign language, and that takes time.

Letters 22–23

As long as there are different languages there will inevitably be problems with translation.

Language Mistake *Letter 22*

From SOUTH KOREA about ***BRAZIL***

> My company employed an agency to translate our material for the Brazilian market. We'd already sent away the material when we discovered that it had been written in Spanish and not Portuguese. Our Brazilian agents have told us that it's useless and they require new material. Are the languages really so different?

As well as being the language of Brazil, Portuguese is widely spoken in Venezuelan cities, and elsewhere in South America that Spanish isn't the primary language. It was lucky that your agents spotted the mistake before the material was printed, for national language forms a vital part of national identity, and not respecting this is asking for trouble. Spanish and Portuguese are closely related languages but they are far from being identical, and Brazilians dislike foreigners who do not appreciate this fact. I can imagine that a similar assumption about the inter-changeability of Swedish, Norwegian, and Danish or the different Chinese languages would cause the same sort of resentment. You really have no choice but to recall the Spanish version and provide a Portuguese version as quickly as possible. If you are interested in doing business in Brazil it would be wise to show an interest in, and a certain background knowledge of, the country so you avoid "putting your foot in it" again. You can consult appropriate books, and the Internet is a great source of useful information.

Interpreters *Letter 23*

From MEXICO about ***JAPAN***

> I'm going to be traveling to Japan with a small group of other managers. We don't speak Japanese and were wondering if we should take an interpreter with us, which would be very expensive, or if we can ask the Japanese firm if they can arrange one for us.

It depends on how much money is at stake. If you're hoping to build a solid long-term relationship that is going to earn your company a fat profit, then it's worth thinking about developing a working relationship with a fluent Japanese speaker (preferably a native speaker) who is bicultural as well as bilingual and knows what your company does.

You can hire an interpreter from an agency in Japan, but then you'd have to make sure you allowed sufficient time in Japan to get to know each other before you met your potential partners. She (most Japanese translators are female) needs to know in advance what ground the talks are going to cover so she can prepare herself. She also needs to become familiar with the communication style of the person or people she's translating for. One more thing: if you do decide to hire an interpreter in Japan, book her well in advance as there are not many Japanese-Spanish translators, and you may have to accept a Japanese-English substitute.

Asking the Japanese company to provide an interpreter may not be a good idea, because even though you can be quite sure she will translate the Japanese side's message correctly (she will probably know their business very well), there's no guarantee your message is going to be expressed as you intended. For example, she may not want to take on the responsibility of delivering a message from you that will not please her fellow citizens. They may not have heard the expression "Don't shoot the messenger," but many interpreters are only too familiar with the meaning behind it.

To minimize the possibilities of misunderstandings, have a written summary of the points you are going to make at the meeting translated and distributed *before* the meeting, and get a written summary of the proceedings translated into Japanese shortly *after* the meeting.

IN A NUTSHELL: A GLOBAL LANGUAGE?

Global Business Standards

For native English speakers: learn at least one foreign language as well as you can.
For non-native English speakers: learn English as well as you can.
For everyone: learn a few words of the language of any country you visit and of any foreign visitor you are going to meet.

- **Argentina:** The official language is Spanish, but it is influenced somewhat by Italian. (See Letters 15 and 22.)
- **Australia:** The language is influenced by both British and American English, but it has a distinctive accent and a special Aussie vocabulary. (See Letter 21.)
- **Austria:** German is spoken with a distinctive accent.
- **Belgium:** Official languages are Flemish (similar to Dutch), French, and German. The language spoken is closely tied to a person's ethnicity, and group loyalty is strong. (See Letters 15 and 18.)
- **Brazil:** Portuguese is spoken here—not Spanish like most of the rest of South America. (See Letters 15 and 22.)
- **Canada:** There are two official languages: English and French. The language spoken is closely tied to a person's ethnicity, and group loyalty is strong. (See Letters 15, 17, and 21.)

- **China:** The official spoken language is Mandarin, a language based on tones. It is also the only form of written language. In some provinces people speak one of four major dialects, but these aren't understood by speakers of the other dialects. (See Letter 20.)
- **Denmark:** Danish is almost indistinguishable to Norwegian in written form. Norwegians, Danes, and Swedes can often understand each other.
- **Finland:** The language is similar to Hungarian (!). In some areas Finns also speak Swedish.
- **France:** You are judged according to how well you speak French, and your command of the language is seen as an indicator of your education and intelligence. There is a big difference between using the familiar *tu* (informal) and the more formal *vous*. (See Letters 15 and 16.)
- **Germany:** There is a big difference between using the familiar *Du* and the formal *Sie*.
- **Hong Kong:** English, Cantonese, and Mandarin are widely spoken. (See Letter 20.)
- **India:** There are eighteen official languages and about as many dialects distributed geographically (e.g., Hindi, Punjabi, and Gujarati, and Urdu, which is spoken mostly by Muslim minority). English is widely spoken by educated people. Many people are bilingual or multilingual.
- **Indonesia:** There are more than 300 ethnic languages. Bahasa Indonesia, the major unifying language, is adapted from Bhasa Melayu (Malay). (See Letter 20.)
- **Italy:** About 60 percent of Italians speak a dialect, which may be impossible for other Italians to understand. The vast majority also speaks standard Italian.
- **Japan:** Spoken Japanese and Chinese are quite different. Basic literacy requires mastery of three alphabets, one of which is derived from Chinese and contains about two thousand characters. (See Letters 20 and 23.)
- **Mexico:** Spanish is spoken by 98 percent of the population. (See Letters 15 and 21.)
- **Netherlands:** Dutch is spoken. It is almost identical to Flemish, which is spoken in Belgium. It is also the ancestor of South Africa's Afrikaans. The Dutch are some of the best speakers of English as a foreign language in the world. (See Letter 16.)
- **Norway:** There are two distinct and rival versions of Norwegian. Norwegian is almost indistinguishable to Danish in written form. Norwegians, Danes, and Swedes can often understand each other.
- **Poland:** Polish is a Slavic language, but unlike Russian, it uses the Latin script.
- **Russia:** Russian uses the Cyrillic alphabet. Words are pronounced as they are spelled. Russian is spoken by most people, but Russia is made up of about a hundred ethnic groups, many with their own languages.

- **Saudi Arabia:** Arabic is the official language of the country and is widely spoken in the whole region. (See Letter 15.)
- **South Africa:** There are eleven official languages. English, Afrikaans (related to Dutch), and Zulu are the main ones.
- **South Korea:** Compared to Chinese and Japanese, the alphabet is easy to learn. Foreign (English) words are readily integrated into Korean. There is much pressure on young Koreans to learn English. (See Letters 20 and 22.)
- **Spain:** The Castilian dialect is the accepted standard. There are also three regional languages. Catalan (as well as Castilian) is spoken widely in Barcelona, Spain's second-largest city. There are some differences from the Spanish of Latin America. (See Letter 15.)
- **Sweden:** A sharp intake of breath can mean *yes*. Norwegians, Danes, and Swedes can often understand each other. (See Letter 15.)
- **Switzerland:** There are four official languages and most Swiss speak at least two fluently. The result of the most recent census shows the breakdown of first language speakers as follows: (Swiss) German 63.9%, French 19.5%, Italian 6.6%, Romansh 0.5%, others 9.5%.
- **Taiwan:** Mandarin is the official language, but 70 percent of the population speaks Southern Fujianese, often called Taiwanese. They do not use the modernized Chinese script currently used in China.
- **Thailand:** Like Chinese, Thai is a tonal language. The written script is based on ancient Indian languages. Fellow Thais usually understand regional and ethnic dialects. (See Letter 20.)
- **Turkey:** Turkey is an oral culture. What is said and heard is taken more seriously than what is written.
- **U.K.:** Differences between British and American English may lead to misunderstandings. (See Letters 15, 19, 20, and 21.)
- **U.S.:** Differences between British and American English may lead to misunderstandings. Spanish is widely spoken by Latin American immigrants in southern states and California. (See Letters 15, 19, 20, and 21.)
- **Venezuela:** Spanish is spoken. There is a distinctive Venezuelan accent, and some specifically Venezuelan vocabulary exists. In major cities Portuguese is quite common. (See Letters 15 and 22.)

9 The Importance of Memos, Letters, and E-mail

Sharon J. Gerson and Steven M. Gerson

Sharon J. Gerson and Steven M. Gerson are noted educators, authors, and consultants in the field of business communication.

WHICH COMMUNICATION CHANNEL SHOULD YOU USE?

Memos, letters, and e-mail messages are three common types of communication channels. [Table 1 shows the significance of e-mails, memos, and letters in the workplace.] Other communication channels include reports, Web sites, blogs, PowerPoint presentations, oral communication, and instant messages. When should you write an e-mail message instead of a memo? When should you write a memo instead of a letter? Is an instant message appropriate to the situation? You will make these decisions based on your audience (internal or external), the complexity of your topic, the speed with which your message can be delivered, and security concerns.

For example, e-mail is a convenient communication channel. It is easy to write a short e-mail message, which can be sent almost instantaneously to your audience at the click of a button. However, e-mail might not be the best communication channel to use. If you are discussing a highly sensitive topic such as a pending merger, corporate takeover, or layoffs, an e-mail message would be less secure than a letter sent in a sealed envelope.

You might need to communicate with employees working in a manufacturing warehouse. Not all of these employees will necessarily have an office or access to a computer. If you sent an e-mail message, how would they access this correspondence? A memo posted in the break room would be a better choice of communication channel.

THE DIFFERENCES AMONG MEMOS, LETTERS, AND E-MAIL

To clarify the distinctions among memos, letters, and e-mail, review Table 9–1.

TABLE 9–1 Memos versus Letters versus E-mails

Characteristics	Memos	Letters	E-mail
Destination	Internal: correspondence written to colleagues within a company.	External: correspondence written outside the business.	Internal and external: correspondence written to friends and acquaintances, coworkers within a company, and clients and vendors.
Format	Identification lines include "Date," "To," "From," and "Subject," The message follows.	Includes letterhead address, date, reader's address, salutation, text, complimentary close, and signatures.	Identification lines: To and subject. The Date and From are computer generated. Options include cc (complimentary copy), Ref (reference), and Distribution (other recipients of the e-mail message).
Audience	Generally high tech or low tech, mostly business colleagues.	Generally low tech and lay readers, such as vendors, clients, stakeholders, and stockholders.	Multiple readers due to the internal and external nature of e-mail.
Topic	Generally topics related to internal corporate decisions; abbreviations and acronyms often allowed.	Generally topics related to vendor, client, stakeholder, and stockholder interests; abbreviations and acronyms usually defined.	A wide range of diverse topics determined by the audience.
Complexity and Length of Communication	Memos usually are limited to a page of text. If you need to write longer correspondence and develop a topic in more detail, you might consider using a different communication channel, such as a short report.	Letters usually are limited to a page of text, though you might write a two- or three-page report using a letter format. If you need to develop a topic in greater detail than can be conveyed in one to three pages, you might want to use a different communication channel, such as a longer, formal report.	An effective e-mail message usually is limited to one viewable screen (requiring no scrolling) or two screens. E-mail, generally, is not the best communication channel to use for complex information or long correspondence. If your topic demands more depth than can be conveyed in a screen or two, you might want to write a report instead.

(*Continued*)

Characteristics	Memos	Letters	E-mail
Tone	Informal due to peer audience.	More formal due to audience of vendors, clients, stakeholders, and stockholders.	A wide range of tones due to diverse audiences. Usually informal when written to friends, informal to coworkers, more formal to management.
Attachments or Enclosures	Hard-copy attachments can be stapled to the memo. Complimentary copies (cc) can be sent to other readers.	Additional information can be enclosed within the envelope. Complimentary copies can be sent to other readers.	Computer word processing files, HTML files and Web links, PDF files, RTF files, or downloadable graphics can be attached to e-mail. Complimentary copies (cc) can be sent to other readers. Size of these files is an issue, because large documents can crash a reader's system. A good rule is to limit files to 750 kilobytes (K).
Delivery Time	Determined by a company's in-house mail procedure.	Determined by the destination (within the city, state, or country). Letters could be delivered within 3 days but may take more than a week.	Often instantaneous, usually within minutes. Delays can be caused by system malfunctions or excessively large attachments.
Security	If a company's mail delivery system is reliable, the memo will be placed in the reader's mailbox. Then, what the reader sees on the hard-copy page will be exactly what the writer wrote. Security depends on the ethics of coworkers and whether the memo was sent in an envelope.	The U.S. Postal Service is very reliable. Once the reader opens the envelope, he or she sees exactly what the writer wrote. Privacy laws protect the letter's content.	E-mail systems are not secure. E-mail can be tampered with, read by others, and sent to many people. E-mail stays within a company's computer backup system and is the property of the company. Therefore, e-mail is not private.

FAQs: Memos vs. E-Mail

Q: Why write a memo? Haven't memos been replaced by e-mail?

A: E-mail is rapidly overtaking memos in the workplace, but employees still write memos for the following reasons.

1. Not all employees work in offices or have access to computers. Many employees who work in warehouses or in the field cannot easily access an e-mail account. They must depend on hard-copy documentation like memos.
2. Not all companies have e-mail. This may be hard to believe in the twenty-first century, but still it's a fact. These companies depend on hard-copy documentation like memos.
3. Many unions demand that hard-copy memos be posted on walls, in break rooms, in offices, and elsewhere, to ensure that all employees have access to important information. Sometimes, unions even demand that employees initial the posted memos, thus acknowledging that the memos have been read.
4. Some information cannot be transmitted electronically via e-mail. A bank we've worked with, for example, sends hard-copy cancelled checks as attachments to memos. They cannot send the actual cancelled check via e-mail.
5. E-mail messages are easy to disregard. We get so many e-mail messages (many of them spam) that we tend to quickly delete them. Memos, in contrast, make more of an official statement. People might take hard-copy memos more seriously than e-mail messages.

MEMOS

Reasons for Writing Memos

Memos are an important means by which employees communicate with each other. Memos, hard-copy correspondence written within your company, are important for several reasons.

First, you will write memos to a wide range of readers. This includes your supervisors, coworkers, subordinates, and multiple combinations of these audiences. Memos usually are copied (cc: complimentary copies) to many readers, so a memo sent to your boss could be read by an entire department, the boss's boss, and colleagues in other departments.

Because of their frequency and widespread audiences, memos could represent a major component of your interpersonal communication skills within your work environment.

Furthermore, memos are very flexible and can be written for many different purposes:

- **Documentation**—expenses, incidents, accidents, problems encountered, projected costs, study findings, hirings, firings, reallocations of staff or equipment
- **Confirmation**—a meeting agenda, date, time, and location; decisions to purchase or sell; topics for discussion at upcoming teleconferences; conclusions arrived at; fees, costs, or expenditures
- **Procedures**—how to set up accounts, research on the company intranet, operate new machinery, use new software, apply online for job opportunities through the company intranet, create a new company Web site, or solve a problem
- **Recommendations**—reasons to purchase new equipment, fire or hire personnel, contract with new providers, merge with other companies, revise current practices, or renew contracts
- **Feasibility**—studying the possibility of changes in the workplace (practices, procedures, locations, staffing, equipment, or missions/visions)
- **Status**—daily, weekly, monthly, quarterly, biannually, yearly statements about where you, the department, or the company is regarding many topics (sales, staffing, travel, practices, procedures, or finances)
- **Directive (delegation of responsibilities)**—informing subordinates of their designated tasks
- **Inquiry**—asking questions about upcoming processes or procedures
- **Cover**—prefacing an internal proposal, long report, or other attachments

Criteria for Writing Memos

Memos contain the following key components.

- Memo identification lines—Date, To, From, and Subject
- Introduction
- Discussion
- Conclusion
- Audience recognition
- Appropriate memo style and tone

Figure 9–1 shows an ideal, all-purpose organizational template that works well for memos, letters, and e-mail.

The memo checklist will give you the opportunity for self-assessment and peer evaluation of your writing. Input from peers can be an important way for you to gauge the response to your memo, determine if content should be added or deleted, and check for correctness.

Introduction: A lead-in or overview stating *why* you are writing and *what* you are writing about.

Discussion: Detailed development, made accessible through highlighting techniques, explaining *exactly what*

-
-
-

Conclusion: State *what* is next, *when* this will occur, and *why* the date is important.

FIGURE 9–1
All-Purpose Template for Memos, Letters, and E-mail

MEMO CHECKLIST

___ 1. Does the memo contain identification lines (Date, To, From, and Subject)?

___ 2. Does the subject line contain a topic and a focus?

___ 3. Does the introduction clearly state
- Why this memo has been written?
- What topic the memo is discussing?

___ 4. Does the body explain exactly what you want to say?

___ 5. Does the conclusion
- Tell when you plan a follow-up or when you want a response?
- Explain why this dated action is important?

___ 6. Are highlighting techniques used effectively for document design?

___ 7. Is the memo concise?

___ 8. Is the memo clear,
- Achieving specificity of detail?
- Answering reporter's questions?

___ 9. Does the memo recognize audience,
- Defining acronyms or abbreviations where necessary for various levels of readers (high tech, low tech and lay)?

___ 10. Did you avoid grammatical errors? Errors will hurt your professionalism. . . .

FAQs: Letters vs. E-Mail

Q: Why write a letter? Haven't letters been replaced by e-mail?

A: Though e-mail is quick, it might not be the best communication channel, for the following reasons.

1. E-mail might be too quick. In the workplace, you will write about topics that require a lot of thought. Because e-mail messages can be written and sent quickly, people too often write hurriedly and neglect to consider the impact of the message.
2. E-mail messages tend to be casual, conversational, and informal. Not all correspondence, however, lends itself to this level of informality. Formal correspondence related to contracts, for example, requires the more formal communication channel of a letter. The same applies to audience. You might want to write a casual e-mail to a coworker, but if you were writing to the president of a company, the mayor of a city, or a foreign dignitary, a letter would be a better, more formal choice of communication channel.
3. E-mail messages tend to be short. For content requiring more detail, a longer letter would be a better choice.
4. We get so many e-mail messages a day that they are easy to disregard—even easy to delete. Letters carry more significance. If you want to ensure that your correspondence is read and perceived as important, you might want to write a letter instead of an e-mail.
5. Letters allow for a "greater paper trail" than e-mail. Most employees' e-mail inboxes fill up quickly. To clean these inboxes up, people tend to delete messages that they don't consider important. In contrast, hard-copy letters are wonderful documentation.

LETTERS

Reasons for Writing Letters

Letters are external correspondence that you send from your company to a colleague working at another company, a vendor, a customer, a prospective employee, and stake-holders and stockholders. Letters leave your work site (as opposed to memos, which stay within the company).

Because letters are sent to readers in other locations, your letters not only reflect your communication abilities but also are a reflection of your company. This section provides letter components, formats, criteria, and examples to help you write . . . [various] kinds of letters:. . . .

Essential Components of Letters

Your letter should be typed or printed on 8½ × 11 inch paper. Leave 1 to 1½ inch margins at the top and on both sides. Choose an appropriately businesslike font (size and style), such as Times New Roman or Arial (12 point). Though "designer fonts," such as Comic Sans and Shelley Volante, are interesting, they tend to be harder to read and less professional.

Your letter should contain the essential components shown in Figure 9–2.

Writer's Address

This section contains either your personal address or your company's address. If the heading consists of your address, then you will include your street address, the city, state, and zip code. The state may be abbreviated with the appropriate two-letter abbreviation.

If the heading consists of your company's address, you will include the company's name, street address, and city, state, and zip code.

Date

Document the month, day, and year when you write your letter. You can write your date in one of two ways: May 31, 2008 or 31 May 2008. Place the date one or two spaces below the writer's address.

Reader's Address

Place the reader's address two lines below the date.

- Reader's name (If you do not know the name of this person, begin the reader's address with a job title or the name of the department.)
- Reader's title (optional)
- Company name
- Street address
- City, state, and zip code

Salutation

The traditional salutation, placed two spaces beneath the reader's address, is *Dear* and your reader's last name, followed by a colon (Dear Mr. Smith:).

You can also address your reader by his or her first name if you are on a first-name basis with this person (Dear John:). If you are writing to a woman and are unfamiliar with her marital status, address the letter *Dear Ms. Jones*. However, if you know the woman's marital status, you can address the letter accordingly (Dear Miss Jones *or* Dear Mrs. Jones:).

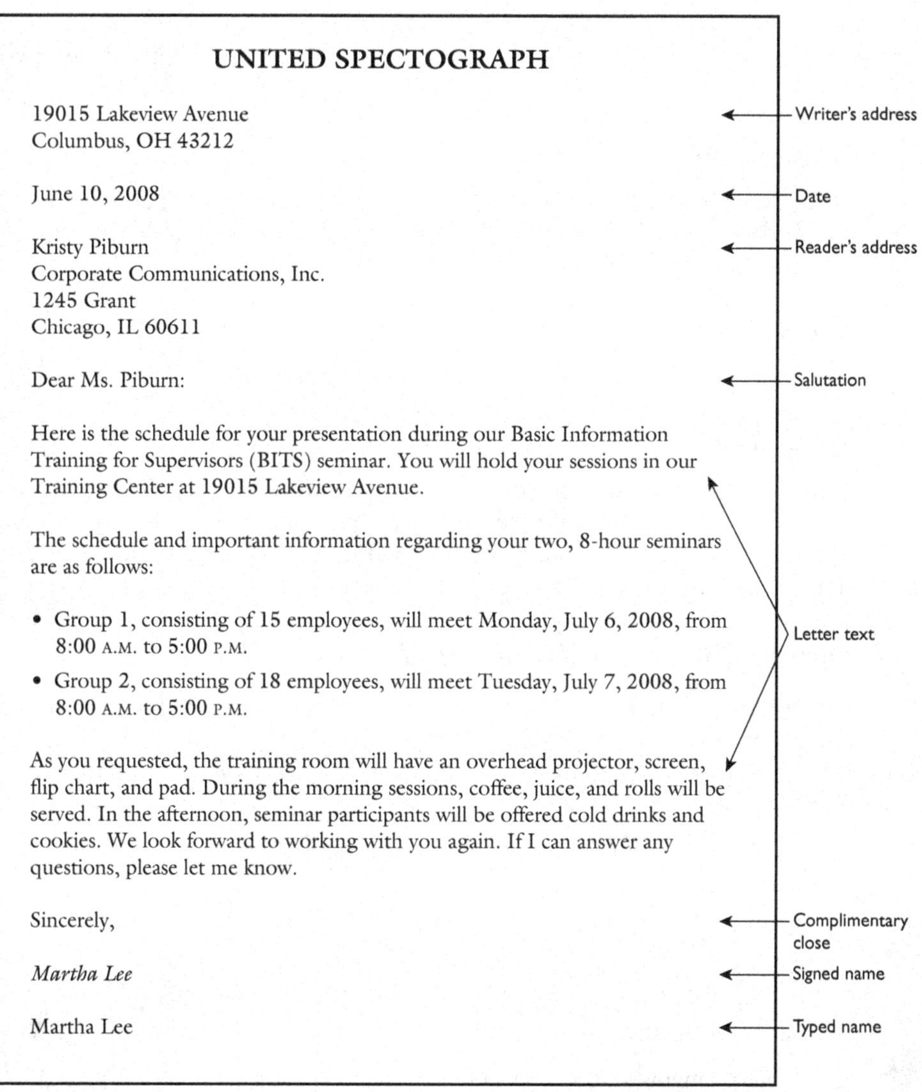
UNITED SPECTOGRAPH

19015 Lakeview Avenue
Columbus, OH 43212

June 10, 2008

Kristy Piburn
Corporate Communications, Inc.
1245 Grant
Chicago, IL 60611

Dear Ms. Piburn:

Here is the schedule for your presentation during our Basic Information Training for Supervisors (BITS) seminar. You will hold your sessions in our Training Center at 19015 Lakeview Avenue.

The schedule and important information regarding your two, 8-hour seminars are as follows:

- Group 1, consisting of 15 employees, will meet Monday, July 6, 2008, from 8:00 A.M. to 5:00 P.M.
- Group 2, consisting of 18 employees, will meet Tuesday, July 7, 2008, from 8:00 A.M. to 5:00 P.M.

As you requested, the training room will have an overhead projector, screen, flip chart, and pad. During the morning sessions, coffee, juice, and rolls will be served. In the afternoon, seminar participants will be offered cold drinks and cookies. We look forward to working with you again. If I can answer any questions, please let me know.

Sincerely,

Martha Lee

Martha Lee

FIGURE 9–2
Essential Letter Components

Letter Body

Begin the body of the letter two spaces below the salutation. The body includes your introductory paragraph, discussion paragraph(s), and concluding paragraph. The body should be single spaced with double spacing between paragraphs. Whether you indent the beginning of paragraphs or leave them flush with the left margin is determined by the letter format you employ.

Complimentary Close

Place the complimentary close, followed by a comma, two spaces below the concluding paragraph. Typical complimentary closes include "Sincerely," "Yours truly," and "Sincerely yours."

Signed Name

Sign your name legibly beneath the complimentary close.

Typed Name

Type your name four spaces below the complimentary close. You can type your title one space beneath your typed name. You also can include your title on the same line as your typed name, with a comma after your name.

Optional Components of Letters

In addition to the letter essentials, you can include the following optional components.

Subject Line

Place a subject line two spaces below the reader's address and two spaces above the salutation.

> Dr. Ron Schaefer
> Linguistics Department
> Southern Illinois University
> Edwardsville, IL 66205
>
> Subject: Linguistics Conference Registration Payment
>
> Dear Dr. Schaefer:

You also could use a subject line instead of a salutation.

> Linguistics Department
> Southern Illinois university
> Edwardsville, IL 66205
>
> Subject: Linguistics Conference Registration Payment

A subject line not only helps readers understand the letter's intent but also (if you are uncertain of your reader's name) avoids such awkward salutations as "To Whom It May Concern," "Dear Sirs," and "Ladies and Gentlemen." In the simplified format, both the salutation and the complimentary close are omitted, and a subject line is included.

New-Page Notations

If your letter is longer than one page, cite your name, the page number, and the date on all pages after page 1. Place this notation either flush with the left margin at the top of subsequent pages or across the top of subsequent pages. (You must have at least two lines of text on the next page to justify another page.)

Left margin, subsequent page notation	Across top of subsequent pages
Mabel Tinjaca Page 2 May 31. 2008	Mabel Tinjaca 2 May 31, 2008

Writer's and Typist's Initials

If the letter was typed by someone other than the writer, include both the writer's and the typist's initials two spaces below the typed signature. The writer's initials are capitalized, the typist's initials are typed in lowercase, and the two sets of initials are separated by a colon. If the typist and the writer are the same person, this notation is not necessary.

Sincerely,

W. T. Winnery

WTW: mm

Enclosure Notation

If your letter prefaces enclosed information, such as an invoice or report, mention this enclosure in the letter and then type an enclosure notation two spaces below the typed signature (or two spaces below the writer and typist initials). The enclosure notation can be abbreviated "Enc."; written out as "Enclosure"; show the number of enclosures, such as "Enclosures (2)"; or specify what has been enclosed—"Enclosure: January Invoice."

Copy Notation

If you have sent a copy of your letter to other readers, show this in a copy notation. A complimentary copy is designated by a lowercase "cc." List the other readers' names following the copy notation. Type the copy notation two spaces below the typed signature or two spaces below either the writer's and typist's initials or the enclosure notation.

> Sincerely,
>
> Brian Altman
> Enclosure: August Status Report
> cc: Marcia Rittmaster and Larry Rochelle

Formatting Letters

Three common types of letter formats include full block (Figure 9–3), full block with subject line (Figure 9–4), and simplified (Figure 9–5) [pp. 234–235]. Two popular and professional formats used in business are full block and full block with subject line. With both formats, you type all information at the left margin without indenting paragraphs, the date, the complimentary close, or signature. The full block with subject line differs only with the inclusion of a subject line.

Another option is the simplified format. This type of letter layout is similar to the full block format in that all text is typed margin left. The two significant omissions include no salutation ("Dear ________:") and no complimentary close ("Sincerely,"). Omitting a salutation is useful in the following instances:

- You do not know your reader's name (NOTE: Avoid the trite salutation, "To Whom It May Concern:")
- You are writing to someone with a nongender-specific name (Jesse, Terry, Stacy, Chris, etc.) and you do nor know whether to use "Mr.," "Mrs.," or "Ms." . . .

The Administrative Management Society (AMS) suggests that if you omit the salutation, you also should omit the complimentary close. Some people feel that omitting the salutation and the complimentary close will make the letter cold and unfriendly. However, the AMS says that if your letter is warm and friendly, these omissions will not be missed. More importantly, if your letter's content is negative, beginning with "Dear" and ending with "Sincerely" will not improve the letter's tone or your reader's attitude toward your comments. . . .

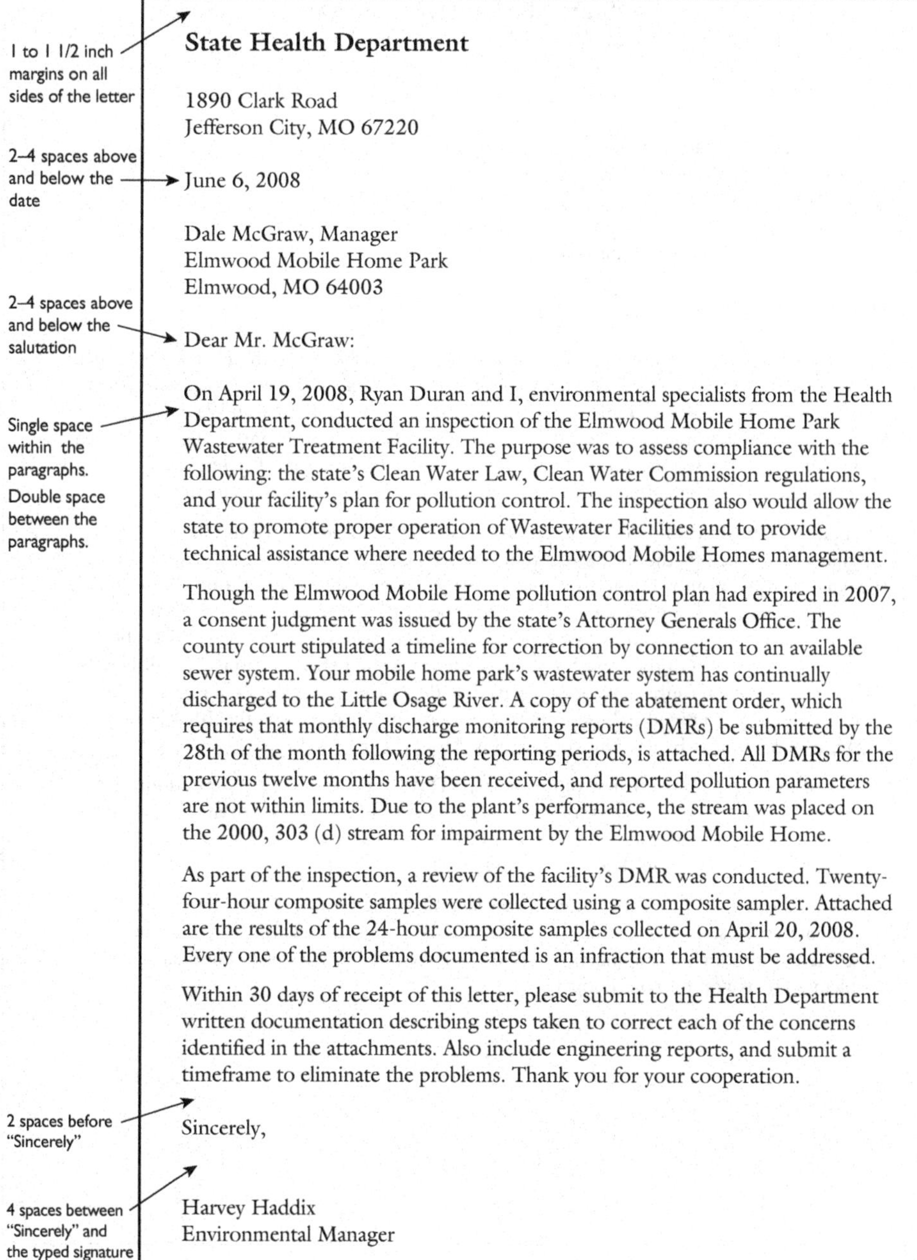

State Health Department

1890 Clark Road
Jefferson City, MO 67220

June 6, 2008

Dale McGraw, Manager
Elmwood Mobile Home Park
Elmwood, MO 64003

Dear Mr. McGraw:

On April 19, 2008, Ryan Duran and I, environmental specialists from the Health Department, conducted an inspection of the Elmwood Mobile Home Park Wastewater Treatment Facility. The purpose was to assess compliance with the following: the state's Clean Water Law, Clean Water Commission regulations, and your facility's plan for pollution control. The inspection also would allow the state to promote proper operation of Wastewater Facilities and to provide technical assistance where needed to the Elmwood Mobile Homes management.

Though the Elmwood Mobile Home pollution control plan had expired in 2007, a consent judgment was issued by the state's Attorney Generals Office. The county court stipulated a timeline for correction by connection to an available sewer system. Your mobile home park's wastewater system has continually discharged to the Little Osage River. A copy of the abatement order, which requires that monthly discharge monitoring reports (DMRs) be submitted by the 28th of the month following the reporting periods, is attached. All DMRs for the previous twelve months have been received, and reported pollution parameters are not within limits. Due to the plant's performance, the stream was placed on the 2000, 303 (d) stream for impairment by the Elmwood Mobile Home.

As part of the inspection, a review of the facility's DMR was conducted. Twenty-four-hour composite samples were collected using a composite sampler. Attached are the results of the 24-hour composite samples collected on April 20, 2008. Every one of the problems documented is an infraction that must be addressed.

Within 30 days of receipt of this letter, please submit to the Health Department written documentation describing steps taken to correct each of the concerns identified in the attachments. Also include engineering reports, and submit a timeframe to eliminate the problems. Thank you for your cooperation.

Sincerely,

Harvey Haddix
Environmental Manager

Attachment

FIGURE 9–3
Full Block Format

State Health Department
1890 Clark Road Jefferson City, MO 67220

June 6, 2008

Dale McGraw, Manager
Elmwood Mobile Home Park
Elmwood, MO 64003

Subject: Pollution Control Inspection

Dear Mr. McGraw:

On April 19, 2008, Ryan Duran and I, environmental specialists from the Health Department, conducted an inspection of the Elmwood Mobile Home Park Wastewater Treatment Facility. The purpose was to assess compliance with the following: the state's Clean Water Law, Clean Water Commission regulations, and your facility's plan for pollution control. The inspection also would allow the state to promote proper operation of Wastewater Facilities and to provide technical assistance where needed to the Elmwood Mobile Homes management.

Though the Elmwood Mobile Home pollution control plan had expired in 2007, a consent judgment was issued by the state's Attorney Generals Office. The county court stipulated a timeline for correction by connection to an available sewer system. Your mobile home park's wastewater system has continually discharged to the Little Osage River. A copy of the abatement order, which requires that monthly discharge monitoring reports (DMRs) be submitted by the 28th of the month following the reporting periods, is attached. All DMRs for the previous twelve months have been received, and reported pollution parameters are not within limits. Due to the plant's performance, the stream was placed on the 2000, 303 (d) stream for impairment by the Elmwood Mobile Home.

As part of the inspection, a review of the facility's DMR was conducted. Twenty-four-hour composite samples were collected using a composite sampler. Attached are the results of the 24-hour composite samples collected on April 20, 2008. Every one of the problems documented is an infraction that must be addressed.

Within 30 days of receipt of this letter, please submit to the Health Department written documentation describing steps taken to correct each of the concerns identified in the attachments. Also include engineering reports, and submit a timeframe to eliminate the problems. Thank you for your cooperation.

Sincerely,

Harvey Haddix
Environmental Manager

Attachment

FIGURE 9–4
Full Block Format with Subject Line

State Health Department
1890 Clark Road
Jefferson City, MO 67220

June 6, 2008

Dale McGraw, Manager
Elmwood Mobile Home Park
Elmwood, MO 64003

Subject: Pollution Control Inspection

On April 19, 2008, Ryan Duran and I, environmental specialists from the Health Department, conducted an inspection of the Elmwood Mobile Home Park Wastewater Treatment Facility. The purpose was to assess compliance with the following: the state's Clean Water Law, Clean Water Commission regulations, and your facility's plan for pollution control. The inspection also would allow the state to promote proper operation of Wastewater Facilities and to provide technical assistance where needed to the Elmwood Mobile Homes management.

Though the Elmwood Mobile Home pollution control plan had expired in 2007, a consent judgment was issued by the state's Attorney Generals Office. The county court stipulated a timeline for correction by connection to an available sewer system. Your mobile home park's wastewater system has continually discharged to the Little Osage River. A copy of the abatement order, which requires that monthly discharge monitoring reports (DMRs) be submitted by the 28th of the month following the reporting periods, is attached. All DMRs for the previous twelve months have been received, and reported pollution parameters are not within limits. Due to the plant's performance, the stream was placed on the 2000, 303 (d) stream for impairment by the Elmwood Mobile Home.

As part of the inspection, a review of the facility's DMR was conducted. Twenty-four-hour composite samples were collected using a composite sampler. Attached are the results of the 24-hour composite samples collected on April 20, 2008. Every one of the problems documented is an infraction that must be addressed.

Within 30 days of receipt of this letter, please submit to the Health Department written documentation describing steps taken to correct each of the concerns identified in the attachments. Also include engineering reports, and submit a timeframe to eliminate the problems. Thank you for your cooperation.

Harvey Haddix
Environmental Manager

Attachment

FIGURE 9–5
Simplified Format Omitting "Dear . . ." and "Sincerely"

LETTERS CHECKLIST

____ 1. **Letter Essentials:** Does your letter include the eight essential components (writer's address, date, recipient's address, salutation, text, complimentary close, writer's signed name, and writer's typed name)?

____ 2. **Introduction:** Does the introduction state what you are writing about and why you are writing?

____ 3. **Discussion:** Does your discussion clearly state the details of your topic depending on the type of letter?

____ 4. **Highlighting/Page Layout:** Is your text accessible? To achieve reader-friendly ease of access, use headings, boldface, italics, bullets, numbers, underlining, or graphics (tables and figures). These add interest and help your readers navigate your letter.

____ 5. **Organization:** Have you helped your readers follow your train of thought by using appropriate modes of organization? These include chronology, importance, problem/solution, or comparison/contrast.

____ 6. **Conclusion:** Does your conclusion give directive action (tell what you want the reader to do next and when) and end positively?

____ 7. **Clarity:** Is your letter clear, answering . . . [the reader's] questions and providing specific details that inform, instruct, or persuade?

____ 8. **Conciseness:** Have you limited the length of your words, sentences, and paragraphs?

____ 9. **Audience Recognition:** Have you written appropriately to your audience? This includes avoiding biased language, considering the multicultural/cross-cultural nature of your readers, and your audience's role (supervisors, subordinates, coworkers, customers, or vendors). Have you created a positive tone to build rapport?

___ 10. **Correctness:** Is your text grammatically correct? Errors will hurt your professionalism. . . .

E-MAIL

Why Is E-mail Important?

E-mail (electronic mail) is different from hard-copy memos and letters in many ways. The primary difference is that people read online text differently than they read hard-copy text. E-mail has become a predominant means of routine correspondence. Many companies are "geared to operate with e-mail," creating what the Harvard Business school calls "e-mail cultures" for the following reasons ("The Transition to General Management."

FAQs: Professionalism in E-Mail Messages

Q: E-mail messages are just casual communication, right? So writing an e-mail message is easy, isn't it, since you don't have to worry about grammar or correct style?

A: Nothing could be further from the truth. E-mail might be your major means of communication in the workplace. Therefore, you must pay special attention to correctness.

Listen to what managers at an engineering company say about e-mail messages:

- "Most business communication is now via e-mail. Business e-mail needs to be almost as formal and as carefully written as a letter because it is a formal and legal document. Never send an e-mail that you would not be comfortable seeing on the front page of a newspaper, because some day you may."
- "I see more and more new hires wanting to rely on e-mail. It is a totally ineffective way to resolve many issues on an engineering project. But they seem to feel it is OK for almost any communication. I suspect the general acceptance by their peers for this form of communication has led them to mistakenly assume the same is true for a business setting."
- "Many young people tend to be very 'social' in e-mails. Your employer owns your e-mails written on your work computers. They are NOT private. They can be used not only against you, but against your firm in court. For example, if I send an e-mail to a coworker that states in it somewhere what a lousy job Frank is doing on the such-and-such project and that project goes bad, it is possible that e-mail could end up in court and be used against my employer. In my mind all I was doing was venting my frustrations to an understanding friend and co-worker. But, in reality, I am creating a permanent record of anything I say."

Steven M. Gerson, et al. ("Core Competencies." Survey. Prentice Hall. 2004)

Harvard Business School. 1998. November 12, 2002. www.hbs.edu/gm/index.html).

Time

"Everything is driven by time. You have to use what is most efficient" (Carolyn Miller, et al. "Communication in the Workplace." *Center for Communication in Science, Technology, and Management.* October 1996, 10). The primary driving force behind e-mail's prominence is time. E-mail is quick. Whereas a posted letter might take several days to deliver, e-mail messages can be delivered within seconds.

Convenience

With wireless communication, you can send e-mail from notebooks to handhelds. Current communication systems combine a voice phone, personal digital assistant, and e-mail into a package that you can slip into a pocket or purse. Then, you can access your e-mail messages anywhere, anytime.

Internal/External

E-mail allows you to communicate internally to coworkers and externally to customers and vendors. Traditional communication channels, like letters and memos, have more limited uses. Generally, letters are external correspondence written from one company to another company; memos are internal correspondence transmitted within a company.

Cost

E-mail is cost effective because it is paper free. With an ability to attach files, you can send many kinds of documentation without paying shipping fees. This is especially valuable when considering international business.

Documentation

E-mail provides an additional value when it comes to documentation. Because so many writers merely respond to earlier e-mail messages, what you end up with is a "virtual paper trail" (Miller, 15). When e-mail is printed out, often the printout will contain dozens of e-mail messages, representing an entire string of dialogue. This provides a company an extensive record for future reference. In addition, most companies archive e-mail messages in backup files.

Reasons for Writing E-mail Messages

E-mail is used to convey many types of information in business and industry. You can write an e-mail message to accomplish any of the following purposes.

- **Directive**—inform a subordinate or a team of employees to complete a task.
- **Cover/transmittal**—inform a reader or readers that you have attached a document, and list the key points that are included in the attachment.
- **Documentation**—report on expenses, incidents, accidents, problems encountered, projected costs, study findings, hiring, firings, and reallocations of staff or equipment.
- **Confirmation**—inform a reader about a meeting agenda, date, time, and location; decisions to purchase or sell; topics for discussion at upcoming teleconferences; conclusions arrived at; fees, costs, or expenditures.
- **Procedures**—explain how to set up accounts, research on the company intranet, operate new machinery, use new software, apply online for job opportunities through the company intranet, create a new company Web site, or solve a problem.
- **Recommendations**—provide reasons to purchase new equipment, fire or hire personnel, contract with new providers, merge with other companies, revise current practices, or renew contracts.
- **Feasibility**—study the possibility of changes in the workplace (practices, procedures, locations, staffing, or equipment).
- **Status**—provide a daily, weekly, monthly, quarterly, biannual, or yearly report about where you, the department, or the company is regarding a topic of your choice (class project, sales, staffing, travel, practices, procedures, or finances).
- **Inquiry**—ask questions about upcoming processes, procedures, or assignments.

Techniques for Writing Effective E-mail Messages

To convey your messages effectively and to ensure that your e-mail messages reflect professionalism, follow these tips for writing e-mail.

Recognize Your Audience. E-mail messages can be sent to managers, coworkers, subordinates, vendors, and customers, among other audiences. Your e-mail readers will be high tech, low tech, and lay people. Thus, you must factor in levels of knowledge.

If an e-mail message is sent internationally, you also might have to consider your readers' language. Remember that abbreviations and acronyms are not universal. Dates, times, measurements, and monetary figures differ from country to country. . . . In addition, your reader's e-mail system might not have the same features or capabilities that you have. Hard-copy text will look the same to all readers. E-mail platforms, such as in AOL, Outlook, Juno, HotMail, and Yahoo, display text differently. To communicate effectively, recognize your audience's level of knowledge, unique language, and technology needs.

Identify Yourself

Identify yourself by name, affiliation, or title. You can accomplish this either in the "From" line of your e-mail or by creating a signature file or .sig file. This .sig file acts like an online business card. Once this identification is complete, readers will be able to open your e-mail without fear of corrupting their computer systems.

Provide an Effective Subject Line

Readers are unwilling to open unsolicited or unknown e-mail, due to fear of spam and viruses. In addition, corporate employees receive approximately 50 e-mail messages each day. They might not want to read every message sent to them. To ensure that your e-mail messages are read, avoid uninformative subject lines, such as "Hi," "What's New," or "Important Message." Instead, include an effective subject line, such as "Subject: Meeting Dates for Tech Prep Conference."

Keep Your E-mail Message Brief

E-readers skim and scan. To help them access information quickly, "Apply the 'top of the screen' test. Assume that your readers will look at the first screen of your message only" (Mary Munter, et al. "Business E-Mail: Guidelines For Users." *Business Communication Quarterly* 66 (March 2003): 31). Limit your message to one screen (if possible).

Organize Your E-mail Message

Successful writing usually contains an introductory paragraph, a discussion paragraph or paragraphs, and a conclusion. Although many e-mail messages are brief, only a few sentences, you can use the introductory sentences to tell the reader why you are writing and what you are writing about. In the discussion, clarify your points thoroughly. Use the concluding sentences to tell the reader what is next, possibly explaining when a follow-up is required and why that date is important.

Use Highlighting Techniques Sparingly

Many e-mail packages will let you use highlighting techniques, such as boldface, italics, underlining, computer-generated bullets and numbers, centering, font color highlighting, and font color changes. Many other e-mail platforms will not display such visual enhancements. To avoid having parts of the message distorted, limit your highlighting to asterisks (*), numbers, double spacing, and all-cap headings.

Proofread Your E-mail Message

Errors will undermine your professionalism and your company's credibility. Recheck your facts, dates, addresses, and numerical information before you send the message. Try these tips to help you proofread an e-mail message.

- Type your text first in a word-processing package, such as Microsoft Word.
- Print it out. Sometimes it is easier to read hard-copy text than text online. Also, your word-processing package, with its spell check and/or grammar check, will help you proofread your writing.

Once you have completed these two steps (writing in Word or WordPerfect and printing out the hard-copy text), copy and paste the text from your word-processing file into your e-mail.

Make Hard Copies for Future Reference

Making hard copies of all e-mail messages is not necessary because most companies archive e-mail. However, in some instances, you might want to keep a hard copy for future reference. These instances could include transmissions of good news. For example, you have received compliments about your work and want to save this record for your annual job review. You also might save a hard copy of an e-mail message regarding flight, hotel, car rental, or conference arrangements for business-related travel.

Be Careful When Sending Attachment

When you send attachments, tell your reader within the body of the e-mail message that you have attached a file; specify the file name of your attachment and the software application that you have used (HTML, PowerPoint, PDF, RTF [rich text format], Word, or Works); and use compression (Zip) files to limit your attachment size. Zip files are necessary only if an attachment is quite large.

Practice Netiquette

When you write your e-mail messages, observe the rules of "netiquette."

- **Be courteous.** Do not let the instantaneous quality of e-mail negate your need to be calm, cool, deliberate, and professional.

- **Be professional.** Occasionally, e-mail writers compose excessively casual e-mail messages. They will lowercase a pronoun like "i," use ellipses (. . .) or dashes instead of more traditional punctuation, use instant messaging shorthand language such as "LOL," or "BRB," and depend on emoticons A K. These e-mail techniques might not be appropriate in all instances. Don't forget that your e-mail messages represent your company's professionalism. Write according to the audience and communication goal.
- **Avoid abusive, angry e-mail messages.** Because of its quick turnaround abilities, e-mail can lead to negative correspondence called flaming. Flaming is sending angry e-mail, often TYPED IN ALL CAPS. . . .

E-MAIL CHECKLIST

___ 1. Does the e-mail use the correct address?

___ 2. Have you identified yourself? Provide a "sig" (signature) line.

___ 3. Did you provide an effective subject line? Include a topic and a focus.

___ 4. Have you effectively organized your e-mail?
Consider including the following:
- Opening sentence(s) telling *why* you are writing and what you are writing about.
- Discussion unit with itemized points telling what exactly the e-mail is discussing.
- Concluding sentence(s), *summing up* your e-mail message or telling your audience what to do next

___ 5. Have you used highlighting techniques sparingly?
- Avoid boldface, italics, color, or underlining.
- Use asterisks (*) for bullets, numbers, and double spacing for access.

___ 6. Did you practice netiquette?
- Be polite, courteous, and professional.
- Don't flame.

___ 7. Is the e-mail concise?

___ 8. Did you identify and limit the size of attachments?
- Tell your reader(s) if you have attached files and what types of files are attached (PPT, PDF, RTF, Word, etc.).
- Limit the files to 750 K.

___ 9. Does the memo recognize audience?
- Define acronyms or abbreviations where necessary.
- Consider a diverse audience (factoring in issues, such as multiculturalism or gender).

___10. Did you avoid grammatical errors?

INSTANT MESSAGING

E-mail could be too slow for today's fast-paced workplace. Instant messaging (IM) could replace e-mail in the workplace within the next five years. Studies suggest IM pop-ups are already providing businesses many benefits.

Benefits of Instant Messaging

Following are benefits of instant messaging.

- Increased speed of communication.
- Improved efficiency for geographically dispersed workgroups.
- Collaboration by multiple users in different locations.
- Communication with colleagues and customers at a distance in real time, such as the telephone.
- Avoidance of costly long distance telephone rates (Note: Voice-over IP [VoIP] services, which allow companies to use the Internet for telephone calls, could be more cost efficient than IM.)
- More "personal" link than e-mail.
- Communication channel that is less intrusive than telephone calls.
- Communication channel that allows for multitasking (With IM, you can speak to a customer on the telephone or via an e-mail message and *simultaneously* receive product updates from a colleague via IM.)
- Quick way to find out who is in the office, out of the office, available for conversation, or unavailable due to other activities. [Jeff Hoffman. "Instant Messaging in the Workplace." *Intercom* (February 2004): 16-17; Deb Shinder. "Instant Messaging: Does It Have a Place in Business Networks?" *WindowSecurity.com.* June 8, 2005. i.e. www.windowsecurity.com/articles/Instant-Messaging-Business-Networks.html.]

Challenges of Instant Messaging

For business purposes, IM is so new that corporate standards have not been formalized. Software companies have not yet redesigned IM home versions for the workplace. This leads to numerous potential problems, including security, archiving, monitoring, and the following (Hoffman 2004; Shinder 2005):

- **Security issues.** This is the biggest concern. IM users are vulnerable to hackers, electronic identity theft, and uncontrolled transfer of documents. With unsecured IM, a company could lose confidential documents, internal users could download copyrighted software, or external users could send virus-infected files.

- **Lost productivity.** Use of IM on the job can lead to job downtime. First, we tend to type more slowly than we talk. Next, the conversational nature of IM leads to "chattiness." If employees are not careful, or monitored, a brief IM conversation can lead to hours of lost productivity.
- **Employee abuse.** IM can lead to personal messages rather than job-related communication with coworkers or customers.
- **Distraction.** With IM, a bored colleague easily can distract you with personal messages, online chats, and unimportant updates.
- **Netiquette.** As with e-mail, due to the casual nature of IM, people tend to relax their professionalism and forget about the rules of polite communication. IM can lead to rudeness or just pointless conversations.
- **Spim.** IM lends itself to "spim," instant messaging spam—unwanted advertisements, pornography, pop-ups, and viruses.

Techniques for Successful Instant Messaging

To solve potential problems, consider these 10 suggestions.

1. **Choose the correct communication channel.** Use IM for speed and convenience. If you need length and detail, other options—e-mail messages, memos, reports, letters—are better choices. In addition, sensitive topics or bad news should never he handled through IM. These deserve the personal attention provided by telephone calls or face-to-face meetings.
2. **Document important information.** For future reference, you must archive key text. IM does not allow for this. Therefore, you will need to copy and paste IM text into a word-processing tool for long-term documentation.
3. **Summarize decisions.** IM is great for collaboration; however, all team members might not be online when decisions are made. Once conclusions have been reached that affect the entire team, the designated team leader should e-mail everyone involved. In this e-mail, the team leader can summarize key points, editorial decisions, timetables, and responsibilities.
4. **Tune in, or turn off.** The moment you log on, IM software tells everyone who is active online. Immediately, your IM buddies can start sending messages, IM pop-ups can be distracting. Sometimes, in order to get your work done, you might need to turn off your IM system. Your IM product might give you status options, such as "on the phone," "away from my desk," or "busy." Turning on IM could infringe upon your privacy and time. Turning off might be the answer.
5. **Limit personal use.** Your company owns the instant messaging in the workplace. IM should be used for business purposes only.

6. **Create "buddy" lists.** Create limited lists of IM users, including legitimate business contacts (colleagues, customers, and vendors).
7. **Avoid public directories.** This will help ensure that your IM contacts are secure and business related.
8. **Disallow corporate IM users from installing their own IM software.** A company should require standardized IM software for safety and control.
9. **Never use IM for confidential communication.** Use another communication channel if your content requires security.
10. **Use IM software that allows you to archive and record IM communications.** As with e-mail, IM programs can let systems administrators log and review IM conversations. Some programs create reports that summarize archived information and let users search for text by keywords or phrases. These systems are perfect for future reference (Hoffman 2004; Shinder 2005).

10 How to Use Bottom-Line Writing in Corporate Communications

John S. Fielden and Ronald E. Dulek

When they wrote this article, John S. Fielden and Ronald Dulek were Professors of Management Communications at the University of Alabama. Jointly, they also authored a series of books on effective business writing.

Every top executive complains about "wordy" memos and reports. From Eisenhower to Reagan, stories have circulated about their refusal to read any memo longer than one page. The CEO of one of the largest companies in the United States actually demands reports so short they can be typed on a three-by-five card. And J. P. Morgan is reputed to have refused audience to anyone who could not state his purpose on the back of a calling card.

"Don't be wordy!" "Be brief, brief, brief!" "Be succinct!" One writing expert after another exhorts business people with these slogans. And who will disagree?

We do.

As a result of an in-depth study of the writing done at the division headquarters of a very large and successful company, we are absolutely convinced that advice such as "Be brief!" is not only useless, it does not even address itself to the real writing problem.

What causes trouble in corporate writing is not the length of communications (for most business letters, memos, and reports are short), but a lack of efficiency in the organizational pattern used in these communications. And, as you will see, it is for the most part a lack of organizational efficiency on the part of writers that is often deliberate, or, if not consciously deliberate, so deeply ingrained in their behavioral programming that it causes an irresistible impulse to beat around the bush.

Put simply, people organize messages backwards, putting their real purpose last. But people read frontwards and need to know the writer's purpose immediately. That purpose is what we eventually came to call the message's bottom line.

At the beginning of the study we wondered, why do people write backwards? One possibility is that they are writing histories of their mental processes as they think their way through a problem. Since their conclusion could only be arrived at after analysis, the report therefore would state its conclusions last. But if that were the reason, it would only be analytical memos and reports that would be organized backwards.

Such was not the case in the study we did. Almost *all* memos and reports put their purpose last. Why? We determined to study the problem to see if we could design a cure for such blatantly inefficient writing.

COMPREHENSION IS THE KEY

In the division headquarters we worked with, 9,000,000 (internal and external) messages of all types are distributed annually. Our study began with an intense analysis of a sample of 2,000 letters, memos, and reports randomly drawn from company files. The typical communication was one page. Only in rare cases did any memo or report exceed three pages. These various documents were well-written in the sense of being above average in terms of mechanical correctness and aptness of word choice.

Yet only one in twenty of these communications was organized efficiently. Below is one of the actual memos we analyzed (disguised, of course). Look at your watch before you read it. Keep a record of how many times you have to read it before you really *comprehend* its message, and how long it takes to understand the report's purpose.

Memo A

> The Facilities people have been working on consolidating HQ Marketing Functions into the new building at Pebble Brook. As presently envisioned, Marketing Research will remain in its current location but be provided with additional space for expansion. The following functions will be moved into the new facility—Business Analysis, Special Applications, and Market Planning. It is expected that Public Sector will be relocated in a satellite location. The above moves will consolidate all of Marketing into the Pebble Brook location with the exception noted above.
>
> Attached is a preliminary outline of the new building by floor and whom it will house. I am interested in knowing if this approach is in agreement with your thoughts.

This memo seems brief on the surface. It contains only 115 words. But let's measure brevity not by words but by the length of time it takes a reader to comprehend a message.

We feel that if you were really the addressee, you would have had to read this memo twice. Why? Because you didn't know *why* you were reading it until the last paragraph. Once you discover the purpose—that you are being asked to approve a plan—you want to reread the memo to see if you do, in fact, agree with the moves. The memo suddenly (and, unfortunately, at its end) informed you that you were on the hook. Obviously, there is a big difference between the way you will read a memo containing information of general (and casual) interest and one which requires you to make a decision involving the physical moving and reshuffling of hundreds of powerful and sensitive people. Yet organizationally this memo as presented does not show even a foggy awareness of this difference.

Now read the revision. Notice how your comprehension time would have dropped significantly had you received this revision instead of the original.

Memo B

Attached is a preliminary outline—by floor—of the new building at Pebble Brook and a statement of whom it will house. I am interested in knowing if this approach is in agreement with your thinking.

Our suggestion is that we make the following changes:

1. Business Analysis, Special Applications, and Market Planning will. . . .
2. Public Sector will be. . . .
3. Marketing Research will remain. . . .

In terms of comprehension, the revision lets you know right away that you are expected to make a decision. Whether or not you would mull over that decision, we cannot tell. But we do know this: in terms of actual time expended in comprehending what is being asked of the reader, Memo B can be comprehended in one-third the time required by Memo A. And, if we measure brevity in terms of comprehension time, rather than number of words, Memo B produces a 66 percent savings in comprehension time.

We learned immediately in our study that comprehension time drops dramatically when a memo states its purpose—why it is being written for the reader—at the very beginning.

Confirm this point by reading Memo C, another disguised memo drawn from the division headquarters. Time your comprehension as before.

Memo C

The first of a series of meetings of the Strategic Marketing planning group will be held on Thursday, September 7, from 1 to 4 P.M. in Conference Room C. These important meetings are for the purpose of monitoring and suggesting changes in overall market strategies and product support. Attached is a list of those managers who should attend on a regular basis. These managers should specifically be prepared to review alternative strategies for the new product line. The purpose of this reminder is to ask your help in encouraging attendance and direct participation by your representatives. Please have them contact Frank Persons for any further information and to confirm their attendance.

Now read Memo D and compare comprehension time once again.

Memo D

Please encourage those of your managers whose names are listed on the attachment to attend regularly and directly participate in the meetings of the Strategic Marketing Planning group.

The next meeting is to be held on Thursday, September 7, from 1 to 4 P.M. in Conference Room C.

Please have your representative(s):

1. Contact Frank Persons for any further information and to confirm attendance.
2. Be prepared specifically to review alternative strategies for the new F–62 line.
3. Be ready to discuss changes in overall market strategies and product support.

Memo D is obviously more efficient. Why? Not only because it begins by stating its purpose but also because it itemizes the actions requested of the reader, organizing them in an easy-to-digest checklist. The original gives extensive background about the meetings but buries the requested action in a fat paragraph. Most readers would have to read the original at least twice just to be able to ferret out exactly what is being asked of them.

The time being saved, of course, seems insignificant on communications as short as Memos A and C. But consider how significant the savings would be corporate-wide if every manager's comprehension time in reading all messages could be reduced by even a small percentage.

HIGH COST OF COMPREHENSION

A recent study done by International Data Corporation states that managers in information industries spend an astonishing 60 percent of their time reading and writing; professionals spend 50 percent.[1] If cost accounted, how much would, say, a 20 percent to 30 percent savings in reading and writing time amount to for companies in this industry alone? The possibilities are arresting.

We made some cost estimates for the communications undertaken by the division headquarters we studied. The 9,000,000 messages distributed annu-

[1] *Automated Business Communications: The Management Workstation.* (Framingham, Mass.: International Data Corporation, 1981): 21.

TABLE 10–1 Estimated Division Headquarters Writing Costs

Number of messages sent annually	9,000,000
Percent individually composed	12%
Total individually composed	1,800,000
Composition cost (per message)	$10
Minimum total composition cost	$10,800,000

ally by the division headquarters included, of course, all sorts of mailings and multiple copies of such things as new product announcements, price changes, and the like, often running into the thousands of copies. Therefore, it was not fair to assume all 9,000,000 messages mailed were individually composed. Instead, we determined through conservative estimates that 12 percent of the 9,000,000 mailings were individual communications. And for each of these we will assume, for the purpose of this article, the ridiculously low figure of $10 to be the cost of creating, typing, and distributing. Based on these estimates, the minimum total composition cost for this one divisional headquarters would be $10,800,000 a year (see Table 10–1).

But writing time is, of course, only part of the story. What about the cost of comprehending all 9,000,000 of these messages? For while we estimate that only 12 percent of these messages were individually composed (that is, not copies), all 9,000,000 messages were presumably intended to be read. Again, in an attempt to dramatize through understatement, we will use a low salary figure: $20,000 per year. You can, of course, substitute the actual salary and other figures for your own company and determine for yourself at least roughly the magnitude of your company's reading costs.

As Table 10–2 shows, we approximated the division's minimum reading costs to be over $4,500,000. Of course, this figure is bound to be far below actual costs. Not only are our salary estimates unrealistically low, but we haven't taken into account the fact that many of the documents were read by multiple readers. In fact, many memos urged recipients to pass information on to colleagues and subordinates.

TABLE 10–2 Estimated Division Headquarters Reading Costs

Low-median salary	$20,000 $10/hour 17¢/minute
Average* reading time	3 minutes
Reading cost per document	$0.51
Reading cost for 9,000,000 messages	$4,590,000

*Assumed that some messages read in depth; some not given more than a glance; some barely looked at.

USING DIRECT PATTERNS

While these dollar figures were somewhat astonishing and the possibilities of dollar savings enticing, the company under study evidenced the greater concern about the waste of productivity involved in such inefficient communications having become the norm. The specter of hard-working employees' time being wasted by an inundation of inefficiently organized memos and letters was distressing. The company asked us to teach people how to report in a "bottom-line" fashion. Therefore, we taught people to tell readers immediately what was their purpose in writing and what they expected of the reader, if anything. If people had no purpose in writing, they probably shouldn't write in the first place. If they didn't expect anything of the reader and were just offering possibly useful information, we told them to say so right away.

In short, we were teaching people to use a direct organizational pattern. We were urging them to eschew the circuitous pattern in which writers, because of some sensitivity (real or imagined), withhold their purpose and do not let their readers know why they are being written to and what is being asked of them until their minds have been conditioned to accept the points the writers are trying to get across.

Obviously, there is nothing wrong with a circuitous organizational pattern in certain circumstances. But in this company, and we suspect in many other companies across the country, the circuitous pattern has become the norm for all types of communication in all situations.

Just ask yourself: how sensible is it to always write backwards, in a way that is just the opposite of how people comprehend information? Look at one more illustrative letter from our study:

Memo E

> This is in reference to the letter sent you by Joe Smith of ABC Materials, Inc.
>
> Mr. Smith requested information available from Product Analysis Reports (PAR's). As soon as information was made available to me from this source, I orally relayed the response to Mr. Smith.
>
> Making use of the Planning Application Model, I was able to respond to Mr. Smith's request for further information about potential new products of possible interest to ABC. It was not until I received the copy of Mr. Smith's letter that I was aware that the data provided for him was not sufficient.
>
> I have used all the resources that I am aware of to resolve Mr. Smith's concerns. Mr. Smith has informed me he is more than satisfied with the work done and considers the project completed. He has also announced an intention of doing further business with us.

Attached are copies of all the requests that I've been asked to submit during the six months that I have been assigned to this account. Also attached is a copy of an ABC analysis, submitted by my predecessor, which related to one of the items referenced in his letter. Upon request, I will forward copies of all of the relevant analysis that are in my files.

Where's the bottom line? What's this writer trying to get across? Isn't it the following?

Memo F

I have reviewed and acted upon the letter sent to you by Joe Smith of ABC Materials. Mr. Smith has informed me he is more than satisfied with the work done and considers the project completed. He has also announced an intention of doing further business with us.

Here in some detail are the steps I have taken for Mr. Smith... .

Since what this writer is reporting is good news, the communication is not sensitive. There's no need to report this information as circuitously as we might well be tempted to do if we had bungled the situation with Mr. Smith and had lost his business.

What percentage of all communications would you estimate to fall into the sensitive category that may call for a circuitous organizational pattern? Ten percent is the outer limit of possibility, unless one has a specialized job such as handling complaints, writing sales letters, dealing with shareholders, or the like. Why, then, upon analyzing these 2,000 sample letters, memos, and reports from this corporate division, did we find that almost all documents were organized circuitously? Why, in this extremely well-managed and successful company, was it the exceedingly rare letter or memo that did not bury its purpose somewhere in the third or fourth paragraph, and most frequently in the last sentence?

At the time, we had no idea of the etiology of the disease, but we felt we had a simple cure. We would tell people how to organize their thoughts so that the bottom line of their message would be immediately highlighted and promptly presented in everything they wrote. To facilitate this goal, we invented a series of bottom-line reporting principles which, if followed, would enable writers to communicate in a direct, straightforward, no-nonsense fashion in all situations that were not fraught with sensitivity. This would, we thought, save writing time and expense (see Table 10–3).

And readers, too, would benefit—instead of having to search through a memo to find out what purpose the writer had in writing to them and what the writer wanted or expected them to do, they could look at the first paragraph and see the answer to these vital questions. Moreover, if the purpose and topic seemed irrelevant to their interests or needs, they could reject reading it, or merely give it a glance. Significant reading time and dollar savings should certainly result.

TABLE 10–3 Principles of Bottom-Line Reporting

Principle 1:	State your purpose first unless there are overriding reasons for not doing so.
Principle 2:	State your purpose first, even if you believe your readers need a briefing before they can fully understand the purpose of your communication.
Principle 3:	Present information in order of its importance to the reader.
Principle 4:	Put information of dubious utility or questionable importance to the reader into an appendix or attachment.
Principle 5:	In persuasive situations, where you do not know how your reader will react to what you ask for, state your request at the start in all cases except: a. Those where you don't (or barely) know the reader, and to ask something immediately of a relative (or absolute) stranger would probably be perceived as being "pushy." b. Those where the relationship between you and your reader is not close or warm.
Principle 6:	Think twice before being direct in negative messages upward.

The program was instituted throughout the division. Did it work? Yes, in terms of getting the principles across and in terms of getting intellectual acceptance of these principles.

But getting emotional commitment to these principles was quite another story. We sensed in discussions that writers' commitment to being circuitous was not merely a bad habit. It was something else, something that was so ingrained that forcing personnel to be direct actually caused disquiet in many people. What could have been the reason?

PROGRAMMING FOR INEFFICIENCY

Obviously, people who work in large organizations were not born there. They have come to those organizations programmed by their social upbringing and by their educational experiences. And both of these earlier programmings strongly contribute to resistance to bottom-line reporting.

Social Upbringing

People seldom are conscious of how their social upbringing programs them to be indirect. Yet almost every sensitive social situation reinforces the wisdom of being circuitous, of not being direct. Aren't most brief answers to sensitive questions regarded as brusqueness or curtness, as being short with someone?

It begins early. The children are asked, "Do you want to go to Aunt Alice's house?" The children answer, honestly and directly, "No!" Unacceptable! The children are scolded and soon learn to beat around the bush the next time, all the while searching for some plausible excuse to forestall the visit. It is not surprising that as adults, the same children, when asked by the boss, "What do you think of my new plan? Think it'll work?" think twice before responding, "No!"

Educational Programming

Having been thoroughly programmed by their families that being direct is being impolite, the children now go to school. Here they soon learn that a twenty-page term report gets a high grade; a two-page report gets a low grade. A five-page answer to a test question is good; a one-paragraph answer is bad. Regardless of what teachers may profess, they invariably give extra credit for "effort." And effort is most easily measured by numbers of words or by pounds of pages. A premium is placed on long-windedness, and long-windedness is achieved by being circuitous rather than direct.

Indoctrination into Anxiety

On their first jobs in a large organization, young people are naturally nervous. They are very concerned that whatever they write or say not make people upset. They are also very concerned about "getting good grades." Therefore, they fall back upon the same behavior that was rewarded in school. They are going to do everything possible not to look lazy. They are going to be thorough in everything they write. Every chance to write a report to a superior is a chance to write that blockbuster of a term paper that could not fail to impress the boss. They are going to get that "A."

The fact that young people enter organizations at the bottom provides a final step in their programming for being circuitous and indirect. Everybody knows that writing *up* in an organization is far different from writing *down*. When young people enter an organization, the only direction they *can* write is up. Therefore, all the early experiences received in corporations consist of writing situations where they have to write information to people who are in fact, or may someday be, their superiors. Naturally, they become very uneasy.

Now let's suppose the company institutes a program to encourage personnel to be more direct. Imagine yourself as that newly hired young person in the organization. Are you going to believe any program suggesting that you be blunt and direct in your upward or lateral communications, when your entire lifetime programming has proved to you over and over again that bluntness is all too frequently suicidal? No chance!

Young people may give lip service to such a program, but in any real-life situation in which they feel threatened (in actuality, almost all situations) they will avoid coming to the point with an almost religious passion. And in negative or sensitive situations, the last thing they are going to do is state their purposes and requests directly.

By contrast, their higher level superiors, having enjoyed years of power positions in the hierarchy (from whence they could write down to anyone in any fashion they pleased), take a far different view of writing. The superiors now pride themselves on directness and bewail long-windedness on the part of their subordinates. But the subordinates' desires for self-preservation (reinforced by all their preorganizational programming) force them to give lip service at best to corporate attempts to "get to the point."

And, let's face it, in the corporate pyramid almost everybody is somebody's subordinate and, perhaps because of files, one never knows who is going to read what has been written. Therefore, circuitous writing is partly the habit of a lifetime and partly CYA.

WHAT YOUR ORGANIZATION CAN DO

Is a cure then impossible? Is inefficient, circuitous writing simply to be endured and its costs in lost productivity and wasted dollars merely written off?

No; a cure for inefficient writing is possible. But a thorough organization-wide cure requires that:

- People recognize and reject their social and educational programming for being circuitous in all non-sensitive writing situations. This deprogramming is the responsibility of the individual.
- People learn to write efficiently; that is, learn to organize their messages in such a way as to make it easy (and fast) for readers to comprehend the message. Teaching the bottom-line principles will impart this skill. But implementing the bottom-line principles requires strong high-level management support.
- People must develop the self-confidence necessary to send bottom-line messages upward in nonsensitive (or slightly sensitive) messages. A long-range cure depends to a great extent on attitude, on reducing the tensions inherent in superior subordinate communications. Most writing insecurities stem from real, not imagined, failures on the part of superiors to communicate clearly and unequivocally their willingness to accept bottom-lined messages from subordinates.

Higher level executives have to appreciate how threatening directness can be to subordinates. Superiors, therefore, need to be persuaded not only to have the following credo taped to the wall above their desks but also communicated to all subordinates with whom they relate:

The Superior's Credo

1. I will ask all subordinates to be direct in their messages to me and I will not become angry if subordinates do so politely—even when those thoughts run counter to mine.
2. I will recognize and appreciate subordinates' attempts to conserve my time (and other readers' time) in all memos and reports they write to me, or for my signature.
3. I will work out with subordinates some general understanding of how much detail I require in various circumstances.
4. I will make clear to subordinates that I judge their communications not by length and weight, but by directness and succinctness.
5. And when I myself report up in the organization, I will be as direct as I expect my subordinates to be.

Once senior executives have adopted and put this credo into practice, all subordinates should recognize that there is now no excuse for them not to live by the following credo:

The Subordinate's Credo

1. I will have the courage (in all but the most sensitive or negative situations) to state at the beginning of messages my purpose in writing, exactly what information I am trying to convey, and/or precisely what action(s) I want my reader to take (if possible, itemized in checklist form for easy comprehension).
2. My readers, especially if they are my superiors, are extremely busy. I must not waste their time by making them read unnecessary undigested detail any more than I would waste their time chattering on in a face-to-face interview.
3. I will make a judgment as to how much my readers need to know in order to take the action required by the communication.
4. If I am in doubt as to whether specific information is necessary to my readers, I will either put this information in summary form in attachments, or tell readers that I stand ready to offer more information if so requested.
5. I will avoid the arsenal of the con man. If I want something of a superior, I will ask for it forthrightly.

11 Audience Analysis: The Problem and a Solution

J. C. Mathes and Dwight W. Stevenson

J. C. Mathes and Dwight W. Stevenson are both Professors Emeriti of Technical Communications in the College of Engineering at the University of Michigan.

Every communication situation involves three fundamental components: a writer, a message, and an audience. However, many report writers treat the communication situation as if there were only two components: a writer and his message. Writers often ignore their readers because writers are preoccupied with their own problems and with the subject matter of the communication. The consequence is a poorly designed, ineffective report.

As an example, a student related to the class her first communication experience on a design project during summer employment with an automobile company. After she had been working on her assignment for a few weeks, her supervisor asked her to jot him a memo explaining what she was doing. Not wanting to take much time away from her work and not thinking the report very important, she gave him a handwritten memo and continued her technical activities. Soon after, the department manager inquired on the progress of the project. The supervisor immediately responded that he had just had a progress report, and thereupon forwarded the engineer's brief memo. Needless to say, the engineer felt embarrassed when her undeveloped and inadequately explained memo became an official report to the organization. The engineer thought her memo was written just to her supervisor, who was quite familiar with her assignment. Due to her lack of experience with organizational behavior, she made several false assumptions about her report audience, and therefore about her report's purpose.

The inexperienced report writer often fails to design his report effectively because he makes several false assumptions about the report writing situation. If the writer would stop to analyze the audience component, he would realize that:

1. It is false to assume that the person addressed is the audience.
2. It is false to assume that the audience is a group of specialists in the field.
3. It is false to assume that the report has a finite period of use.
4. It is false to assume that the author and the audience always will be available for reference.
5. It is false to assume that the audience is familiar with the assignment.
6. It is false to assume that the audience has been involved in daily discussions of the material.
7. It is false to assume that the audience awaits the report.
8. It is false to assume that the audience has time to read the report.

Assumptions one and two indicate a writer's lack of awareness of the nature of his report audience. Assumptions three, four, and five indicate his lack of appreciation of the dynamic nature of the system. Assumptions six, seven, and eight indicate a writer's lack of consideration of the demands of day-by-day job activity.

A report has value only to the extent that it is useful to the organization. It is often used primarily by someone other than the person who requested it. Furthermore, the report may be responding to a variety of needs within the organization. These needs suggest that the persons who will use the report are not specialists or perhaps not even technically knowledgeable about the report's subject. The specialist is the engineer. Unless he is engaged in basic research, he usually must communicate with persons representing many different areas of operation in the organization.

In addition, the report is often useful over an extended period of time. Each written communication is filed in several offices. Last year's report can be incomprehensible if the writer did not anticipate and explain his purpose adequately. In these situations, even within the office where a report originated, the author as well as his supervisor will probably not be available to explain the report. Although organizational charts remain unchanged for years, personnel, assignments, and professional roles change constantly. Because of this dynamic process, even the immediate audience of a report sometimes is not familiar with the writer's technical assignment. Thus, the report writer usually must design his report for a dynamic situation.

Finally, the report writer must also be alert to the communication traps in relatively static situations. Not all readers will have heard the coffee break chats that fill in the details necessary to make even a routine recommendation convincing. A report can arrive at a time when the reader's mind is churning with other concerns. Even if it is expected, the report usually meets a reader who needs to act immediately. The reader usually does not have time to read through the whole report; he wants the useful information clearly and succinctly. To the reader, time probably is the most important commodity. Beginning report writers seldom realize they must design their reports to be used efficiently rather than read closely.

The sources of the false assumptions we have been discussing are not difficult to identify. The original source is the artificial communication a student is required to perform in college. In writing only for professors, a student learns to write for audiences of one, audiences who know more than the writer knows, and audiences who have no instrumental interests in what the report contains. The subsequent source, on the job, is the writer's natural attempt to simplify his task. The report writer, relying upon daily contact and familiarity, simply finds it easier to write a report for his own supervisor than to write for a supervisor in a different department. The writer also finds it easier to concentrate upon his own concerns than to consider the needs of his readers. He finds it difficult to address complex audiences and face the design problems they pose.

AUDIENCE COMPONENTS AND PROBLEMS THEY POSE

To write a report you must first understand how your audience poses a problem. Then you must analyze your audience in order to be able to design a report structure that provides an optimum solution. To explain the components of the report audience you must do more than just identify names, titles, and roles. You must determine who your audiences are as related to the purpose and content of your report. "Who" involves the specific operational functions of the persons who will read the report, as well as their educational and business backgrounds. These persons can be widely distributed, as is evident if you consider the operational relationships within a typical organization.

Classifying audiences only according to directions of communication flow along the paths delineated by the conventional organizational chart, we can identify three types of report audiences: *horizontal, vertical,* and *external.* For example, in the organization chart in Figure 11–1, *Part of Organization Chart for Naval Ship Engineering Center,*[1] horizontal audiences exist on each level. The Ship Concept Design Division and the Command and Surveillance Division form horizontal audiences for each other. Vertical audiences exist between levels. The Ship Concept Design Division and the Sur-

[1]A reference in H. B. Benford and J. C. Mathes, *Your Future in Naval Architecture,* Richards Rosen, New York, 1968.

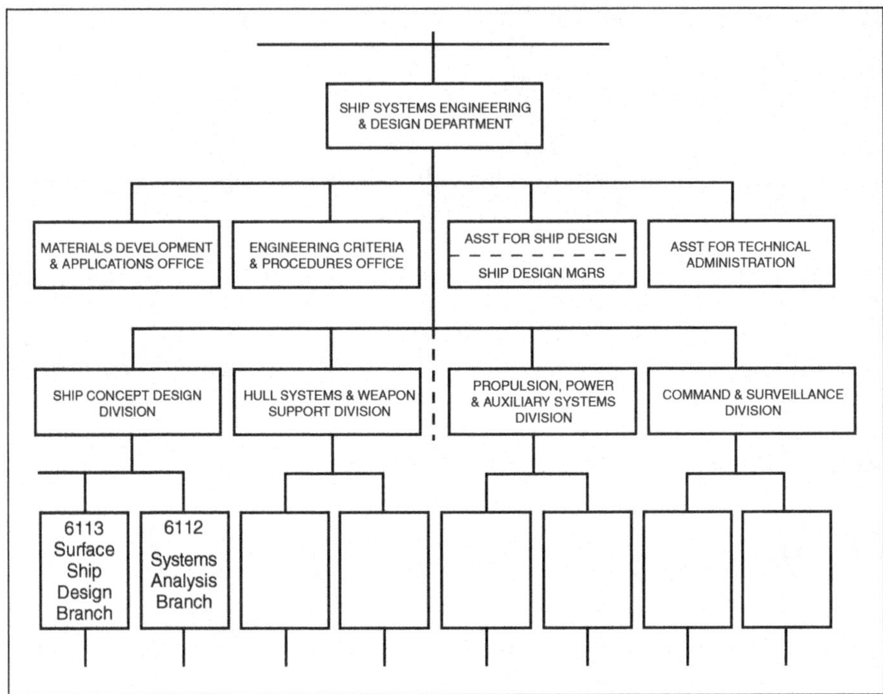

FIGURE 11–1
Part of Organization Chart for Naval Ship Engineering Center

face Ship Design Branch form vertical audiences for each other. External audiences exist when any unit interacts with a separate organization, such as when the Surface Ship Design Branch communicates with the Newport News Shipbuilding Company.

What the report writer first must realize is the separation between him and any of these three types of audiences. Few reports are written for horizontal audiences within the same unit, such as from one person in the Surface Ship Design Branch to another person or project group within the Surface Ship Design Branch itself. Instead, a report at least addresses horizontal audiences within a larger framework, such as from the Surface Ship Design Branch to the Systems Analysis Branch. Important reports usually have complex audiences, that is, vertical and horizontal, and sometimes external audiences as well.

An analysis of the problems generated by horizontal audiences—often assumed to pose few problems—illustrates the difficulties most writers face in all report writing situations. A systems engineer in the Systems Analysis Branch has little technical education in common with the naval architect in the Surface Ship Design Branch. In most colleges he takes only a few of the same mathematics and engineering science courses. The systems engineer would not know the wave resistance theory familiar to the naval architect, although he could use the results of his analysis. In turn, the naval architect would not know stochastics and probability theory, although he could understand systems models. But the differences between these audiences and writers go well beyond differences in training. In addition to having different educational backgrounds, the audiences will have different concerns, such as budget, production, or contract obligations. The audiences will also be separated from the writer by organizational politics and competition, as well as by personality differences among the people concerned.

When the writer addresses a horizontal audience in another organizational unit, he usually addresses a person in an organizational role. When addressed to the role rather than the person, the report is aimed at a department or a group. This means the report will have audiences in addition to the person addressed. It may be read primarily by staff personnel and subordinates. The addressee ultimately may act on the basis of the information reported, but at times he serves only to transfer the report to persons in his department who will use it. Furthermore, the report may have audiences in addition to those in the department addressed. It may be forwarded to other persons elsewhere, such as lawyers and comptrollers. The report travels routinely throughout organizational paths, and will have unknown or unanticipated audiences as well.

Consequently, even when on the same horizontal organizational level, the writer and his audience have little in common beyond the fact of working for the same organization, of having the same "rank" and perhaps of having the same educational level of attainment. Educational backgrounds can be entirely different; more important, needs, values, and uses are different. The report writer may recommend the choice of one switch over another on the basis of cost-efficiency analysis; his audiences may be concerned for business relationships, distribution patterns, client preferences, and budgets. Therefore, the writer should not assume that his audience has technical competence in the field, familiarity with the technical assignment, knowledge of him or of personnel in his group, similar value perspectives, or even complementary motives. The differences between writer and audience are distinctive, and may even be irreconcilable.

The differences are magnified when the writer addresses vertical audiences. Reports directed at vertical audiences, that is, between levels of an organization chart, invariably have horizontal audience components also. These complex report writing situations pose significant communication problems for the writer. Differences between writer and audience are fundamental. The primary audiences for the reports, especially informal reports, must act or make decisions on the basis of the reports. The reports thus have only instrumental value, that is, value insofar as they can be used effectively. The writer must design his report primarily according to how it will be used.

In addition to horizontal audiences and to vertical audiences, many reports are also directed to external audiences. External audiences, whether they consist of a few or many persons, have the distinctive, dissimilar features of the complex vertical audience. With external audiences these features invariably are exaggerated, especially those involving need and value. An additional complication is that the external audience can judge an entire organization on the basis of the writer's report. And sometimes most important of all, concerns for tact and business relationships override technical concerns.

In actual practice the writer often finds audiences in different divisions of his own company to be "external" audiences. One engineer encountered this problem in his first position after graduation. He was sent to investigate the inconsistent test data being sent to his group from a different division of the company in another city. He found that the test procedures being used in that division were faulty. However, at his supervisor's direction he had to write a report that would not "step on any toes." He had to write the report in such a manner as to have the other division correct its test procedures while not implying that the division was in any way at fault. An engineer who assumes that the purpose of his report is just to explain a technical investigation is poorly prepared for professional practice.

Most of the important communication situations for an engineer during his first five years out of college occur when he reports to his supervisor, department head, and beyond. In these situations, his audiences are action-oriented line management who are uninterested in the technical details and may even be unfamiliar with the assignment. In addition, his audiences become acquainted with him professionally through his reports; therefore, it is more directly the report than the investigation that is important to the writer's career.

Audience components and the significant design problems they pose are well illustrated by the various audiences for a formal report written by an engineer on the development of a process to make a high purity chemical, as listed in Figure 11–2, *Complex Audience Components for a Formal Report by a Chemical Engineer on a Process to Make a High Purity Chemical.* The purpose of the report was to explain the process; others would make a feasibility study of the process and evaluate it in comparison to other processes.

The various audiences for this report, as you can determine just by reading their titles, would have had quite different roles, backgrounds, interests, values, needs, and uses for the report. The writer's brief analysis of the audiences yielded the following:

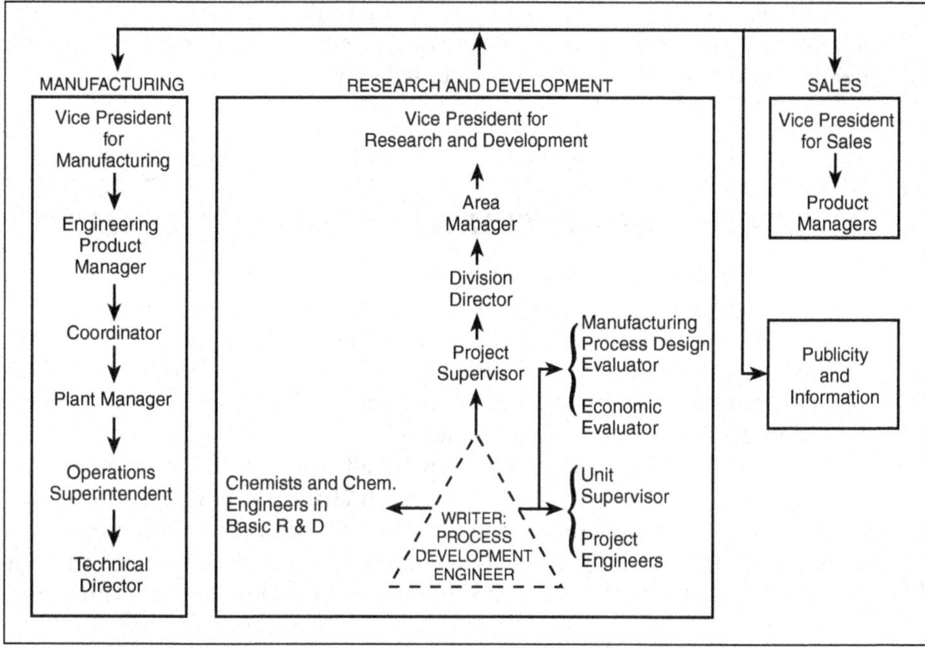

FIGURE 11–2
Complex Audience Components for a Formal Report by a Chemical Engineer on a Process to Make a High Purity Chemical

He could not determine the nature of many of his audiences, who they were, or what the specifics of their roles were.

His audiences had little familiarity with his assignment.

His report would be used for information, for evaluation of the process, and for evaluation of the company's position in the field.

Some of his audiences would have from a minute to a half hour to glance at the report, some would take the report home to study it, and some would use it over extended periods of time for process analysis and for economic and manufacturing feasibility studies.

The useful lifetime of the report could be as long as twenty years.

The report would be used to evaluate the achievements of the writer's department.

The report would be used to evaluate the writing and technical proficiencies of the writer himself.

This report writer classified his audiences in terms of the conventional organization chart. Then to make them more than just names, titles, and roles he asked himself what they would know about his report and how they would use it. Even then he had only partially solved his audience problem and had just begun to clarify the design problems he faced. To do so he needed to analyze his audiences systematically.

A METHOD FOR SYSTEMATIC AUDIENCE ANALYSIS

To introduce the audience problem that report writers must face, we have used the conventional concept of the organization chart to classify audiences as *horizontal, vertical,* and *external.* However, when the writer comes to the task of performing an instrumentally useful audience analysis for a particular report, this concept of the organization and this classification system for report audiences are not very helpful.

First, the writer does not view from outside the total communication system modeled by the company organization chart. He is within the system himself, so his view is always relative. Second, the conventional outsider's view does not yield sufficiently detailed information about the report audiences. A single bloc on the organization chart looks just like any other bloc, but in fact each bloc represents one or several human beings with distinctive roles, backgrounds, and personal characteristics. Third, and most importantly, the outsider's view does not help much to clarify the specific routes of communication, as determined by audience needs, which an individual report will follow. The organization chart may describe the organization, but it does not describe how the organization functions. Thus many of the routes a report follows—and consequently the needs it addresses—will not be signaled by the company organization chart.

In short, the conventional concept of report audiences derived from organization charts is necessarily abstract and unspecific. For that reason a more effective method for audience analysis is needed. In the remaining portion of this . . . [selection], we will present a three-step procedure. The procedure calls for preparing an egocentric organization chart to identify individual report readers, characterizing these readers, and classifying them to establish priorities. Based upon an egocentric view of the organization and concerned primarily with what report readers need, this system should yield the information the writer must have if he is to design an individual report effectively.

Prepare an Egocentric Organization Chart

An egocentric organization chart differs from the conventional chart in two senses. First, it identifies specific individuals rather than complex organizational units. A bloc on the conventional chart may often represent a number of people, but insofar as possible the egocentric chart identifies particular individuals who are potential readers of reports a writer produces. Second, the egocentric chart categorizes people in terms of their proximity to the report writer rather than in terms of their hierarchical relationship to the report writer. Readers are not identified as organizationally superior, inferior, or equal to the writer but rather as near or distant from the writer. We find it effective to identify four different degrees of distance as is illustrated in Figure 11–3, *Egocentric Organization Chart.* In this figure, with the triangle representing the writer, each circle is an individual reader identified by his organizational title and by his primary operational concerns. The four degrees of distance are identified by the four concentric rings. The potential readers in the first ring are those people with whom the writer associates daily. They are typically those people in his same office or project group. The readers in the second ring are those people in other offices with whom the writer must normally interact in order to perform his job. Typically, these are persons in adjacent and management groups. The readers in the third ring are persons relatively more distant but still within the same organization. They are distant management, public relations, sales, legal department, production, purchasing, and so on. They are operationally dissimilar persons. The readers in the fourth ring are persons beyond the organization. They may work for the same company but in a division in another city. Or they may work for an entirely different organization.

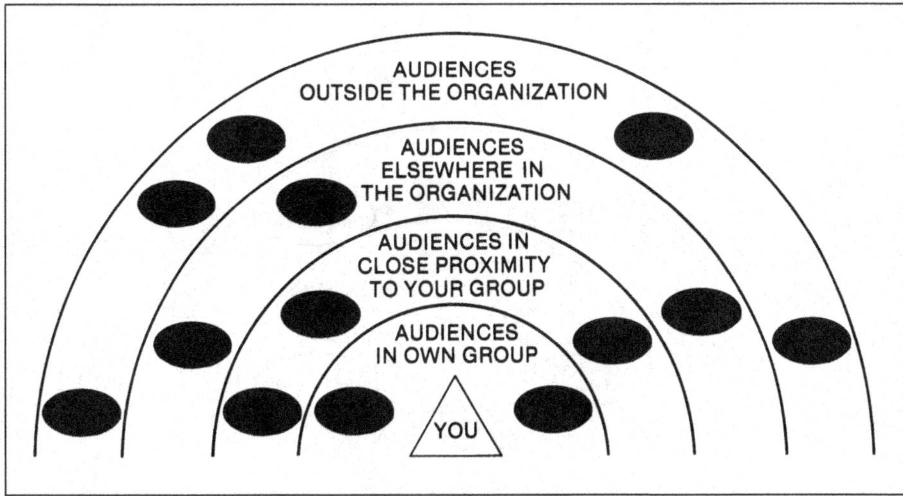

FIGURE 11–3
Egocentric Organization Chart

Having prepared the egocentric organization chart, the report writer is able to see himself and his potential audiences from a useful perspective. Rather than seeing himself as an insignificantly small part of a complex structure—as he is apt to do with the conventional organizational chart—the writer sees himself as a center from which communication radiates throughout an organization. He sees his readers as individuals rather than as faceless blocs. And he sees that what he writes is addressed to people with varying and significant degrees of difference.

A good illustration of the perspective provided by the egocentric organization chart is the chart prepared by a chemical engineer working for a large corporation, Figure 11–4, *Actual Egocentric Organization Chart of an Engineer in a Large Corporation.* It is important to notice how the operational concerns of the persons even in close proximity vary considerably from those of the development engineer. What these people need from reports written by this engineer, then, has little to do with the processes by which he defined his technical problems.

The chemical engineer himself is concerned with the research and development of production processes and has little interest in, or knowledge of, budgetary matters. Some of the audiences in his group are chemists concerned with production—not with research and development. Because of this they have, as he said, "lost familiarity with the technical background,

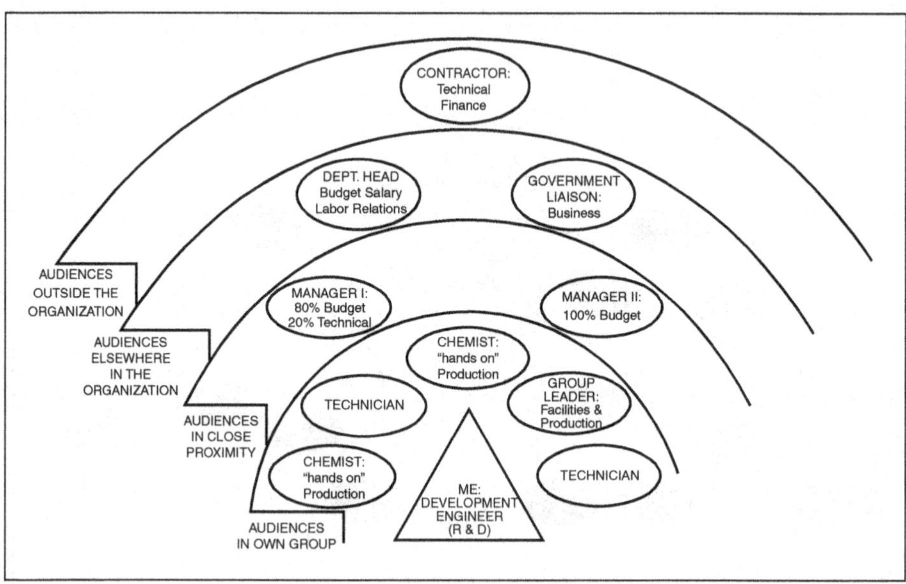

FIGURE 11–4
Actual Egocentric Organization Chart of an Engineer in a Large Corporation

and instead depend mostly on experience." Other audiences in his group are technicians concerned only with operations. With only two years of college, they have had no more than introductory chemistry courses and have had no engineering courses.

Still another audience in his group is his group leader. Rather than being concerned with development, this reader is concerned with facilities and production operations. Consequently, he too is "losing familiarity with the technical material." Particularly significant for the report writer is that his group leader in his professional capacity does not use his B.S.Ch.E. degree. His role is that of manager, so his needs have become administrative rather than technical.

The concerns of the chemical engineer/report writer's audiences in close proximity to his group change again. Instead of being concerned with development or production operations, these audiences are primarily concerned with the budget. They have little technical contact, and are described as "business oriented." Both Manager I and Manager II are older, and neither has a degree in engineering. One has a Ph.D. degree in chemistry, the other an M.S. degree in technology. Both have had technical experience in the lab, but neither can readily follow technical explanations. As the chemical engineer said, both would find it "difficult to return to the law."

The report writer's department head and other persons through whom the group communicates with audiences elsewhere in the organization, and beyond it, have additional concerns as well as different backgrounds. The department head is concerned with budget, personnel, and labor relations. The person in contact with outside funding units—in this case, a government agency—has business administration degrees and is entirely business oriented. The person in contact with subcontractors has both technical and financial concerns.

Notice that when this writer examined his audiences even in his own group as well as those in close proximity to him, he saw that the natures, the backgrounds, and especially the operational concerns of his audiences vary and differ considerably. As he widened the scope of his egocentric organization chart, he knew less and less about his audiences. However, he could assume they will vary even more than those of the audiences in close proximity.

Thus, in the process of examining the audience situation with an egocentric organization chart, a report writer can uncover not only the fact that audiences have functionally different interests, but also the nature of those functional differences. He can proceed to classify the audiences for each particular report in terms of audience needs.

Preparation of the egocentric organization chart is the first step of your procedure of systematic audience analysis. Notice that this step can be performed once to describe your typical report audience situation but must be particularized for each report to define the audiences for that report. Having prepared the egocentric chart once, the writer revises his chart for subsequent reports by adding or subtracting individual audiences.

Characterize the Individual Report Readers

In the process of preparing the egocentric organization chart, you immediately begin to think of your individual report readers in particular terms. In preparing the egocentric chart discussed above, the report writer mentioned such items as a reader's age, academic degrees, and background in the organization as well as his operational concerns. All of these particulars will come to mind when you think of your audiences as individuals. However, a systematic rather than piecemeal audience analysis will yield more useful information. The second step of audience analysis is, therefore, a systematic characterization of each person identified in the egocentric organization chart. A systematic characterization is made in terms of *operational, objective,* and *personal* characteristics.

The *operational characteristics* of your audiences are particularly important. As you identify the operational characteristics for a person affected by your report, try to identify significant differences between his or her role and yours. What are his professional values? How does he spend his time? That is, will his daily concerns and attitudes enable him to react to your report easily, or will they make it difficult for him to grasp what you are talking about? What does he know about your role, and in particular, what does he know or remember about your technical assignment and the organizational problem that occasioned your report to come to him? You should also consider carefully what he will need from your report. As you think over your entire technical investigation, ask yourself if that person will involve staff personnel in action on your report, of if he will in turn activate other persons elsewhere in the organization, when he receives the report. If he should, you must take their reactions into account when you write your report.

In addition, you should ask yourself, "How will my report affect his role?" A student engineer recently told us of an experience he had during summer employment when he was asked to evaluate the efficiency of the plant's waste treatment process. Armed with his fresh knowledge from advanced chemical engineering courses, to his surprise he found that, by making a simple change in the process, the company could save more than $200,000 a year. He fired off his report with great anticipation of glowing accolades—none came. How had his report affected the roles of some of his audiences? Although the writer had not considered the report's consequences when he wrote it, the supervisor, the manager, and related personnel now were faced with the problem of accounting for their waste of

$200,000 a year. It should have been no surprise that they were less than elated over his discovery.

By *objective characteristics* we mean specific, relevant background data about the person. As you try to identify his or her educational background, you may note differences you might have otherwise neglected. Should his education seem to approximate yours, do not assume he knows what you know. Remember that the half-life of engineering education today is about five years. Thus, anyone five to ten years older than you, if you are recently out of college, probably will be only superficially familiar with the material and jargon of your advanced technical courses. If you can further identify his past professional experiences and roles, you might be able to anticipate his first-hand knowledge of your role and technical activities as well as to clarify any residual organizational commitments and value systems he might have. When you judge his knowledge of your technical area, ask yourself, "Could he participate in a professional conference in my field of specialization?"

For *personal characteristics,* when you identify a person by name, ask yourself how often the name changes in this organizational role. When you note his or her approximate age, remind yourself how differences in age can inhibit communication. Also note personal concerns that could influence his reactions to your report.

A convenient way to conduct the audience analysis we have been describing and to store the information it yields is to use an analysis form similar to the one in Figure 11–5, *Form for Characterizing Individual Report Readers* [p. 272]. It may be a little time-consuming to do this the first time around, but you can establish a file of audience characterizations. Then you can add to or subtract from this file as an individual communication situation requires.

One final point: This form is a means to an end rather than an end in itself. What is important for the report writer is that he thinks systematically about the questions this form raises. The novice usually has to force himself to analyze his audiences systematically. The experienced writer does this automatically.

Classify Audiences in Terms of How They Will Use Your Report

For each report you write, trace out the communication routes on your egocentric organization chart and add other routes not on the chart. Do not limit these routes to those specifically identified by the assignment and the addresses of the report. Rather, think through the total impacts of your report on the organization. That is, think in terms of the first, second, and even some third-order consequences of your report, and trace out the significant

NAME: TITLE:

A. OPERATIONAL CHARACTERISTICS:

1. His role within the organization and consequent value system:
2. His daily concerns and attitudes:
3. His knowledge of your technical responsibilities and assignment:
4. What he will need from your report:
5. What staff and other persons will be activated by your report through him:
6. How your report could affect his role:

B. OBJECTIVE CHARACTERISTICS:

1. His education—levels, fields, and years:
2. His past professional experiences and roles:
3. His knowledge of your technical area:

C. PERSONAL CHARACTERISTICS:

Personal characteristics that could influence his reactions—age, attitudes, pet concerns, etc.

FIGURE 11–5
Form for Characterizing Individual Report Readers

communication routes involved. All of these consequences define your actual communication.

When you think in terms of consequences, primarily you think in terms of the uses to which your report will be put. No longer are you concerned with your technical investigation itself. In fact, when you consider how readers will use your report, you realize that very few of your potential readers will have any real interest in the details of your technical investigation. Instead, they want to know the answers to such questions as "Why was this investigation made? What is the significance of the problem it addresses? What am I supposed to do with the results of this investigation? What will it cost? What are the implications—for sales, for production, for the unions? What happens next? Who does it? Who is responsible?"

It is precisely this audience concern for nontechnical questions that causes so much trouble for young practicing engineers. Professionally, much of what the engineer spends his time doing is, at most, of only marginal concern to many of his audiences. His audiences ask questions about things which perhaps never entered his thoughts during his own technical activities when he received the assignment, defined the problem, and performed his investigation. These questions, however, must enter into his considerations when he writes his report.

Having defined the communication routes for a report you now know what audiences you will have and what questions they will want answered. The final step in our method of audience analysis is to assign priorities to your audiences. Classify them in terms of how they will use your report. In order of their importance to you (not in terms of their proximity to you), classify your audiences by these three categories:

- *Primary audiences*—who make decisions or act on the basis of the information a report contains.
- *Secondary audiences*—who are affected by the decisions and actions.
- *Immediate audiences*—who route the report or transmit the information it contains.

The *primary audience* for a report consists of those persons who will make decisions or act on the basis of the information provided by the report. The report overall should be designed to meet the needs of these users. The primary audience can consist of one person who will act in an official capacity, or it can consist of several persons representing several offices using the report. The important point here is that the primary audience for a report can consist of persons from any ring on the egocentric organization chart. They may be distant or in close proximity to the writer. They may be his organizational superiors, inferiors, or equals. They are simply those readers for whom the report is primarily intended. They are the top priority users.

In theory at least, primary audiences act in terms of their organizational roles rather than as individuals with distinctive idiosyncracies, predilections, and values. Your audience analysis should indicate when these personal concerns are likely to override organizational concerns. A typical primary audience is the decision maker, but his actual decisions are often determined by the evaluations and recommendations of staff personnel. Thus the report whose primary audience is a decision maker with line responsibility actually has an audience of staff personnel. Another type of primary audience is the production superintendent, but again his actions are often contingent upon the reactions of others.

In addition, because the report enters into a system, in time both the line and staff personnel will change; roles rather than individuals provide continuity. For this reason, it is helpful to remember the words of one engineer when he said, "A complete change of personnel could occur over the lifetime of my report." The report remains in the file. The report writer must not assume that his primary audience will be familiar with the technical assignment. He must design the report so that it contains adequate information concerning the reasons for the assignment, details of the procedures used, the results of the investigation, and conclusions and recommendations. This information is needed so that any future component of his primary audience will be able to use the report confidently.

The *secondary audience* for a report consists of those persons other than primary decision makers or users who are affected by the information the report transmits into the system. These are the people whose activities are affected when a primary audience makes a decision, such as when production supervision has to adjust to management decisions. They must respond appropriately when a primary audience acts, such as when personnel and labor relations have to accommodate production line changes. The report writer must not neglect the needs of his secondary audiences. In tracing out his communication routes, he will identify several secondary audiences. Analysis of their needs will reveal what additional information the report should contain. This information is often omitted by writers who do not classify their audiences sufficiently.

The *immediate audience* for a report are those persons who route the report or transmit the information it contains. It is essential for the report writer to identify his immediate audiences and not to confuse them with his primary audiences. The immediate audience might be the report writer's supervisor or another middle management person. Yet usually his role will be to transmit information rather than to use the information directly. An information system has numerous persons who transmit reports but who may not act upon the information or who may not be affected by the information in ways of concern to the report writers. Often, a report is addressed to the writer's supervisor, but except for an incidental memo report, the supervisor serves only to transmit and expedite the information flow throughout the organizational system.

A word of caution: at times the immediate audience is also part of the primary audience; at other times the immediate audience is part of the secondary audience. For each report you write, you must distinguish those among your readers who will function as conduits to the primary audience.

As an example of these distinctions between categories of report audiences, consider how audiences identified on the egocentric organization chart, Figure 11–4 [p. 268], can be categorized. Assume that the chemical engineer writes a report on a particular process improvement he has designed. The immediate audience might be his Group Leader. Another would be Manager I, transmitting the report to Manager II. The primary audiences might be Manager II and the Department Head; they would ask a barrage of nontechnical questions similar to those we mentioned a moment ago. They will decide whether or not the organization will implement the improvement recommended by the writer. The Department Head also could be part of the secondary audience by asking questions relating to labor relations and union contracts. Other secondary audiences, each asking different questions of the report, could be:

> The person in contact with the funding agency, who will be concerned with budget and contract implications.
>
> The person in contact with subcontractors, determining how they are affected.
>
> The Group Leader, whose activities will be changed.
>
> The "hands on" chemist, whose production responsibilities will be affected.
>
> The technicians, whose job descriptions will change.

In addition to the secondary audiences on the egocentric organization chart, the report will have other secondary audiences throughout the organization—technical service and development, for example, or perhaps waste treatment.

At some length we have been discussing a fairly detailed method for systematic audience analysis. The method may have seemed more complicated than it actually is. Reduced to its basic ingredients, the method requires you, first, to identify all the individuals who will read the report, second, to characterize them, and third, to classify them. The *Matrix for Audience Analysis,* Figure 11–6, is a convenient device for characterizing and classifying your readers once you have identified them. At a glance, the matrix reveals what information you have and what information you still need to generate. Above all, the matrix forces you to think systematically. If you are able to fill in a good deal of specific information in each cell (particularly in the first six cells), you have gone a long way towards seeing how the needs of your audiences will determine the design of your report.

We have not introduced a systematic method for audience analysis with the expectation that it will make your communication task easy. We have

Characteristics / Types of audiences	Operational	Objective	Personal
Primary	①	④	⑦
Secondary	②	⑤	⑧
Immediate	③	⑥	⑨

FIGURE 11–6
Matrix for Audience Analysis

introduced you to the problems you must account for when you design your reports—problems you otherwise might ignore. You should, at least, appreciate the complexity of a report audience. Thus, when you come to write a report, you are less likely to make false assumptions about your audience. To develop this attitude is perhaps as important as to acquire the specific information the analysis yields. On the basis of this attitude, you now are ready to determine the specific purpose of your report.

12 How to Lie with Statistics

Darrell Huff

Darrell Huff, a freelance writer, expanded this article into a book with the same title (Norton, 1954).

"The average Yaleman, Class of '24," *Time* magazine reported last year after reading something in the New York *Sun,* a newspaper published in those days, "makes $25,111 a year."

Well, good for him!

But, come to think of it, what does this improbably precise and salubrious figure mean? Is it, as it appears to be, evidence that if you send your boy to Yale you won't have to work in your old age and neither will he? Is this average a mean or is it a median? What kind of sample is it based on? You could lump one Texas oilman with two hundred hungry freelance writers and report *their* average income as $25,000-odd a year. The arithmetic is impeccable, the figure is convincingly precise, and the amount of meaning there is in it you could put in your eye.

In just such ways is the secret language of statistics, so appealing in a fact-minded culture, being used to sensationalize, inflate, confuse, and oversimplify. Statistical terms are necessary in reporting the mass data of social and economic trends, business conditions, "opinion" polls, this year's census. But without writers who use the words with honesty and understanding and readers who know what they mean, the result can only be semantic nonsense.

In popular writing on scientific research, the abused statistic is almost crowding out the picture of the white-jacketed hero laboring overtime without time-and-a-half in an ill-lit laboratory. Like the "little dash of powder, little pot of paint," statistics are making many an important fact "look like what she ain't." Here are some of the ways it is done.

The sample with the built-in bias. Our Yale men—or Yalemen, as they say in the Time-Life building—belong to this flourishing group. The exaggerated estimate of their income is not based on all members of the class nor on a random or representative sample of them. At least two interesting categories of 1924-model Yale men have been excluded.

First there are those whose present addresses are unknown to their classmates. Wouldn't you bet that these lost sheep are earning less than the boys from prominent families and the others who can be handily reached from a Wall Street office?

There are those who chucked the questionnaire into the nearest wastebasket. Maybe they didn't answer because they were not making enough money to brag about. Like the fellow who found a note clipped to his first pay check suggesting that he consider the amount of his salary confidential: "Don't worry," he told the boss. "I'm just as ashamed of it as you are."

Omitted from our sample then are just the two groups most likely to depress the average. The $25,111 figure is beginning to account for itself. It may indeed be a true figure for those of the Class of '24 whose addresses are known and who are willing to stand up and tell how much they earn. But even that requires a possibly dangerous assumption that the gentlemen are telling the truth.

To be dependable to any useful degree at all, a sampling study must use a representative sample (which can lead to trouble too) or a truly random one. If *all* the Class of '24 is included, that's all right. If every tenth name on a complete list is used, that is all right too, and so is drawing an adequate number of names out of a hat. The test is this: Does every name in the group have an equal chance to be in the sample?

You'll recall that ignoring this requirement was what produced the *Literary Digest*'s famed fiasco.* When names for polling were taken only from telephone books and subscription lists, people who did not have telephones or *Literary Digest* subscriptions had no chance to be in the sample. They possibly did not mind this underprivilege a bit, but their absence was in the end very hard on the magazine that relied on the figures.

This leads to a moral: You can prove about anything you want to by letting your sample bias itself. As a consumer of statistical data—a reader, for example, of a news magazine—remember that no statistical conclusion can rise above the quality of the sample it is based upon. In the absence of information about the procedures behind it, you are not warranted in giving any credence at all to the result.

The truncated, or gee-whiz, graph. If you want to show some statistical information quickly and clearly, draw a picture of it. Graphic presentation is the thing today. If you don't mind misleading the hasty looker, or if you quite clearly *want* to deceive him, you can save some space by chopping the bottom off many kinds of graph.

---

*Editor's note: The *Literary Digest* predicted that Alfred Landon would defeat Franklin Roosevelt in the 1936 presidential election. Landon carried only two states.

Suppose you are showing the upward trend of national income month by month for a year. The total rise, as in one recent year, is 7 percent. It looks like this:

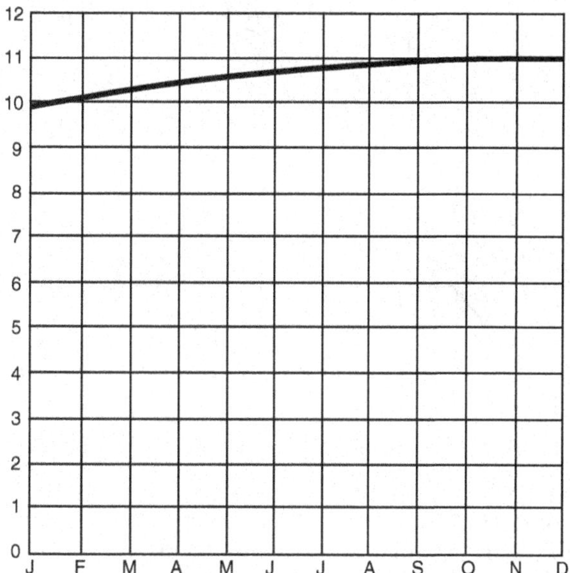

That is clear enough. Anybody can see that the trend is slightly upward. You are showing a 7 percent increase, and that is exactly what it looks like.

But it lacks schmaltz. So you chop off the bottom, this way:

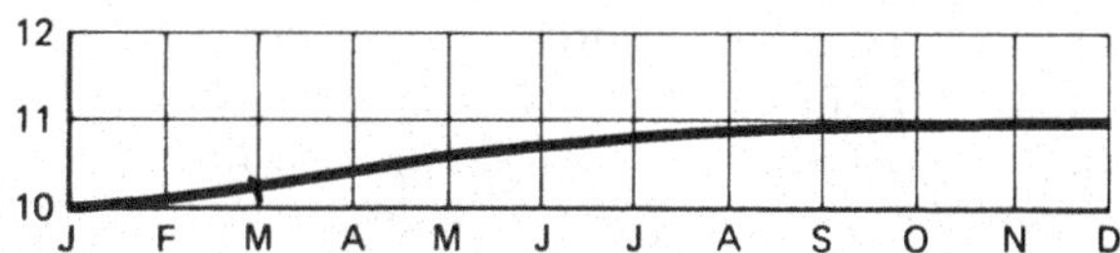

The figures are the same. It is the same graph and nothing has been falsified—except the impression that it gives. Anyone looking at it can just feel prosperity throbbing in the arteries of the country. It is a subtler equivalent of editing "National income rose 7 percent" into ". . . climbed a whopping 7 percent."

It is vastly more effective, however, because of that illusion of objectivity.

The souped-up graph. Sometimes truncating is not enough. The trifling rise in something or other still looks almost as insignficant as it is. You can make that 7 percent look livelier than 100 percent ordinarily does. Simply change the proportion between the ordinate and the abscissa. There's no rule against it, and it does give your graph a prettier shape.

But it exaggerates, to say the least, something awful:

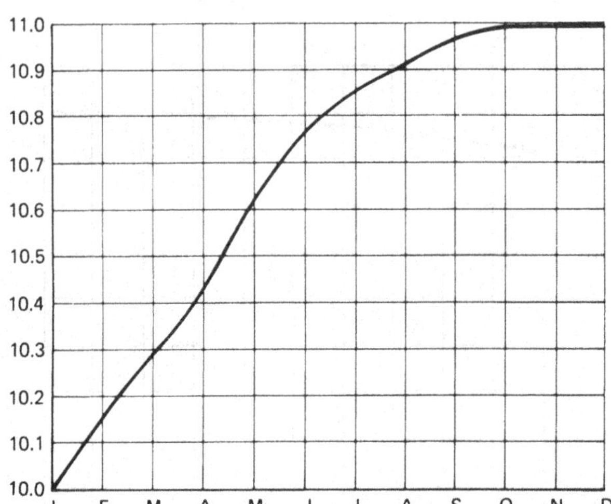

The well-chosen average. I live near a country neighborhood for which I can report an average income of $15,000. I could also report it as $3,500.

If I should want to sell real estate hereabouts to people having a high snobbery content, the first figure would be handy. The second figure, however, is the one to use in an argument against raising taxes, or the local bus fare.

Both are legitimate averages, legally arrived at. Yet it is obvious that at least one of them must be as misleading as an out-and-out lie. The $15,000-figure is a mean, the arithmetic average of the incomes of all the families in the community. The smaller figure is a median; it might be called the income of the average family in the group. It indicates that half the families have less than $3,500 a year and half have more.

Here is where some of the confusion about averages comes from. Many human characteristics have the grace to fall into what is called the "normal" distribution. If you draw a picture of it, you get a curve that is shaped like a bell. Mean and median fall at about the same point, so it doesn't make very much difference which you use.

But some things refuse to follow this neat curve. Income is one of them. Incomes for most large areas will range from under $1,000 a year to upward of $50,000. Almost everybody will be under $10,000, way over on the left-hand side of that curve.

One of the things that made the income figure for the "average Yaleman" meaningless is that we are not told whether it is a mean or a median. It is not that one type of average is invariably better than the other; it depends upon what you are talking about. But neither gives you any real information—and either may be highly misleading—unless you know which of those two kinds of average it is.

In the country neighborhood I mentioned, almost everyone has less than the average—the mean, that is—of $10,500. These people are all small farmers, except for a trio of millionaire week-enders who bring up the mean enormously.

You can be pretty sure that when an income average is given in the form of a mean nearly everybody has less than that.

The insignificant difference or the elusive error. Your two children Peter and Linda (we might as well give them modish names while we're about it) take intelligence tests. Peter's IQ, you learn, is 98 and Linda's is 101. Aha! Linda is your brighter child.

Is she? An intelligence test is, or purports to be, a sampling of intellect. An IQ, like other products of sampling, is a figure with a statistical error, which expresses the precison or reliability of the figure. The size of this probable error can be calculated. For their test the makers of the much-used Revised Stanford-Binet have found it to be about 3 percent. So Peter's indicated IQ of 98 really means only that there is an even chance that it falls between 95 and 101. There is an equal probability that it falls somewhere else—below 95 or above 101. Similarly, Linda's has no better than a fifty-fifty chance of being within the fairly sizeable range of 98 to 104.

You can work out some comparisons from that. One is that there is rather better than one chance in four that Peter, with his lower IQ rating, is really at least three points smarter than Linda. A statistician doesn't like to consider a difference significant unless you can hand him odds a lot longer than that.

Ignoring the error in a sampling study leads to all kinds of silly conclusions. There are magazine editors to whom readership surveys are gospel; with a 40 percent readership reported for one article and a 35 percent for another, they demand more like the first. I've seen even smaller differences given tremendous weight, because statistics are a mystery and numbers are impressive. The same thing goes for market surveys and so-called public opinion polls. The rule is that you cannot make a valid comparison between two such figures unless you know the deviations. And unless the difference between the figures is many times greater than the probable error of each, you have only a guess that the one appearing greater really is.

Otherwise you are like the man choosing a camp site from a report of mean temperature alone. One place in California with a mean annual temperature of 61 is San Nicolas Island on the south coast, where it always stays in the comfortable range between 47 and 87. Another with a mean of 61 is in the inland desert, where the thermometer hops around from 15 to 104. The deviation from the mean marks the difference, and you can freeze or roast if you ignore it.

The one-dimensional picture. Suppose you have just two or three figures to compare—say the average weekly wage of carpenters in the United States and another country. The sums might be $60 and $30. An ordinary bar chart makes the difference graphic.

That is an honest picture. It looks good for American carpenters, but perhaps it does not have quite the oomph you are after. Can't you make that difference appear overwhelming and at the same time give it what I am

afraid is known as eye-appeal? Of course you can. Following tradition, you represent these sums by pictures of money bags. If the $30 bag is one inch high, you draw the $60 bag two inches high. That's in proportion, isn't it?

The catch is, of course, that the American's money bag, being twice as tall as that of the $30 man, covers an area on your page four times as great. And since your two-dimensional picture represents an object that would in fact have three dimensions, the money bags actually would differ much more than that. The volumes of any two similar solids vary as the cubes of their heights. If the unfortunate foreigner's bag holds $30 worth of dimes, the American's would hold not $60 but a neat $240.

You didn't say that, though, did you? And you can't be blamed, you're only doing it the way practically everybody else does.

The ever-impressive decimal. For a spurious air of precision that will lend all kinds of weight to the most disreputable statistics, consider the decimal.

Ask a hundred citizens how many hours they slept last night. Come out with a total of, say, 7.813. Your data are far from precise to begin with. Most people will miss their guess by fifteen minutes or more and some will recall five sleepless minutes as half a night of tossing insomnia.

But go ahead, do your arithmetic, announce that people sleep an average of 7.813 hours a night. You will sound as if you knew precisely what you are talking about. If you were foolish enough to say 7.8 (or "almost" 8) hours it would sound like what it was—an approximation.

The semiattached figure. If you can't prove what you want to prove, demonstrate something else and pretend that they are the same thing. In the daze that follows the collision of statistics with the human mind, hardly anybody will notice the difference. The semiattached figure is a durable device guaranteed to stand you in good stead. It always has.

If you can't prove that your nostrum cures colds, publish a sworn laboratory report that the stuff killed 31,108 germs in a test tube in eleven seconds. There may be no connection at all between assorted germs in a test tube and the whatever-it-is that produces colds, but people aren't going to reason that sharply, especially while sniffling.

Maybe that one is too obvious and people are beginning to catch on. Here is a trickier version.

Let us say that in a period when race prejudice is growing it is to your advantage to "prove" otherwise. You will not find it a difficult assignment.

Ask that usual cross section of the population if they think . . . [Blacks] have as good a chance as white people to get jobs. Ask again a few months later. As Princeton's Office of Public Opinion Research has found out, people who are most unsympathetic to . . . [Blacks] are the ones most likely to answer yes to this question.

As prejudice increases in a country, the percentage of affirmative answers you will get to this question will become larger. What looks on the face of it like growing opportunity for . . . [Blacks] actually is mounting prejudice and nothing else. You have achieved something rather remarkable: the worse things get, the better your survey makes them look.

The unwarranted assumption, or *post hoc* rides again. The interrelation of cause and effect, so often obscure anyway, can be most neatly hidden in statistical data.

Somebody once went to a good deal of trouble to find out if cigarette smokers make lower college grades than non-smokers. They did. This naturally pleased many people, and they made much of it.

The unwarranted assumption, of course, was that smoking had produced dull minds. It seemed vaguely reasonable on the face of it, so it was quite widely accepted. But it really proved nothing of the sort, any more than it proved that poor grades drive students to the solace of tobacco. Maybe the relationship worked in one direction, maybe in the other. And maybe all this is only an indication that the sociable sort of fellow who is likely to take his books less than seriously is also likely to sit around and smoke many cigarettes.

Permitting statistical treatment to befog casual relationships is little better than superstition. It is like the conviction among the people of the Hebrides that body lice produce good health. Observation over the centuries had taught them that people in good health had lice and sick people often did not. *Ergo,* lice made a man healthy. Everybody should have them.

Scantier evidence, treated statistically at the expense of common sense, has made many a medical fortune and many a medical article in magazines, including professional ones. More sophisticated observers finally got things straightened out in the Hebrides. As it turned out, almost everybody in those circles had lice most of the time. But when a man took a fever (quite possibly carried to him by those same lice) and his body became hot, the lice left. Here you have cause and effect not only reversed, but intermingled.

There you have a primer in some ways to use statistics to deceive. A well-wrapped statistic is better than Hitler's "big lie": it misleads, yet it can't be pinned onto you.

Is this little list altogether too much like a manual for swindlers? Perhaps I can justify it in the manner of the retired burglar whose published reminiscences amounted to a graduate course in how to pick a lock and muffle a footfall: The crooks already know these tricks. Honest men must learn them in self-defense.

Appendix
Writing Handbook

Chapter 1 divided the writing process into three stages: planning, drafting, and revising. This Appendix will help you fix problems that occur during the revision stage of writing. It includes alphabetized entries on style, grammar, and usage. These three terms are defined as follows:

> **Style** includes features such as word choice, sentence length, paragraph organization, and active and passive voice. These are matters of choice, not right and wrong. For example, both the wordy and concise versions of a passage may be grammatically correct, but the concise version is a better stylistic choice.
>
> **Grammar** consists of the actual rules that determine how language should be used, as opposed to stylistic options one can choose. Examples of such right/wrong issues include comma placement and correct use of modifiers.
>
> **Usage** defines contexts for the correct use of problem words—especially word pairs such as effect/affect and complement/compliment.

Each entry in this Appendix has two parts: an explanation of the meaning and one or more correct examples.

Of course, when you're preparing a document for your boss or client, you don't separate problems by style, grammar, or usage. You just want to produce a draft that is easy to read and free of errors. Thus all entries in this Appendix are alphabetized for easy reference. Following are two separate tables of contents—alphabetical and topical.

ALPHABETIZED TABLE OF CONTENTS

TOPICAL TABLE OF CONTENTS

Style

Grammar

Usage

A/AN

These two words are different forms of the same article. *A* occurs before words that start with consonants or consonant sounds. Examples:

- *a* three-pronged plug
- *a* once-in-a-lifetime job (though its first letter is a vowel, *once* begins with the consonant sound of "w")
- *a* historic moment (because *history* begins with a consonant sound)
- *An* occurs before words that begin with vowels or vowel sounds. Examples:
- *an* earthly paradise
- *an* hour (though its first letter is a consonant, *hour* begins with a vowel sound)
- *an* eager new employee

A LOT/ALOT

The correct form is the two-word phrase *a lot.* (*Alot* is not acceptable usage.) Although acceptable in casual discourse, *a lot* should be replaced by more formal diction in technical writing. Examples:

- My father had *a lot* of patience.
- They retrieved *many* [not *a lot of*] soil samples from the site.

ABBREVIATIONS: RULES

Technical writing uses many abbreviations. Without this shorthand form, you would produce much longer reports and proposals—without adding content. Follow six basic rules in your use of abbreviations:

Do Not Use Abbreviations When Confusion May Result

When you want to use a term just once or twice *and* you are not certain readers will understand an abbreviation, write out the term rather than abbreviating it. Example:

> They were required to remove creosote from the site, according to the directive from the Environmental Protection Agency.

Even though *EPA* is the accepted abbreviation for the agency mentioned, you should write out the name in full *if* you are using the term only once to an audience that may not understand it.

Use Parentheses for Clarity

When you use a term more than *twice* and are not certain your readers will understand it, write out the term the first time it is used and place the abbreviation in parentheses. Then use the abbreviation in the rest of the document. In long reports or proposals, however, you may need to repeat the term with the parenthetical abbreviation in key places. Example:

> According to the directive from the Environmental Protection Agency (EPA), the builders were required to remove the creosote from the construction site. Furthermore, the directive noted that builders could expect to be visited by EPA inspectors every other week.

Include a Glossary When There Are Many Abbreviations

When a document contains many abbreviations that may not be understood, include a glossary at the beginning or end of the document. A glossary simply collects all the terms and abbreviations and places them in one location, for easy reference.

Use Abbreviations for Units of Measure

Most technical documents use abbreviations for units of measure. Do not include a period unless the abbreviation could be confused with a word. Examples:

> mi, ft, oz, in., gal., lb

Note that abbreviations for units of measure have the same form for both singular and plural. Examples:

> ½ in., 1 in., 5 in.

Avoid Spacing and Periods

Avoid internal spacing and internal periods in most abbreviations that contain all capital letters. Examples:

> ASTM, EPA, ASEE

Some common exceptions include professional titles and degrees such as P.E., B.S., and B.A.

Be Careful with Company Names

Abbreviate a company or other organizational name only when you are certain that officials from the organization consider the abbreviation appropriate. IBM (for the company) and UCLA (for the university) are examples of commonly accepted organizational abbreviations. When in doubt, follow the preceding rule regarding parentheses; that is, write the name in full the first time it is used, followed by the abbreviation in parentheses.

ABBREVIATIONS: COMMON EXAMPLES

The following common abbreviations are appropriate for most technical writing. They are placed into three main categories of measurements, locations, and titles:

Measurements

Use these abbreviations when you use numbers with measurements.

ac: alternating current
amp: ampere
bbl: barrel
BTU: British thermal unit
bu: bushel
C: Celsius
cal: calorie
cc: cubic centimeter
circ: circumference
cm: centimeter
cos: cosine
cot: cotangent
cps: cycles per second
cu ft: cubic foot (feet)
db: decibel
dc: direct current
dm: decimeter
doz or dz: dozen

f: farad
F: Fahrenheit
Fbm: foot board measure
fig.: figure
fl oz: fluid ounce
ft: foot (feet)
g: gram
gal. or gl: gallon
gpm: gallons per minute
hp: horsepower
hr: hour
Hz: hertz
in.: inch
J: joule
K: Kelvin
ke: kinetic energy
kg: kilogram
km: kilometer

kW: kilowatt
kWh: kilowatt hour
L: liter
lb: pound
lin: linear
lm: lumen
log: logarithm
m: meter
min: minute
mm: millimeter
oz: ounce
ppm: parts per million
psf: pounds per square foot (feet)
psi: pounds per square inch
pt: pint
qt: quart
rev: revolution
rpm: revolutions per minute
sec: second
sq: square
sq ft: square foot (feet)
tn: ton
tan: tangent
V: volt
va: volt-ampere
W: watt
wk: week
wl: wavelength
yd: yard
yr: year

Locations

Use these common abbreviations for addresses—on envelopes and letters, for example. However, write out the words in full in other contexts.

AL: Alabama
AK: Alaska
AS: American Samoa
AZ: Arizona
AR: Arkansas
CA: California
CZ: Canal Zone
CO: Colorado
CT: Connecticut
DE: Delaware
DC: District of Columbia
FL: Florida
GA: Georgia
GU: Guam
HI: Hawaii
ID: Idaho
IL: Illinois
IN: Indiana
IA: Iowa
KS: Kansas
KY: Kentucky
LA: Louisiana
ME: Maine
MD: Maryland
MA: Massachusetts
MI: Michigan
MN: Minnesota
MS: Mississippi
MO: Missouri
MT: Montana

NE: Nebraska
NV: Nevada
NH: New Hampshire
NJ: New Jersey
NM: New Mexico
NY: New York
NC: North Carolina
ND: North Dakota
OH: Ohio
OK: Oklahoma
OR: Oregon
PA: Pennsylvania
PR: Puerto Rico
RI: Rhode Island
SC: South Carolina
SD: South Dakota
TN: Tennessee
TX: Texas
UT: Utah
VT: Vermont
VI: Virgin Islands
VA: Virginia
WA: Washington
WV: West Virginia
WI: Wisconsin
WY: Wyoming
AB: Alberta
BC: British Columbia
MB: Manitoba
NB: New Brunswick
NF: Newfoundland
NWT: North West Territories
NS: Nova Scotia
ON: Ontario
PEI: Prince Edward Island
QC: Quebec
SK: Saskatchewan
YK: Yukon

Titles

Some abbreviations of titles go before the name (such as Dr., Mr., and Messrs.), whereas others go after the name (such as college degrees, Jr., and Sr.).

Atty.: Attorney
B.A.: Bachelor of Arts
B.S.: Bachelor of Science
D.D.: Doctor of Divinity
Dr.: Doctor (used mainly with medical and dental degrees but also with other doctorates)
Drs.: plural of Dr.
D.V.M.: Doctor of Veterinary Medicine
Hon.: Honorable
Jr.: Junior
LL.D.: Doctor of Laws
M.A.: Master of Arts

M.S.: Master of Science

M.D.: Doctor of Medicine

Messrs.: Plural of Mr.

Mr.: Mister

Mrs.: used to designate a married, widowed, or divorced woman

Ms.: used increasingly for all women, especially when one is uncertain about a woman's marital status

Ph.D.: Doctor of Philosophy

Sr.: Senior

ACCEPT/EXCEPT

These words have different meanings and often are different parts of speech. *Accept* is a verb that means "to receive." *Except* is a preposition and means "to make an exception or special case of." Examples:

- I *accepted* the service award from my office manager.
- Everyone *except* Jonah attended the marine science lecture.

ACCURATE WORDING

Good technical writing style demands accuracy in phrasing. Indeed, many technical professionals place their reputation and even their financial lives on the line with every document that goes out their door. That fact makes clear the importance of taking your time on any editing pass that deals with accuracy of phrasing. Accuracy often demands more words, not fewer. The main rule, then, is never to sacrifice clarity for conciseness. Following are some rules for writing accurately. They also will help you to avoid unnecessary exposure to liability.

Distinguish Facts from Opinions

Always identify your opinions and judgments as such by using phrases like "we recommend," "we believe," "we suggest," and "in our opinion." If you want to avoid repetitious use of these phrases, group your opinions into a series or list. Thus a single lead-in can indicate to the reader that opinions, not facts, are forthcoming. Examples:

- In our opinion, spread footings would be an acceptable foundation for the building you plan at the site.
- On the basis of our site visit and our experience at similar sites, we believe that (1) __________, (2) __________, and (3) __________.

Include Obvious Qualifying Statements When Needed

Be aware of possible misinterpretations by those who may not know that even technical fields can be inexact. Write carefully, but without becoming overly defensive. In other words, your readers—especially those who are nontechnical—want to know what you did do *and* what you did not do. Example:

> Our summary of soil conditions is based only on information obtained during a brief visit to the site. We did not drill any soil borings.

Avoid Absolutes Unless You Mean Them

Some words may convey a stronger meaning than you intend. One notable example is *minimize*, which means to reduce to the lowest possible level or amount. If a report claims that a particular piece of equipment will "minimize" breakdowns on the assembly line, the passage could be interpreted as an absolute commitment. In theory, the reader could consider any breakdown at all to be a violation of the report's implications. If instead the writer had used the verb *limit* or *reduce*, the wording would have been more accurate and less open to misunderstanding.

> **Original:** If you follow our recommendations, pollution will be minimized at the site.
>
> **Revision:** If you follow our recommendations, pollution will be greatly reduced at the site.

The original version would be correct only if the writers were able to guarantee that their recommendations would lead to the lowest possible level of pollution.

ACTIVE AND PASSIVE VOICE

This entry defines the active and passive voices and gives examples of each. It also lists some guidelines for using both voices.

The Meaning of Active and Passive

Active voice sentences emphasize the person (or thing) performing the action—that is, somebody (or something) does something ("Matt completed the field study yesterday"). Passive voice sentences emphasize the action itself—that is, something is being done by somebody ("The field study was completed [by Matt] yesterday"). Here are some other examples of the same thoughts expressed in first the active and then the passive voice:

Examples: Active Voice

1. We *reviewed* aerial photographs in our initial assessment of possible fault activity at the site.
2. The study *revealed* that three underground storage tanks had leaked unleaded gasoline into the soil.
3. We *recommend* that you use a minimum concrete thickness of 6 in. for residential subdivision streets.

Examples: Passive Voice

1. Aerial photographs *were reviewed* [by us] in our initial assessment of possible fault activity at the site.
2. The fact that three underground storage tanks had been leaking unleaded gasoline into the soil *was revealed* in the study.
3. *It is recommended* that you use a minimum concrete thickness of 6 in. for residential concrete streets.

Note that passive constructions are wordier than active ones. They tend to leave out the person or thing doing the action. Although occasionally this impersonal approach is appropriate, often the reader becomes frustrated by writing that does not indicate who or what is doing something.

Using Active and Passive Voice

The fact is that both the active and the passive voice have a role in writing. Knowing when to use each is the key. Here are a few guidelines that will help:

Use the Active Voice When You Want to Do the Following:

1. Emphasize who is responsible for an action ("*We recommend* that you consider our firm for the work").
2. Stress the name of a company, whether yours or the reader's ("*PineBluff Contracting has expressed* interest in receiving bids for the Baytown project").
3. Rewrite a top-heavy sentence so that the main idea is up front ("*Figure 1 shows* the approximate locations of the cars that derailed from the northbound freight train").

4. Pare down the verbiage in your writing; because the active voice is always a shorter construction (see the active and passive examples in previous subsections).

Use the Passive Voice When You Want to Do the Following:

1. Emphasize the action rather than the person performing it ("*Samples will be sent* directly from the site to our laboratory in Sacramento").
2. Avoid the kind of egocentric tone that results from repetitious use of "I," "we," and the name of your company ("*The project will be directed* by two programmers from our Boston office").
3. Break the monotony of writing that relies too heavily on active voice sentences.

Technical and business writing depends far too much on the passive voice. This stylistic error results in part from the common misperception that passive writing is more "objective." In fact, overuse of passives only makes writing more tedious to read. In modern business and technical writing, most readers prefer the active voice.

ADVICE/ADVISE/INFORM

Advice is a noun that means "suggestion or recommendation." *Advise* is a verb that means "to suggest or recommend." Do not use the verb *advise* as a substitute for *inform,* which means simply "to provide information." Examples:

- The consultant gave us *advice* on starting a new retirement plan for our employees.
- She *advised* us that a 401(k) plan would be useful for all our employees.
- She *informed* [not *advised*] her clients that they would receive her final report by March 15.

AFFECT/EFFECT

These two words cause much confusion. The key to using them correctly is remembering two simple sentences that cover most (but, unfortunately, not all) usage:

1. *Affect* with an "a" is a verb meaning "to influence."
2. *Effect* with an "e" is a noun meaning "result."

Here is one main exception you also need to know: In special instances, *effect* can be a verb that means "to bring about," as in "He effected considerable change when he became a manager." Examples:

- His progressive leadership greatly *affected* the company's future.
- One *effect* of securing the large government contract was the hiring of several more accountants.
- The president's belief in the future of microcomputers *effected* change in the company's approach to office management. (Less wordy alternative: substitute *changed* for *effected change in.*)

AGREE TO/AGREE WITH

Agree to means that you have *consented to* an arrangement, offer, proposal, etc. *Agree with* suggests only that you are *in harmony with* a certain statement, idea, person, etc. Examples:

- Representatives from our firm *agreed to* alter the contract to reflect the new scope of work.
- We *agree with* you that more study may be needed before the plant is built.

ALL RIGHT/ALRIGHT

All right is an acceptable spelling; *alright* is not. *All right* is an adjective that means "acceptable," an exclamation that means "outstanding," or a phrase that means "correct." Examples:

- Sharon suggested that the advertising copy was *all right* for now but that she would want changes next month.
- Upon seeing his article in print, Zach exclaimed *"All right!"*
- The five classmates were *all right* in their response to the trick questions on the quiz.

ALL TOGETHER/ALTOGETHER

All together is used when items or people are being considered in a group, are working in concert, or are in the same location. *Altogether* is a synonym for "entirely" or "completely." Examples:

- *All together*, the sales team included 50 employees from 15 offices.
- The three firms were *all together* in their support of the agency's plan.
- The managers were *all together* in Cleveland for the conference.
- There were *altogether* too many pedestrians walking near the dangerous intersection.

ALLUSION/ILLUSION/DELUSION/ELUSION

These similar sounding words have distinct meanings. Here is a summary of the differences:

1. **Allusion:** a noun meaning "reference," as in your making an allusion to your vacation in a speech. The related verb is *allude*.
2. **Illusion:** a noun meaning "misunderstanding or false perception." It can be physical (as in seeing a mirage) or mental (as in having the false impression that your hair is not thinning when it is).
3. **Delusion:** a noun meaning a belief based on self-deception. Unlike *illusion*, the word conveys a much stronger sense that someone is out of touch with reality, as in having "delusions of grandeur." The related verb is *delude*.
4. **Elusion:** a noun meaning "the act of escaping or avoiding." The more common form is the verb *elude*, meaning "to escape or avoid."

Examples:

- His report included an *allusion* to the upcoming visit by the government agency in charge of accreditation.
- She harbored an *illusion* that she was certain to receive the promotion. In fact, her supervisor preferred another department member with more experience.
- He had *delusions* that he soon would become company president, even though he started just last week in the mailroom.
- The main point of the report *eluded* him because there was no executive summary.

ALREADY/ALL READY

All ready is a phrase that means "everyone is prepared," whereas *already* is an adverb that means something is finished or completed. Examples:

- They were *all ready* for the presentation to the client.
- George had *already* arrived at the office before the rest of his proposal team members had even left their homes.

ALTERNATELY/ALTERNATIVELY

Because many readers are aware of the distinction between these two words, any misuse can cause embarrassment or even misunderstanding. Follow these guidelines for correct use.

Alternately

As a derivative of *alternate, alternately* is best reserved for events or actions that occur "in turns." Example:

> They used a backhoe during some portions of the project. *Alternately,* they switched to using hand shovels.

Alternatively

A derivative of *alternative, alternatively* should be used when two or more choices are being considered. Example:

> We suggest that you use deep foundations at the site. *Alternatively,* you could consider spread footings.

ALUMNA/ALUMNAE/ALUMNUS/ALUMNI

These terms are derived directly from Latin. An *alumna* is a female graduate, whereas an *alumnus* is a male graduate. The plural forms are *alumnae* for females and *alumni* for males. Some writers prefer to use the plural form *alumni* in situations that involve both male and female graduates. However, the different masculine and feminine forms still are maintained in formal English. Examples:

- As a recent *alumna,* she often helped solicit donations from other *alumnae* of her college.
- He was considered a loyal *alumnus* of the college. Along with 100 other *alumni,* he volunteered every month at the Big Brothers Association of downtown Atlanta.

AMOUNT/NUMBER

Amount is used in reference to items that *cannot* be counted, whereas *number* is used to indicate items that *can* be counted. Examples:

- In the past year we have greatly increased the *amount* of computer paper ordered for the Boston office.
- The past year has seen a huge increase in the *number* [not *amount*] of boxes of computer paper ordered for the Boston office.

AND/OR

This awkward expression probably has its origins in legal writing. It means that there are three separate options to be considered: the item before *and/or*, the item after *and/or*, or both items.

Avoid *and/or* because readers may find it confusing, visually awkward, or both. Instead, replace it with the structure used in the previous sentence. That is, write "A, B, or both," *not* "A and/or B." Example:

> The management trainee was permitted to select two seminars from the areas of computer hardware, communication skills, or both [not *computer hardware and/or communication skills*].

ANTICIPATE/EXPECT

These two words are *not* synonyms. Their meanings are distinctly different. *Anticipate* is used when you mean to suggest or state that steps have been taken *beforehand* to prepare for a situation. *Expect* means only that you consider something likely to occur. Examples:

- *Anticipating* that the contract will be successfully negotiated, Jones Engineering is hiring three new hydrologists.
- We *expect* [not *anticipate*] that you will encounter semi-cohesive and cohesive soils in your excavations at the Park Avenue site.

APOSTROPHES

Apostrophes can be used for contractions, for some plurals, and for possessives. Only the latter two uses cause confusion. Use an apostrophe to indicate the plural form of a word as a word. Example:

> That redundant paragraph contained seven *area*'s and three *factor*'s in only five sentences.

Although some writers also use apostrophes to form the plurals of numbers and full-cap abbreviations, the current tendency is to include only the "s." Examples:

> 7s, ABCs, PCBs, P.E.s.

As for possessives, grammar rules seem to vary, depending on the reference book you're reading. Here are some simple guidelines that reflect this author's view of the best current usage:

Multisyllabic Nouns Ending in "s"

Form the possessive of multisyllabic nouns that end in "s" by adding just an apostrophe, whether the nouns are singular or plural. Examples:

> actress' costume, genius' test score, the three technicians' samples, Jesus' parables, the companies' joint project

Single-Syllable Nouns Ending in "s"

Form the possessive of single-syllable nouns ending in "s" or an "s" sound by adding an apostrophe plus "s." Examples:

> Hoss's horse, Rex's song, the boss's progress report

All Nouns Not Ending in "s"

Form the possessive of all singular and plural nouns not ending in "s" by adding an apostrophe plus "s." Examples:

> the man's hat, the men's team, the company's policy

Paired Nouns

Form the possessive of paired nouns by first determining whether there is joint ownership or individual ownership. For joint ownership, make only the last noun possessive. For individual ownership, make both nouns possessive. Examples:

> Susan and Terry's project was entered in the science fair, but Tom's and Scott's projects were not.

APT/LIABLE/LIKELY

Maintain the distinctions in these three similar words.

1. *Apt* is an adjective that means "appropriate," "suitable," or "has an aptitude for."
2. *Liable* is an adjective that means "legally obligated" or "subject to."
3. *Likely* is either an adjective that means "probable" or "promising" or an adverb that means "probably." As an adverb, it should be preceded by a qualifier such as *quite*.

Examples:

- The successful advertising campaign showed that she could select an *apt* phrase for selling products.

- Jonathan is *apt* at running good meetings. He always hands out an agenda and always ends on time.
- The contract makes clear who is *liable* for any on-site damage.
- Completing the warehouse without an inspection will make the contractor *liable* to lawsuits from the owner.
- A *likely* result of the investigation will be a change in the law. [*likely* as an adjective]
- The investigation will quite *likely* result in a change in the law. [*likely* as an adverb]

ASSURE/ENSURE/INSURE

As a verb meaning "to promise," *assure* is used in reference to people, as in "We want to assure you that our crews will strive to complete the project on time." *Assure* and its derivatives (like *assurance*) should be used with care in technical contexts, for these words can be viewed as a promise or guarantee.

The synonyms *ensure* and *insure* are verbs meaning to "make certain." Like *assure*, they imply a level of certainty that is not always appropriate in engineering and the sciences. When their use is deemed appropriate, the preferred word is *ensure*; reserve *insure* for sentences in which the context is insurance. Examples:

- I can *assure* you that our representatives will be on site to answer questions that the subcontractor may have.
- To *ensure* that the project stays within schedule, we are building in 10 extra days for bad weather. (An alternative that expresses less certainty and obligation: *So that* the project stays within schedule, we are building in 10 extra days for bad weather.)
- We *insured* the truck for $15,000.

AUGMENT/SUPPLEMENT

Augment is a verb that means "to increase in size, weight, number, or importance." *Supplement* is either (1) a verb that means to "add to" something to make it complete or to make up for a deficiency *or* (2) a noun that means "the thing that has been added." Examples:

- The power company supervisor decided to *augment* the line crews in five counties.

- He *supplemented* the deficient audit report by adding the three annual statements requested by the auditors.
- The three accounting *supplements* helped support the conclusions of the audit report.

AWHILE/A WHILE

Although similar in meaning, this pair is used differently. *Awhile* is an adverb that means "for a short time." Because *for* is already a part of its definition, the word cannot be preceded by the preposition *for*. The noun *while*, however, can be preceded by the two words *for a*, giving it essentially the same meaning as *awhile*. Examples:

- Kirk waited *awhile* before trying to restart the generator.
- Kirk waited *for a while* before trying to restart the generator.

BALANCE/REMAINDER/REST

Balance should be used as a synonym for *remainder* only in the context of financial affairs. *Remainder* and *rest* are synonyms to be used in other nonfinancial contexts. Examples:

- The account had a *balance* of $500, which was enough to avoid a service charge.
- The *remainder* [or *rest*, but not *balance*] of the day will be spent on training in oral presentations for proposals.
- During the *rest* [not *balance*] of the session, we learned about the new office equipment.

BECAUSE/SINCE

Maintain the distinction between these two words. *Because* establishes a cause-effect relationship, whereas *since* is associated with time. Examples:

- *Because* he left at 3 p.m., he was able to avoid rush hour.
- *Since* last week, her manufacturing team completed 3,000 units.

Note that *because* should not be used in the wordy construction "the reason is because." Examples:

- John wants the transfer *because* he needs the experience working at another office. [*not* "The reason John needs the transfer is because he needs the experience working at another office."]
- The ship sank *because* it was overloaded. [*not* "The reason the ship sank was because it was overloaded."]

BETWEEN/AMONG

The distinction between these two words has become somewhat blurred. However, many readers still prefer to see *between* used with reference to only two items and *among* used for three or more items. Examples:

- The agreement was just *between* my supervisor and me. No one else in the group knew about it.
- The proposal was circulated *among* all five members of the writing team.
- *Among* Sally, Todd, and Fran, there was little agreement about the long-term benefits of the project.

BI-/SEMI-/BIANNUAL/BIENNIAL

The prefixes *bi* and *semi* can cause confusion. Generally, *bi* means "every two years, months, weeks, etc.," whereas *semi* means "twice a year, month, week, etc." Yet many readers get confused by the difference, especially when they are confronted with a notable exception such as *biannual* (which means twice a year) and *biennial* (which means every two years).

Your goal, as always, is clarity for the reader. Therefore, it is best to write out meanings in clear prose, rather than relying on prefixes that may not be understood. Examples:

- We get paid twice a month [preferable to *semimonthly* or *biweekly*].
- The part-time editor submits articles every other month [preferable to *bimonthly*].
- We hold a company social gathering twice a year [preferable to *biannually* or *semiannually*].
- The auditor inspects our safety files every two years [preferable to *biennially*].

BRACKETS

Use a pair of brackets ([]) to set off explanatory material already contained within another parenthetical statement (see "Parentheses" entry in this

Appendix) or (2) to draw attention to a comment that you, as the writer, are making within a passage you are quoting. Examples:

> Two of our studies have shown that Colony Dam satisfies safety standards. (See Figure 4–3 [Dam Safety Record] for a complete record of our findings.) In addition, the county engineer, Greg Parker, has a letter on file that will give further assurance to homeowners on the lake. Parker notes the following in his letter: "After finishing my three-month study [Parker completed it in July 1995], I have concluded that the Colony Dam meets all required safety standards."

CAPITAL/CAPITOL

Capital is a noun whose main meanings are (1) a city or town that is a government center, (2) wealth or resources, or (3) net worth of a business or the investment that has been made in the business by owners. *Capital* can also be an adjective meaning (1) "excellent," (2) "primary," or (3) "related to the death penalty." Finally, *capital* can be a noun or adjective referring to upper-case letters.

Capitol is a noun or adjective that refers to a building where a legislature meets. With a capital letter, it refers exclusively to the building in Washington, D.C., where the U.S. Congress meets. Examples:

- The *capital* of Pickens County is Jasper, Georgia.
- Our family *capital* was reduced by the tornado and hurricane.
- She had invested significant *capital* in the carpet factory.
- Their proposal contained some *capital* ideas that would open new opportunities for our firm.
- In some countries, armed robbery is a *capital* offense.
- The students visited the *capitol* building in Atlanta. Next year they will visit the *Capitol* in Washington, D.C., where they will meet several members of Congress.

CAPITALIZATION

As a rule, you should capitalize names of specific people, places, and things—sometimes called "proper" nouns. For example, capitalize specific streets, towns, trademarks, geological eras, planets, groups of stars, days of the week, months of the year, names of organizations, holidays, and colleges. Nonspecific nouns—called "common" nouns—are not capitalized.

Of course, if it were this easy there wouldn't be so much confusion about capitalization. There is a tendency in business to overuse capitalization, as in the use of capitals with titles of positions. An example of improper usage follows: "The Director of Marketing visited our office last week." Excessive use of capitals appears pompous and is inappropriate in technical writing. The best practice today includes limited, judicious use of capitals. When in doubt, leave it lowercase. Here are the most frequently capitalized items:

Major Words in Titles of Books and Articles

Capitalize prepositions and articles only when they are the first words in titles. Examples:

- *For Whom the Bell Tolls*
- *In Search of Excellence*
- *The Power of Positive Thinking*

Names of Specific Places and Geographic Locations

Examples:

- Washington Monument
- Rose Bowl
- Dallas, Texas
- Summit County, Ohio

Names of Aircraft and Ships

Examples:

- *Air Force One*
- *SS Arizona*
- *Nina, Pinta,* and the *Santa Maria*

Names of Departments, Offices, and Committees in an Organization

Examples:

- Personnel Department
- International Division
- Benefits Committee

However, when shortened terms are used for these entities, capitals are not used. Example: "Being an elected member of the Benefits Committee, I am concerned that the committee has not met in six months."

Titles That Come before Names

Accepted practice calls for capitalizing titles only when they come directly before the name of the person who holds the title. When titles are used by themselves or follow a person's name, usually they are not capitalized. Examples:

- After breakfast, Chancellor Hairston opened the session.
- To our chagrin, Councilwoman Sharon Jones has served for nine years.
- We thought Professor Ginsberg gave a fine lecture.
- Jane Cannon, a professor in the Math Department, is on leave.
- Rob Smith, president of BGK, Inc., took a well-deserved vacation.
- Our company president was visiting the Singapore office.

The most noteworthy exceptions to this rule are the President of the United States and other heads of state; such titles are usually capitalized in any context. There are few other exceptions. If a company insists on breaking this rule—as in policy documents—it should capitalize *all* positions, not just those at the highest levels.

CENTER ON/REVOLVE AROUND

The key to using these phrases correctly is to think about their literal meaning. For example, you center *on* (not around) a goal, just as you would center on a target with a gun or bow and arrow. Likewise, your hobbies revolve *around* your early interest in water sports, just as the planets revolve around the sun in our solar system. Examples:

- All her selling points in the proposal *centered on* the need for greater productivity in the factory.
- At the latest annual meeting, some stockholders argued that most of the company's recent projects *revolved around* the CEO's interest in attracting attention from the media.

CITE/SITE/SIGHT

1. *Cite* is a verb meaning "to quote as an example, authority, or proof." It can also mean "to commend" or "to bring before a court of law" (as in receiving a traffic ticket).
2. *Site* usually is a noun that means "a particular location." It can also be a verb that means "to place at a location," as with a new school being sited by the town square, but this usage is not preferred. Instead, use a more conventional verb, such as *built.*
3. *Sight* is a noun meaning "the act of seeing" or "something that is seen." Or it can be a verb meaning "to see or observe."

Examples:

- We *cited* a famous geologist in our report on the earthquake.
- Rene was *cited* during the ceremony for her exemplary service to the city of Roswell.
- The officer will *cite* the partygoers for disturbing the peace.
- Although five possible dorm *sites* were considered last year, the college administrators decided to build [preferred over *site*] the dorm at a different location.
- The *sight* of the flock of whooping cranes excited the visitors.
- Yesterday we *sighted* five whooping cranes at the marsh.

COLONS

Colons are quite common in technical writing because they are used with lists. Here are the three main ways they are used:

As a Formal Break before a List

As mentioned in the "Lists" entry in this Appendix, you should place a colon immediately after the last word before a list. Examples:

- Our field study included the tasks listed below:
- In our field study we were asked to complete the following tasks:

Note that a complete clause precedes the colon. Avoid incomplete constructions such as "In our field study, we were asked to:"

As a Formal Break before a Point of Clarification or Elaboration

Examples:

- They were interested in just one issue: quality.
- John loved the dish because of its main ingredient: salmon.

As a Formal Break before a Series within a Sentence

There are two ways to lead into a series within a sentence. First, you can lead smoothly into the series without a break and thus without using a colon. Second, you can include a formal stop that does require a colon. Both options are shown next.

- Next month I will attend conferences in Houston, Austin, Laredo, and Abilene.
- Next month I will attend meetings in four cities: Houston, Austin, Laredo, and Abilene.

COMMAS

Many writers struggle with commas, and for good reason. First, the teaching of punctuation is approached in different, and sometimes contradictory, ways. Second, comma rules are subject to some interpretation. And third, problems with commas sometimes reflect more fundamental problems with sentence structure.

The best strategy is to memorize a few basic rules of comma use. This knowledge will give you confidence in your ability to handle the mechanics of editing. (If you need help understanding any grammatical terms used in the rules, like *compound sentence,* refer to the "Sentence Structure" entries in this Appendix.)

Commas in a Series

Use commas to separate words, phrases, and short clauses written in a series of three or more items. According to current U.S. usage, a comma always precedes the *and* that comes before the last item in a series. Examples:

- The samples contained gray sand, sandy clay, and silty sand.
- The meal included steak, potatoes, and peaches and cream.

In the second example, note that the *and* before the last item in the series (and thus the one that is punctuated) is the one that precedes *peaches.* The other *and*—the one that precedes *cream*—has no comma before it because it connects only two parts of the last element in the series.

Commas in Compound Sentences

Use a comma before the conjunction that joins main clauses in a compound sentence. Example:

> We finished drilling the well, and then we grouted the holes with concrete.

The comma is used here because it separates two complete clauses, each with its own subject and verb ("we finished" and "we grouted"). If the second *we* had been deleted, there would be only one clause containing one subject and two verbs ("we finished and grouted"), thus no comma would be needed. Of course, be certain that you don't use this comma rule to string together intolerably long sentences. Divide long sentences when you can. (See the "Sentence Structure" entries in this Appendix.)

Commas with Nonessential Modifiers

Set off nonessential modifiers with commas—either at the beginning, middle, or end of sentences. Nonessential modifiers are phrases that add more information to a sentence, rather than greatly changing its meaning. When you speak, often there is a pause between this kind of modifier and the main part of the sentence, giving a clue that a comma break is needed. Examples:

- The report, which we submitted three weeks ago, indicated that the company would not be responsible for transporting hazardous wastes.
- The report that we submitted three weeks ago indicated that the company would not be responsible for transporting hazardous wastes.

The first example includes a nonessential modifier. It would be spoken with pauses and therefore uses separating commas. The second example includes an essential modifier. It would be spoken without pauses and therefore includes no separating commas.

Commas with Adjectives in a Series

Use a comma to separate two or more adjectives that modify the same noun. To help you decide if adjectives modify the same noun, use this test: if you can reverse their position and still retain the same meaning, then the adjectives modify the same word and should be separated by a comma. Example:

> Jason opened the two containers in a dry, well-lighted place.

Commas with Introductory Elements

Use a comma after introductory phrases or clauses of about five words or more. Example:

> After completing its topographic survey of the area, the crew returned to headquarters for the weekly project meeting.

Commas like the one after *area* help readers separate secondary or modifying points from the main idea, which of course should be in the main clause. Without these commas, there may be difficulty reading the sentence properly.

Commas in Lists

Use commas in lists that you wish to treat as complete sentences. (See the "Lists" entries in this Appendix for a complete discussion of use and punctuation of listings.)

Commas in Dates, Titles, Etc.

Abide by the conventions of comma usage in punctuating dates, titles, geographic place names, and addresses. Examples:

- May 3, 2009, is the projected date of completion.
- John F. Dunwoody, P.E., has been hired to direct the project because he is a registered engineer.
- McDuff, Inc., has been selected.
- He listed Dayton, Ohio, as his permanent residence.

Note the need for commas after the year "2009," the title "P.E." (as there would be for Ph.D.), the designation "Inc.," and the state name "Ohio."

COMPLEMENT/COMPLIMENT

Both words can be nouns and verbs, and both have adjective forms (*complementary, complimentary*).

Complement

This word is used as a noun to mean "that which has made something whole or complete," as a verb to mean "to make whole, to make complete," or as an adjective to mean "serving as a complement." You may find it easier to remember the word by recalling its mathematical definition: two complementary angles must always equal 90 degrees. Examples:

- (as noun): The *complement* of five technicians brought our crew strength up to 100 percent.
- (as verb): The firm in Canada *complemented* ours in that together we won a joint contract for work in both countries.
- (as adjective): Seeing the project manager and her secretary work so well together made clear their *complementary* relationship in getting office work done.

Compliment

This word is used as a noun to mean "an act of praise, flattery, or admiration," as a verb to mean "to praise, to flatter," or as an adjective to mean "related to praise or flattery, or without charge." Examples:

- (as noun): He appreciated the verbal *compliments,* but he also hoped they would result in a substantial raise.
- (as verb): Howard *complimented* the crew for finishing the job on time and within budget.

- (as adjective): We were fortunate to receive several *complimentary* copies of the new software from the publisher.

COMPOSE/COMPRISE

Compose means "to make up or be included in," whereas *comprise* means "to include or consist of." The easiest way to remember this relationship is to memorize one sentence:

> The parts *compose* the whole, but the whole *comprises* the parts.

One more point to remember: The common phrase "is comprised of" is a substandard, unacceptable replacement for "comprise" or "is composed of." Careful writers don't use it. Examples:

- Seven separate layers *compose* the soils that were uncovered at the site.
- The borings revealed a stratigraphy that *comprises* [not *is comprised of*] seven separate layers.

CONSUL/COUNCIL/COUNSEL

These three words can be distinguished by meaning and, in part, by their use within a sentence.

Consul: A noun meaning an official of a country who is sent to represent that country's interests in a foreign land

Council: A noun meaning an official group or committee

Counsel: A noun meaning an adviser or advice given, or a verb meaning to provide advice

Examples:

- (consul) The Brazilian *consul* met with consular officials from three other countries.
- (council) The Human Resources *Council* of our company recommended a new retirement plan to the company president.
- (counsel as noun) After the tragedy, they received legal *counsel* from their family attorney and spiritual *counsel* from their minister.
- (counsel as verb) As a communications specialist, Roberta helps to *counsel* employees who are involved in various types of disputes.

CONTINUOUS/CONTINUAL

These words have close yet distinctly different meanings. *Continuous* and *continuously* should be used in reference to uninterrupted, unceasing activities. *Continual* and *continually* should be used with activities that are intermittent, or repeated at intervals. If you think your reader may not understand the difference, use synonyms that will be more clear, such as *uninterrupted* for *continuous* and *intermittent* for *continual.* Examples:

- Because it rained *continuously* from 10 a.m. until noon, we were unable to find even a minute of clear sky to move our equipment onto the property.
- We *continually* checked the water pressure for three days before the equipment arrived, while also using the time to set up tests.

CRITERION/CRITERIA

Coming from the Latin language, *criterion* and *criteria* are the singular and plural forms of a word that means "rationale or reasons for selecting a person, place, thing, or idea." A common error is to use *criteria* as both a singular and plural form, but such misuse disregards a distinction recognized by many readers. Maintain the distinction in your writing. Examples:

- Among all the qualifications we established for the new position, the most important *criterion* for success is good communication skills.
- She had to satisfy many *criteria* before being accepted into the honorary society of her profession.

DATA/DATUM

Coming from the Latin, the word *data* is the plural form of *datum.* Traditionalists in the engineering and scientific community still consider *data* a plural form in all cases. However, in recent years some writers have considered *data* a plural form in some cases, when it means "facts," and a singular form in other cases, when it means "information." This book suggests you maintain the traditional use of data as a plural form, unless you have good reason to do otherwise. Examples:

- These *data* show that there is a strong case for building the dam at the other location.
- This particular *datum* shows we need to reconsider recommendations put forth in the original report.

If you consider the traditional singular form—*datum*—to be awkward, use substitutes such as "This item in the data demonstrates our point" or "One of the data demonstrates our point." Singular subjects like *one* or *item* allow you to keep your original meaning without using the word *datum*.

DEFINITE/DEFINITIVE

Although similar in meaning, these two words have slightly different contexts. *Definite* refers to that which is precise, explicit, or final. *Definitive* has the more restrictive meaning of "authoritative" or "final." Examples:

- It is now *definite* that he will be assigned to the London office for six months.
- He received the *definitive* study on the effect of the oil spill on the marine ecology.

DISCRETE/DISCREET/DISCRETION

The adjective *discrete* suggests something that is separate, or something that is made up of many separate parts. The adjective *discreet* is associated with actions that require caution, modesty, or reserve. The noun *discretion* refers to the quality of being "discreet" or the freedom a person has to act on his or her own. Examples:

- The company orientation program includes a writing seminar, which is a *discrete* training unit offered for one full day.
- The orientation program includes five *discrete* units.
- As a member of the human resources staff, Sharon was *discreet* in her handling of personal information about employees.
- Every human resources employee was instructed to show *discretion* in handling personal information about employees.
- By starting a flextime program, the company will give employees a good deal of *discretion* in selecting the time to start and end their workday.

DISINTERESTED/UNINTERESTED

These words have quite different meanings. *Disinterested* means "without prejudice or bias," whereas *uninterested* means "showing no interest." Examples:

- The agency sought a *disinterested* observer who had no stake in the outcome of the trial.
- They spent several days talking to officials from Iceland, but they still remain *uninterested* in performing work in that country.

DUE TO/BECAUSE OF

Mixing these two phrases can also cause confusion. *Due to* is an adjective phrase meaning "attributable to." It usually follows a "to be" verb such as *is, was,* or *were.* It should not be used in place of prepositional phrases such as *because of, owing to,* or *as a result of.* Examples:

- The cracked walls were *due to* the lack of proper fill being used during construction.
- We won the contract *because of* [not *due to*] our thorough understanding of the request for proposal.

EACH OTHER/ONE ANOTHER

Each other occurs in contexts that include only two persons, whereas *one another* occurs in contexts that include three or more persons. Examples:

- Shana and Katie worked closely with *each other* during the project.
- All six members of the team conversed with *one another* regularly through email.

E.G./I.E.

The abbreviation *e.g.* means "for example," whereas *i.e.* means "that is." These two Latin abbreviations are often confused. Thus, many writers prefer to write them out, rather than risk confusion on the part of the reader. Examples:

- He visited many cities where his firm plans to open offices—e.g., [or, preferably, *for example*], Kansas City, New Orleans, and Seattle.
- A spot along the Zayante Fault was the earthquake's epicenter—i.e., [or, preferably, *that is*], the focal point for seismic activity.

ENGLISH AS A SECOND LANGUAGE (ESL)

Technical writing challenges native English speakers and nonnative speakers alike. The purpose of this section is to present a basic description of three grammatical forms: articles, prepositions, and verbs. These forms may require more intense consideration from international students when they complete technical writing assignments. Each issue is described using the ease-of-operation section from the memo in Figure 2–3 on pages 27 to 28. The passage, descriptions, and charts work together to show how these grammar issues function collectively to create meaning.

Articles

Articles are one of the most difficult forms of English grammar for nonnative English speakers, mainly because some language systems do not use them. Thus, speakers of particular languages may have to work hard to incorporate the English article system into their language proficiency.

The English articles include *a, an,* and *the.*

- *A* and *an* express indefinite meaning when they refer to nouns or pronouns or pronouns that are not specific. The writer believes the reader does not know the noun or pronoun.
- *The* expresses definite meaning when it refers to a specific noun or pronoun. The writer believes the reader knows the specific noun or pronoun.

Ease of Operation—Article Usage

The AIM 500 is so easy to operate that **a** novice can learn to transmit **a** document to another location in about two minutes. Here's **the** basic procedure:

1. Press **the** button marked TEL on **the** face of **the** fax machine. You then hear **a** dial tone.
2. Press **the** telephone number of **the** person receiving **the** fax on **the** number pad on **the** face of **the** machine.
3. Lay **the** document facedown on **the** tray at **the** back of **the** machine.

At this point, just wait for **the** document to be transmitted—about 18 seconds per page to transmit. **The** fax machine will even signal **the** user with **a** beep and **a** message on its LCD display when **the** document has been transmitted. Other more advanced operations are equally simple to use and require little training. Provided with **the** machine are two different charts that illustrate **the** machine's main functions.

The size of **the** AIM 500 makes it easy to set up almost anywhere in **an** office. **The** dimensions are 13 inches in width, 15 inches in length, and 9.5 inches in height. **The** narrow width, in particular, allows **the** machine to fit on most desks, file cabinets, or shelves.

ESL writers choose the correct article only when they (1) know the context or meaning, (2) determine whether they share information about the noun with the reader, and (3) consider the type of noun following the article.

The ease-of-operation passage includes 32 articles that represent two types—definite and indefinite. When a writer and a reader share knowledge of a noun, the definite article should be used. On 26 occasions the articles in the passage suggest the writer and reader share some knowledge of a count noun. Count nouns are nouns that can be counted (pen, cloud, memo, etc.). Examples of noncount nouns are *sugar, air,* and *beef.*

For example, the memo writer and the memo recipient share knowledge of the particular model of fax machine—the AIM 500. Thus, "the" is definite when it refers to "the fax machine" in the memo. Notice, however, that "document" becomes definite only after the second time it is mentioned ("Lay the document facedown . . ."). In the first reference to *document, a document* refers to a document about which the writer and reader share no knowledge. The memo writer cannot know which document the reader will fax. Only in the second reference do the writer and reader know the document to be the one the reader will fax.

The indefinite article *a* occurs five times, while *an* occurs once. Each occurrence signals a singular count noun. The reader and the writer share no knowledge of the nouns that follow the *a* or *an,* so an indefinite article is

Articles from "Ease of Operation" Excerpt

Article	Noun	Type	Comment
The	AIM 500	definite	first mention—shared knowledge
A	Novice	indefinite	first mention—no shared knowledge
A	Document	indefinite	first mention—no shared knowledge
The	basic procedure	definite	
The	Button	definite	
The	Face	definite	
The	fax machine	definite	first mention without proper name, with reader/writer shared knowledge
A	dial tone	indefinite	first mention—no shared knowledge
The	telephone number	definite	
The	Person	definite	
The	Fax	definite	
The	number pad	definite	
The	Face	definite	
The	Machine	definite	
The	Document	definite	
The	Tray	definite	
The	Back	definite	
The	Machine	definite	
The	Document	definite	second mention
The	fax machine	definite	
The	User	definite	
A	Beep	indefinite	first mention—no shared knowledge
A	Message	indefinite	first mention—no shared knowledge
The	Document	definite	
The	Machine	definite	
The	machine's main functions	definite	
The	Size	definite	
The	AIM 500	definite	
An	Office	indefinite	first mention—preceding vowel sound—no shared knowledge
The	Dimensions	definite	
The	narrow width	definite	
The	Machine	definite	

appropriate. *A* precedes nouns beginning with consonant sounds. *An* precedes nouns beginning with vowel sounds. Indefinite articles seldom precede non-count nouns unless a non-count functions as a modifier (a beef shortage).

Definite and indefinite articles are used more frequently than other articles; however, other articles do exist. The "generic" article refers to classes or groups of people, objects, and ideas. If the fax machine is thought of in a general sense, the meaning changes. For example, "the fax machine increased office productivity by 33%." *The* now has a generic meaning representing fax machines in general. The same generic meaning can apply to the plural noun, but such generic use requires no article. "Fax machines increased office productivity by 33%."

Verbs

Verbs express time in three ways: simple present, simple past, and future. *Wait, waited,* and *will wait* and *lay* (to put), *laid,* and *will lay* are examples of simple present, simple past, and future tense verbs. Unfortunately, the English verb system is more complicated than that. Verbs express more than time.

Ease of Operation—Verb Usage

The AIM 500 **is** so easy to operate that a novice **can learn** to transmit a document to another location in about two minutes. **Here's** the basic procedure:

1. **Press** the button marked TEL on the face of the fax machine. You then **hear** a dial tone.
2. **Press** the telephone number of the person receiving the fax on the number pad on the face of the machine.
3. **Lay** the document facedown on the tray at the back of the machine.

At this point, just **wait** for the document to be transmitted—about 18 seconds per page to transmit. The fax machine **will** even **signal** the user with a beep and a message on its LCD display when the document **has been transmitted.** Other more advanced operations **are** equally simple to use and **require** little training. **Provided** with the machine **are** two different charts that **illustrate** the machine's main functions.

The size of the AIM 500 **makes** it easy to set up almost anywhere in an office. The dimensions **are** 13 inches in width, 15 inches in length, and 9.5 inches in height. The narrow width, in particular, **allows** the machine to fit on most desks, file cabinets, or shelves.

Verbs in the English language system appear either as regular or irregular forms. Regular verbs follow a predictable pattern.

Regular Verbs

Present	Past	Future
learn	learned	will learn
wait	waited	will wait
press	pressed	will press
signal	signaled	will signal
require	required	will require
provide	provided	will provide
illustrate	illustrated	will illustrate
allow	allowed	will allow
present perfect	**past perfect**	**future perfect**
have learned	had learned	will have learned
have waited	had waited	will have waited
have pressed	had pressed	will have pressed
have signaled	had signaled	will have signaled
have required	had required	will have required
have provided	had provided	will have provided
have illustrated	had illustrated	will have illustrated
have allowed	had allowed	will have allowed

- The form of the simple present tense verbs (such as *walk*) changes to the simple past tense with the addition of *ed* (*walked*).
- The past tense *walked* changes to the perfect tense with the addition of an auxiliary (helping) verb to the simple past tense form. For example, "I have walked" is present perfect, and "I had walked" is past perfect.

Irregular verbs do not follow a predictable pattern.

- Most important, the past tense is not created by adding *ed*. The simple present tense of lay (to put) changes completely in the simple past (*laid*).
- Like regular verbs, the past tense (*laid*) changes to the perfect tense with the addition of an auxiliary verb.

"I have laid the document facedown on the tray" is present perfect, and "I had laid the document facedown on the tray" is past perfect.

Let's examine four specific verb forms in the "Ease of Operation" passage.

1. *Is* represents a being or linking verb in the passage. Being verbs suggest an aspect of an experience or being (existence); for example, "He is still here," and "the fax is broken." Linking verbs connect a subject to a complement (completer); for example, "The fax machine is inexpensive."

Irregular Verbs

Present	Past	Future
is	was	will be
are	were	will be
hear	heard	will hear
do	did	will do
get	got	will get
see	saw	will see
write	wrote	will write
speak	spoke	will speak
present perfect	**past perfect**	**future perfect**
have been (he, she, it)	had been	will have been
have been (they)	had been	will have been
have heard	had heard	will have heard
have done	had done	will have done
have gotten	had gotten	will have gotten
have seen	had seen	will have seen
have written	had written	will have written
have spoken	had spoken	will have spoken

2. *Can learn* is the present tense verb *learn* preceded by a modal. Modals assist verbs to convey meaning. *Can* suggests ability or possibility. Other modals and their meanings appear below.

will	would	could	shall	should	might	must
scientific fact possibility determination	hypothetical	hypothetical	formal will	expectation obligation	possibility	necessity

3. *Here's* shows a linking verb *(is)* connected to its complement *(here)*. The sentence in its usual order—subject first followed by the verb—would appear as, "The basic procedure is here." (article—adjective—noun—linking verb—complement).
4. *Press, lay,* and *wait* (for) share at least four common traits: present tense, singular number, action to transitive, and understood subject of *you*. Although *you* does not appear in the text, the procedure clearly instructs the person operating the fax machine—*you*. Action or transitive verbs express movement, activity, and momentum, and may take objects.

Objects answer the questions who? what? to whom? or for whom? in relation to transitive verbs. For example, "Press the button." "Hear a dial tone." "Press the telephone number." "Lay the document facedown." Press what? Hear what? Lay what?

Verbs from "Ease of Operation" Excerpt

Verb	Tense	Number	Other details
is	present	singular	linking/being (is, was, been)
can learn	present	singular	*can* is a modal auxiliary implying "possibility"
here's (is)	present	singular	linking/being
press	present	singular	understood *you* as subject
hear	present	singular	action/transitive
press	present	singular	understood *you* as subject
lay	present	singular	irregular (lay, laid, laid) singular—understood *you* as subject
wait	present	singular	understood *you* as subject
will signal	future	singular	action to happen or condition to experience—understood *you* as subject
has been	present	singular	passive voice—action that began in
transmitted	perfect		the past and continues to the present
are	present	plural	linking/being
require	present	plural	action/transitive
provided are	present perfect	plural	passive voice—action that began in the past and continues to the present
illustrate	present	plural	action/transitive
makes	present	singular	action/transitive
are	present	plural	linking/being
allows	*present*	*singular*	action/transitive

Prepositions

Prepositions are words that become a part of a phrase composed of the preposition, a noun or pronoun, and any modifiers.

Ease of Operation—Preposition Usage

The AIM 500 is so easy to operate that a novice can learn to transmit a document **to** another location **in** about two minutes. Here's the basic procedure:

1. Press the button marked TEL **on** the face **of** the fax machine. You then hear a dial tone.
2. Press the telephone number **of** the person receiving the fax **on** the number pad **on** the face **of** the machine.
3. Lay the document facedown **on** the tray **at** the back **of** the machine.

At this point, just wait **for** the document to be transmitted—**about** 18 seconds **per** page to transmit. The fax machine will even signal the user **with** a beep and a message **on** its LCD display when the document has been transmitted. Other more advanced operations are equally simple to use and require little training. Provided **with** the machine are two different charts that illustrate the machine's main functions.

The size **of** the AIM 500 makes it easy to set up almost anywhere **in** an office. The dimensions are 13 inches **in** width, 15 inches **in** length, and 9.5 inches **in** height. The narrow width, **in** particular, allows the machine to fit **on** most desks, file cabinets, or shelves.

Notice the relationships expressed within the prepositional phrases and the ways they affect meaning in the sentences. In the "Ease of Operation" passage, about half the prepositional phrases function as adverbs noting place or time. The other half function as adjectives.

Place or	Location	Time
at	above	after
below	around	before
beneath	inside	during
in	near	since
into	on	
outside	out	
over	under	
within	underneath	

One important exception is a preposition that connects to a verb to make a "prepositional" verb, *wait for.* Another interesting quality of prepositions is that sometimes more than one can be used to express a similar meaning. In the "Ease of Operation" passage, for example, both *on* the tray and *at* the back indicate position. Another way to state the same information is *on* the tray *on* the back.

Prepositions from "Ease of Operation" Excerpt

Preposition	Noun Phrase	Comment
to	another location	direction toward
in	(about) two minutes	approximation of time
on	the face	position
of	the fax machine	originating at or from
of	the person	associated with
on	the number	position
on	the face	position
of	the machine	originating at
on	the tray	position
at	the back	position of
of	the machine	originating at
at	this point	on or near the time
for	the document	indication of object of desire
about	18 seconds	adverb = approximation
per	page	for every
with	a beep and a message	accompanying
on	its LCD display	position
with	the machine	accompanying
of	the AIM 500	originating at or from
in	an office	within the area
in	width	with reference to
in	length	with reference to
in	height	with reference to
in	particular	with reference to
on	most desks, file cabinets, or shelves	position

FARTHER/FURTHER

Although similar in meaning, these two words are used differently. *Farther* refers to actual physical distance, whereas *further* refers to nonphysical distance or can mean "additional." Examples:

- The overhead projector was moved *farther* from the screen so that the print would be easier to see.
- *Farther* up the old lumber road, they found footprints of an unidentified mammal.

- As he read *further* along in the report, he began to understand the complexity of the project.
- She gave *further* instructions after they arrived at the site.

FEWER/LESS

The adjective *fewer* is used before items that can be counted, whereas the adjective *less* is used before mass quantities. When errors occur, they usually result from *less* being used with countable items, as in this *incorrect* sentence: "We can complete the job with less men at the site." Examples:

- "The newly certified industrial hygienist signed with us because the other firm in which he was interested offered *fewer* [not *less*] benefits."
- "There was *less* sand in the sample taken from 15 ft than in the one taken from 10 ft."

FLAMMABLE/INFLAMMABLE/NONFLAMMABLE

Given the importance of these words in avoiding injury and death, make sure to use them correctly—especially in instructions.

1. *Flammable* means "capable of burning quickly" and is accepted usage.
2. *Inflammable* has the same meaning as *flammable.* However, it is *not* acceptable usage because readers may confuse it with *nonflammable.*
3. *Nonflammable* means "not capable of burning" and is accepted usage.

Examples:

- They marked the package *flammable* because its contents could be easily ignited by a spark. [Note that *flammable* is preferred here over its synonym, *inflammable.*]
- The supervisor was not worried about placing the crates near the heating unit, because all the contents were *nonflammable.*

FORMER/LATTER

These two words direct the reader's attention to previous points or items. *Former* refers to that which came first, whereas *latter* refers to that which came last. Note that the words are used together only with *two* items or points—*not* with three or more. Also, you should know that some readers may prefer you avoid *former* and *latter* altogether, for the construction may force them to look back to previous sentences to understand your meaning. The second example below gives an alternative.

- (with former/latter) The airline's machinists and flight attendants went on strike yesterday. The *former* left work in the morning, whereas the *latter* left work in the afternoon.
- (without former/latter) The airline's machinists and flight attendants went on strike yesterday. The machinists left work in the morning, whereas the flight attendants left work in the afternoon.

FORTUITOUS/FORTUNATE

The adjective *fortuitous* indicates an action is unexpected, whether it is desirable or not. The adjective *fortunate* indicates an action is desired. A common error is the wrong assumption that "fortuitous" events must also be "fortunate." Examples:

- Seeing McDuff's London manager at the conference was quite *fortuitous,* for I had not been told that he also was attending.
- It was indeed *fortunate* that I encountered the Tokyo manager, for we had the chance to talk about a project involving both our offices.

GENERALLY/TYPICALLY/USUALLY

Words like these can be useful qualifiers in your reports. All three indicate that something is often, but not always, true. Place these adverb modifiers as close as possible to the words they modify. For example, in the first example below it would be inaccurate to write "were typically sampled," because "typically" modifies the entire verb phrase "were sampled." Examples:

- Cohesionless soils *typically* were sampled by driving a 2-inch-diameter, split-barrel sampler. (Active voice alternative: *Typically,* we sampled cohesionless soils by driving a 2-inch-diameter, split-barrel sampler.)
- For projects like the one you propose, *usually* the technician will clean the equipment before returning to the office.
- It *generally* is known that sites for dumping waste should be equipped with appropriate liners.

GOOD/WELL

Although these words have similar meanings, *good* is used as an adjective, and *well* is used as an adverb. A common usage error occurs when writers use the adjective when the adverb is required. Examples:

- It is *good* practice to submit three-year plans on time.
- Although he had a slight case of the flu, he felt *well* enough to attend the seminar.

HOPEFULLY

Use and abuse of this adverb have attracted far more attention than it probably deserves. Yet you should know that some readers will make judgments about your level of literacy by your ability to use *hopefully* correctly. Use the word correctly to avoid drawing attention away from the content of your writing.

Hopefully is an adverb that means "with hope," *not* a one-word substitute for "I hope that." In other words, use *hopefully* only when it serves as an adverb and explicitly means "with hope." Examples:

- I looked *hopefully* through the files for the client's lost report. [That is, I looked "with hope."]
- They waited *hopefully* for the results of the proposal competition. [That is, they waited "with hope."]
- *I hope* I'll find the report before my client arrives for the meeting. [Not "Hopefully, I'll find . . ."]
- *They hoped* their firm would win the proposal competition. [Not "Hopefully, their firm would win . . ."]

IMPLY/INFER

The person doing the speaking or writing "implies." The person hearing or reading the words "infers." Thus the word *imply* requires an active role, whereas the word *infer* requires a passive role. When you imply a point, your words suggest rather than state a point. When you infer a point, you form a conclusion or deduce meaning from someone else's words. Examples:

- The contracts officer *implied* that there would be stiff competition for that $20 million waste treatment project.
- We *inferred* from her remarks that the firm selected for the work must have completed similar projects recently.

ITS/IT'S

These words are often confused. *It's* with the apostrophe is *only* used as a contraction for "it is" or "it has." The other form—*its*—is a possessive pronoun. (*Its'* is not a word.) Examples:

- Because of the rain, *it's* [or *it is*] going to be difficult to move the equipment to the site.
- *It's* [or *it has*] been a long time since we submitted the proposal.
- The company completed *its* part of the agreement on time.

LAY/LIE

These two verbs are troublesome, and you need to know some basic grammar to use them correctly.

1. *Lay* means "to place." It is a transitive verb; thus it takes a direct object to which it conveys action. ("She laid down the printout before starting the meeting.") Its main forms are *lay* (present), *laid* (past), *laid* (past participle), and *laying* (present participle).
2. *Lie* means "to be in a reclining position." It is an intransitive verb; thus it does not take a direct object. ("In some countries, it is acceptable for workers to lie down for a midday nap.") Its main forms are *lie* (present), *lay* (past), *lain* (past participle), and *lying* (present participle).

If you want to use these words with confidence, remember the transitive/intransitive distinction and memorize the principal parts. Examples:

- (lay) I will *lay* the notebook on the lab desk before noon.
- (lay) I have *laid* the notebook there before.
- (lay) I was *laying* the notebook down when the phone rang.
- (lie) The watchdog *lies* motionless at the warehouse gate.
- (lie) The dog *lay* there yesterday too.
- (lie) The dog has *lain* there for three hours today and no doubt will be *lying* there when I return from lunch.

LEAD/LED

Lead is either a noun that names the metallic element or a verb that means "to direct or show the way." *Led* is only a verb form, the past tense of the verb *lead*. Examples:

- The company bought rights to mine *lead* on the land.
- They chose a new president to *lead* the firm into the twenty-first century.
- They were *led* to believe that salary raises would be high this year.

LETTER FORMATS

Many organizations adopt letter formats used uniformly by all employees. Other organizations permit flexibility. In the latter case, you have three basic formats from which to choose: (1) block (with or without indented paragraphs), (2) modified block, or (3) simplified. Figures Appendix–1, Appendix–2, and Appendix–3 (pp. 333–335) provide guidelines for each format.

LIKE/AS

These two words are different parts of speech and thus are used differently in sentences. *Like* is a preposition and therefore is followed by an object—not an entire clause. *As* is a conjunction and thus is followed by a group of words that include a verb. *As if* and *as though* are related conjunctions. Examples:

- Gary looks *like* his father.
- Managers *like* John will be promoted quickly.
- If Teresa writes this report *as* she wrote the last one, our clients will be pleased.
- Our proposals are brief, *as* they should be.
- Our branch manager talks *as though* [or *as if*] the merger will take place soon.

LISTS: GENERAL POINTERS

Lists draw attention to three or more pieces of like information that are important enough to remove from standard text format. In other words, they are an attention-getting strategy. The following are some general pointers for using lists:

Strive for a Range of from Three to Nine Items

Most readers hold up to nine items in short-term memory. More than nine items gives the appearance of a disorganized laundry list; it may confuse rather than clarify an issue. If you have more than nine items, consider grouping them in three or four categories, as you would in an outline. Groups make it easier for readers to grasp and remember many points.

Letterheadof your organization

Two or more blank lines (adjust space to center letter on page)

Date of letter

Two or more blank lines (adjust space to center letter on page)

Address of reader

One blank line

Greeting (salutation)

One blank line

Paragraph: single-spaced (indenting optional)

One blank line

Paragraph: single-spaced (indenting optional)

One blank line

Paragraph: single-spaced (indenting optional)

One blank line

Complimentary close

Three blank lines (for signature)

Typed name and title

One blank line

Typist's initials (optional: writer's initials before typist's initials)

Computer file # (if applicable)

One blank line (optional)

Enclosure notation

One blank line (optional)

Copy notation

FIGURE APPENDIX–1
Letter format: Block
Adapted from *Technical Communication: A Practical Approach*, 6th ed, (p. 242) by W. S. Pfeiffer, 2006, Upper Saddle River, NJ: Prentice Hall. Reprinted by permission.

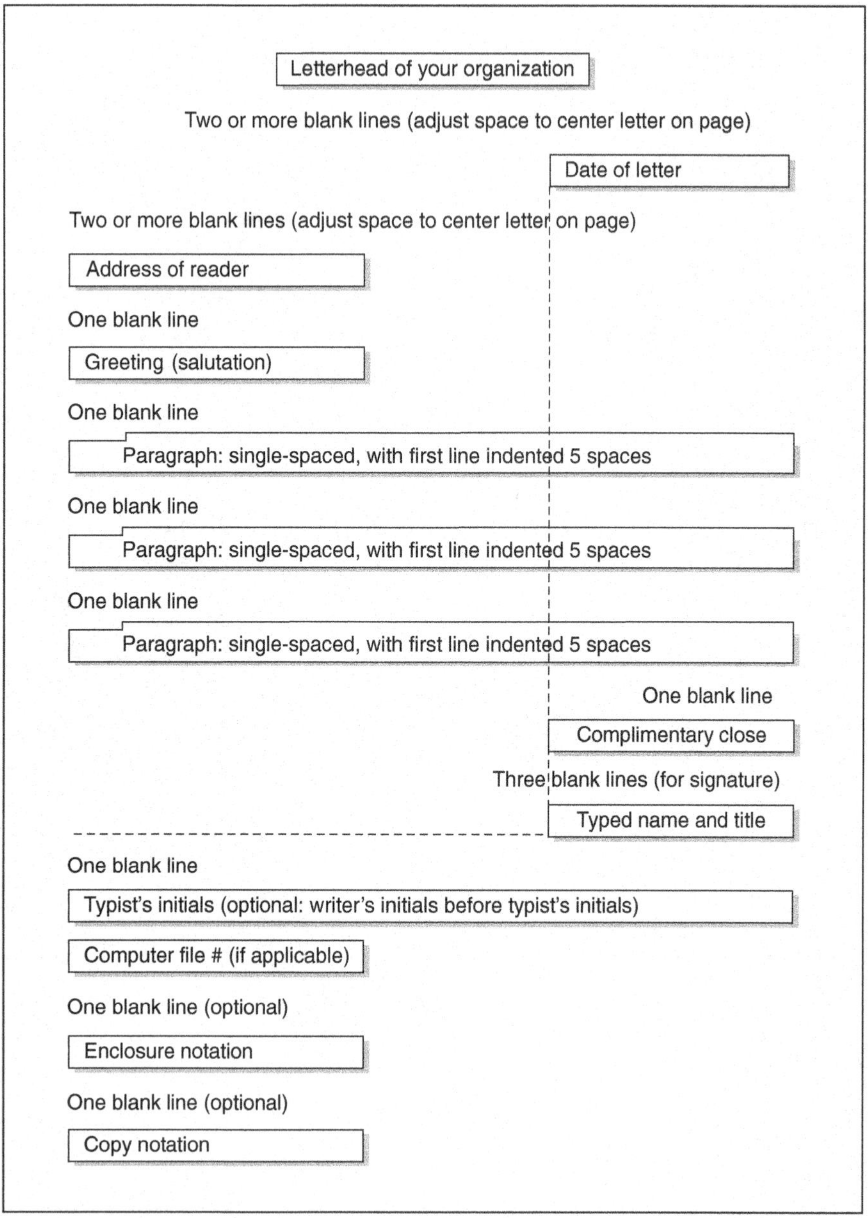

FIGURE APPENDIX–2
Letter format: Modified block
Source: Technical Communication: A Practical Approach, 6th ed, (p. 243) by W. S. Pfeiffer, 2006, Upper Saddle River, NJ: Prentice Hall. Reprinted by permission.

Letterhead of organization

Two or more blank lines (adjust space to center letter on page)

Date of letter

Two or more blank lines (adjust space to center letter on page)

Address of reader

Three blank lines

Short subject line

Three blank lines

Paragraph: single-spaced, no indenting

One blank line

Paragraph: single-spaced, no indenting

One blank line

Paragraph: single-spaced, no indenting

Five blank lines (for signature)

Typed name and title

One blank line (optional)

Typist's initials (optional: writer's initials before typist's initials)

Computer file # (if applicable)

One blank line (optional)

Enclosure notation

One blank line (optional)

Copy notation

FIGURE APPENDIX–3
Letter format: Simplified
Source: Technical Communication: A Practical Approach, 6th ed, (p. 244) by W. S. Pfeiffer, 2006, Upper Saddle River, NJ: Prentice Hall. Reprinted by permission.

Use Bullets (•) for Groupings That Do Not Involve Sequence

The single round bullets are best. Avoid strange-shaped bullets that draw more attention to themselves than to your ideas.

Use Numbers to Convey Sequence

Numbers work best when you are listing ordered items such as steps, procedures, or ranked alternatives.

KEEP POINTS PARALLEL

Parallel means that all points in the same list are in the same grammatical form—whether a complete sentence, verb phrase, or noun phrase. If you change form in the midst of a listing, you risk upsetting the flow of your text. Example:

To complete this project, we planned the following tasks:

- Survey the site
- Take samples from the three boring locations
- Test selected samples in our lab
- Report on the results of the study

The items above are in verb form (note the introductory words *survey, take, test,* and *report*). An alternative would be to put them in noun form, with a different lead-in.

LISTS: PUNCTUATION

You have three main options for punctuating lists. In all three you should (1) precede the list with a lead-in that is a complete thought, as in the preceding example, (2) place a colon after the last word of the lead-in, and (3) capitalize the first letter of the first word of each listed item.

Option A: Place No Punctuation after Listed Items

This style is particularly appropriate when a list includes only short phrases. More and more writers are choosing this option. Example:

In this study we will develop recommendations that address the following concerns in your project:

- Site preparation
- Foundation design

- Sanitary sewer design
- Storm sewer design
- Geologic surface faulting
- Projections for regional land subsidence

Option B: Treat the List like a Sentence Series

In this case you place commas or semicolons between items and a period at the end of the series. Whether you choose Option A or B largely depends on your own style. Example:

> In this study we developed recommendations that dealt with four topics:
>
> - Site preparation,
> - Foundation design,
> - Sewer construction, and
> - Geologic faulting.

This option requires that you place an *and* after the comma that appears before the last item. Another variation of Option B occurs when you have internal commas within one or more of the items. In this case, you need to change the commas that follow the listed items into semicolons. Yet you still keep the *and* before the last item. Example:

> Last month we completed environmental assessments at three sites:
>
> - A gas refinery in Dallas, Texas;
> - A chemical plant in Little Rock, Arkansas; and
> - A waste pit outside of Baton Rouge, Louisiana.

Option C: Treat Each Item like a Separate Sentence

When items in a list are complete sentences, you can punctuate each one as a separate sentence, placing a period at the end of each. Example:

> The main conclusions of our preliminary assessment are summarized here:
>
> - At five of the six borehole locations, petroleum hydrocarbons were detected at concentrations greater than a background concentration of 10 mg/kg.
> - No PCB concentrations were detected in the subsurface soils we analyzed. We will continue the testing, as outlined in our proposal.
> - Sampling and testing should be restarted three weeks from the date of this report.

LOOSE/LOSE

Loose, which rhymes with *goose,* is an adjective that means "unfastened, flexible, or unconfined." *Lose,* which rhymes with *choose,* is a verb that means to "misplace." Examples:

- The power failure was linked to a *loose* connection at the switchbox.
- Because of poor service, the copying machine company may *lose* its contract with our San Francisco office.

MEMO FORMAT

With minor variations, most memoranda (memos) look much the same. The date/to/from/subject information hangs at the top left margin, in whatever order your organization requires. These lines help you avoid lengthy introductory information in the memo itself. Figure Appendix–4 outlines the format for a typical memo. Pay special attention to the subject line, for it immediately conveys the meaning of the memo to readers. In fact, readers use it to decide when, or if, they will read the complete memo. Be brief, but engage interest.

MODIFIERS

Words, phrases, and even dependent clauses can serve as modifiers in a sentence. Their purpose is to qualify, or add meaning to, other elements in the sentence.

Modifiers need to be clearly connected to what they modify. When the connection is not clear, modification errors can occur. Such errors occur most often with phrases that include verbals. There are three types of verbals:

1. **Gerunds:** Nouns that are formed by adding *-ing* to a verb form—for example, "Skiing is his favorite hobby."
2. **Participles:** Adjectives that are formed by adding *-ing* or *-ed* to a verb form—for example, "John is very particular about his writing utensils."
3. **Infinitives:** A phrase that includes the word *to* and a verb root—for example, "To attend college was his main goal."

Facsimile reference
One or more blank lines
Date of memo
Reader's name (and position, if appropriate)
Writer's name (and position, if appropriate)
Subject of memo
One or more blank lines
Paragraph: Single-spaced (optional: first line indented)
One blank line
Paragraph: Single-spaced (optional: first line indented)
One blank line
Paragraph: Single-spaced (optional: first line indented)
One blank line
Typist's initials (optional: writer's initials before typist's initials)
One blank line
Enclosure notation
One blank line
Copy notation

FIGURE APPENDIX–4
Memorandum format
Source: Technical Communication: A Practical Approach, 6th ed, (p. 245) by W. S. Pfeiffer, 2006, Upper Saddle River, NJ: Prentice Hall. Reprinted by permission.

Modification errors can occur with all verbals. However, they are most common with participles and come in the form of dangling or misplaced modifiers.

Dangling Modifiers

When a verbal phrase "dangles," the sentence in which it is used contains no specific word for the phrase to modify. As a result, the meaning of the sentence can be confusing to the reader. You can correct dangling modifiers either by (1) rewording the sentence to give the participle a specific noun to modify (see Revision 1) or by (2) recasting the sentence to remove the participle (see Revision 2).

Original: Using an angle of friction of 20 degrees and a vertical weight of 300 tons, the sliding resistance would be as shown on Table 2.

Revision 1: Using an angle of friction of 20 degrees and a vertical weight of 300 tons, we computed a sliding resistance as shown on Table 2.

Revision 2: If the angle of friction is 20 degrees and the vertical weight is 300 tons, the sliding resistance should be as shown on Table 2.

Misplaced Modifiers

When a verbal phrase is misplaced, it appears to refer to a word that it does not modify. At best, misplaced modifiers can lead to unintentionally amusing prose. At worst, they can cause confusion about the agent of action in technical tasks. Correct the error by recasting the sentence, with modifiers clearly connected to what they modify.

Original: Floating peacefully near the oil rig, we saw two humpback whales. [The sentence should indicate the whales are floating.]

Revision: We saw two humpback whales floating peacefully near the oil rig.

Original: Before beginning to dig the observation trenches, we recommend that the contractors submit their proposed excavation program for our review.

Revision: We recommend the following: Before the contractors begin digging observation trenches, they should submit their proposed excavation program for our review.

NUMBERS

Like rules for abbreviations, those for numbers may vary from profession to profession and even from company to company. Most technical writing subscribes to the approach that numbers are best expressed in figures (45) rather than words (forty-five). Note that this style may differ from that in other types of writing. Unless the preferences of a particular reader suggest you do otherwise, use the following common rules for numbers:

Follow the 10-or-over Rule

In general, use figures for numbers of 10 or more, words for numbers below 10. Examples:

> Three technicians at the site; 15 reports submitted last month; one rig contracted for the job

Do Not Start Sentences with Figures

Begin sentences with the word form of numbers, not with figures. Example:

> Forty-five containers were shipped back to the lab.

Use Figures as Modifiers

Whether above or below 10, numbers are usually expressed as figures when used as modifiers with units of measurement, time, and money. Examples:

> 4 in., 7 hr, 17 ft-lb, $5 per hour

Use Figures in a Group of Mixed Numbers

Use only figures when the numbers grouped together in a passage (usually just one sentence) are both above and below 10. Example:

> For that project they assembled 15 samplers, 4 rigs, and 25 large containers.

In other words, this rule argues for consistency within a writing unit.

Use the Figure Form in Illustration Titles

Use the figure (numeric) form when labeling specific tables and figures in your reports. Example:

> Figure 3, Table 14–B

Be Careful with Fractions

Express fractions as words when they stand alone, but as figures when they are used as modifiers or are joined to whole numbers. Example:

> We have completed two-thirds of the project using the 2½-in. pipe.

Use Figures and Words with Numbers in Succession

When two numbers appear in succession in the same unit, write the first as a word and the second as a figure. Example:

> We found fifteen 2-ft pieces of pipe in the bin.

Only Rarely Use Numbers in Parentheses

Except in legal documents, avoid the practice of placing figures in parentheses after their word equivalents. Example:

> The second party will pay the first party forty-five (45) dollars on or before the first of each month.

Note that the parenthetical amount is placed immediately after the figure, not after the unit of measurement.

Use Figures with Dollars

Use figures with all dollar amounts, with the exception of the context noted in the preceding rule. Avoid cents columns unless exactness to the penny is necessary.

Use Commas in Four-Digit Figures

To prevent possible misreading, use commas in figures of four digits or more. Example:

> 15,000; 1,247; 6,003

Use Words for Ordinals

Usually spell out the ordinal form of numbers. Example:

> The judge informed the first, second, and third choices [not *1st, 2nd,* and *3rd* choices] in the design competition.

A notable exception is graphics, where space limitations could argue for use of the abbreviated form.

NUMBER OF/TOTAL OF

These two phrases can take singular or plural verbs, depending on the context. Here are two simple rules for correct usage:

1. If the phrase is preceded by *the,* it takes a singular verb because emphasis is placed on the group.

2. If the phrase is preceded by *a*, it takes a plural verb because emphasis is placed on the many individual items.

Examples:

- *The number of* projects going over budget *has* decreased dramatically.
- *The total of* 90 lawyers *believes* the courtroom guidelines should be changed.
- *A number* of projects *have* stayed within budget recently.
- *A total of* 90 lawyers *believe* the courtroom guidelines should be changed.

ORAL/VERBAL

Oral refers to words that are spoken, as in *oral presentation. Verbal* refers to spoken or written language, as opposed to "nonverbal" communication such as body language. Avoid the common error of using *verbal* as a substitute for *oral*. Examples:

- In its international operations, our firm has learned that some countries still rely on *oral* [not *verbal*] contracts.
- Their *oral* [not *verbal*] agreement last month was followed by a *written* [not *verbal*] contract this month.

PARAGRAPH GUIDELINES

Paragraphs have two objectives. First, they must state and then develop a topic. Second, they must maintain reader interest in the main idea. These objectives sometimes seem to work at cross-purposes, for many writers force paragraphs to bear the burden of too much detail. Remember that readers become frustrated by (and even tend to skip over) paragraphs that go beyond six or eight lines.

Here are five rules to help you write clear, thoughtful, and engaging paragraphs:

Put the Main Point First

Start the paragraph with your main idea. Do not delay or bury the main point in the middle of the paragraph. Readers who skim documents will usually focus on the first sentences of paragraphs. If you fail to put the main point there, they may miss your point entirely.

Keep Paragraphs Short

Restrict paragraph length to six or eight lines. Most people do not want to read more than that without a visual break. If your idea requires more thorough treatment, divide the topic at a convenient point and use two paragraphs to develop it.

Use Lists

Take groups of related points and form bulleted or numbered lists within the paragraph. Readers lose patience when information could have been more clearly presented in listings.

Avoid Extensive Use of Numbers

Paragraphs are the worst format for presenting data of any kind, especially numbers that describe costs. Readers may ignore or miss data that are packed into paragraphs. Usually tables or figures would be a clearer and more appropriate format. Also, be aware that some readers may think that cost data couched in paragraph form represent an attempt to hide important information.

Give Readers Some Variety

Alter the length of paragraphs, to make your writing more visually appealing. Remember that a very short paragraph should emphasize a major point or provide a transition between two longer paragraphs.

PARENTHESES

Use parentheses sparingly because long parenthetical expressions can distract readers. But they are useful for enclosing the following items:

- An abbreviation immediately following the complete term
- A brief explanation that provides extra, subordinate information
- Reference citations within the text

As for punctuation, a period goes after the close parenthesis when the parenthetical information is part of the sentence (as in this sentence). (However, the period goes inside the close parenthesis when the parenthetical information forms its own sentence, as in the sentence you are reading.)

PARTS OF SPEECH

This term refers to the eight main groups of words in English grammar. A word's placement into one of these groups is based on its function within the sentence, as described here. For additional information on some parts of speech, see the "English as a Second Language (ESL)" entry in this Appendix.

Nouns

Nouns name persons, places, objects, or ideas. The two major categories are (1) proper nouns and (2) common nouns. Proper nouns name specific persons, places, objects, or ideas, and they are capitalized. Examples:

> Cleveland, Mississippi River, Apple Computer, Student Government Association, Susan Jones, Taoism

Common nouns name general groups of persons, places, objects, and ideas, and they are not capitalized. Examples:

> trucks, farmers, engineers, assembly lines, philosophy, committee

Verbs

Verbs express action or state of being. As such they give movement to the sentence and form the core of meaning in your writing. Examples:

> explore, grasp, write, develop, is, has

Pronouns

Pronouns act as substitutes for nouns. Some sample pronoun categories include the following:

- Personal pronouns (I, we, you, she, he)
- Relative pronouns (who, whom, that, which)
- Reflexive and intensive pronouns (myself, yourself, itself)
- Demonstrative pronouns (this, that, these, those)
- Indefinite pronouns (all, any, each, anyone)

Adjectives

Adjectives modify nouns and thus add meaning to them. Examples:

> horizontal, stationary, green, large, simple

Adverbs

Adverbs modify verbs, adjectives, other adverbs, or whole statements. Examples:

soon, generally, well, very, too, greatly

Prepositions

Prepositions show the relationship between nouns or pronouns (called the objects of prepositions) and other elements in a sentence. The preposition and its object, which together form a prepositional phrase, can reveal relationships such as location, time, and direction. Examples:

- They went *over the hill.* (location)
- He left *after the meeting.* (time)
- She walked *toward the office.* (direction)

Conjunctions

Conjunctions are connecting words that link words, phrases, or clauses. They are called coordinate conjunctions when they link like elements, such as two main clauses. They are called subordinate conjunctions when they link two different elements, such as a dependent clause and an independent clause. Examples:

- Coordinate: and, but, for, nor, or, so, yet
- Subordinate: after, although, as if, because, before, even though, if, now that, once, since, so that, though, unless, until, when, whenever, where, whereas, while

Interjections

As an expression of emotion, these words can stand alone (*Look out!*), or they can be inserted into another sentence (*Oh,* now I understand what you meant in your proposal).

PASSED/PAST

Passed is the past tense of the verb *pass,* whereas *past* is an adjective, preposition, or noun that means "previous" or "beyond" or "a time before the present." Examples:

- He *passed* the survey marker on his way to the construction site.
- The *past* president attended last night's meeting. [adjective]

- He worked *past* midnight on the project. [preposition]
- In the distant *past,* the valley was a tribal hunting ground. [noun]

PER

Coming from the Latin, this word should be reserved for business and technical expressions that involve statistics or measurement—such as "per annum" or "per mile." It should *not* be used as a stuffy substitute for "in accordance with." Examples:

- Her *per diem* travel allowance of $150 covered hotels and meals.
- During the oil crisis, gasoline prices increased by more than 50 cents *per gallon.*
- *As you requested* [not *per your request*], we have enclosed brochures on our products.

PER CENT/PERCENT/PERCENTAGE

Per cent and *percent* have basically the same usage and occur with exact numbers. The one word *percent* is preferred. Even more common in technical writing, however, is the use of the percentage sign (%) after numbers. The word *percentage* is used only to express general amounts, not exact numbers. Examples:

- After completing a marketing survey, we discovered that 83 *percent* [or 83%] of our current clients have hired us for previous projects.
- A large *percentage* of the defects can be linked to the loss of two experienced inspectors.

PRACTICAL/PRACTICABLE

Although close in meaning, these two words have quite different implications. *Practical* refers to an action that is known to be effective. *Practicable* refers to an action that can be accomplished or put into practice, without regard for its effectiveness or practicality. Examples:

- His *practical* solution to the underemployment problem led to a 30% increase in employment last year.

- The department head presented a *practicable* response, for it already had been put into practice in another branch.

PRINCIPAL/PRINCIPLE

When these two words are misused, the careful reader will notice. After reading the sections that follow, you will understand why "the principal principle maintained by the principals of the bank is the importance of both interest and principal."

Principal

Principal can be either a noun or adjective and has three basic uses:

1. As a noun meaning "head official" or "person who plays a major role."
2. As a noun meaning "the main portion of a financial account upon which interest is paid."
3. As an adjective meaning "main or primary."

Examples:

- The *principals* of the firm each purchased 1,000 shares of stock.
- We withdrew the interest—but not the *principal*—from our account.
- We believe that the *principal* reason for contamination at the site is the leaky underground storage tank.

Principle

Principle is a noun that means "basic truth, belief, or theorem." Examples:

- He acted on his *principles* when he reported a fellow employee for over-charging a customer.
- The *principle* of free speech means the government allows people to speak even when it detests what they are saying.
- Avogadro's *principle* states that if two equal volumes of gases are at the same temperature and pressure, they contain the same number of molecules.

PRONOUN AGREEMENT AND REFERENCE

Pronouns—like *this, she, anyone,* and *they*—are words that substitute for nouns. The nouns to which pronouns refer are called "antecedents" of their respective pronouns. Pronouns provide a useful strategy for varying your style and avoiding needless repetition of nouns. However, their use requires vigilance in avoiding errors in agreement and reference. Here are the main rules:

Make Pronouns Agree with Antecedents

Check every pronoun to make certain it agrees with its antecedent in number. That is, both noun and pronoun must be singular, or both must be plural. Of special concern are the pronouns *it* and *they.* Examples:

- Norax, Inc., will complete *its* [not *their*] Argentina project next month.
- The committee released *its* [not *their*] recommendations to all departments.

Be Clear about the Antecedent of Every Pronoun

Leave no doubt about what noun a pronoun replaces. Any confusion about the antecedent of a pronoun can change the entire meaning of a sentence. To avoid such reference problems, rewrite a sentence or even repeat a noun rather than use a pronoun. Do whatever is necessary to prevent misunderstanding by your reader.

Original: The gas filters for these tanks are so dirty that they should not be used.

Revision: These filters are so dirty that they should not be used.

Follow This with a Noun

A common stylistic error is the vague use of *this* as a pronoun, especially as the subject of a sentence. Sometimes the reference is totally confusing; sometimes it may be clear after several readings; and sometimes it is fairly clear but still a sign of a vague writing style. Using *this* as a pronoun often makes readers want to ask, "This what?" Make the subject of your sentence concrete, either by adding a noun after the *this* or by recasting the sentence.

Original: He talked every day about his upcoming trip to Europe. This irritated his colleagues.

Revision: He talked every day about his upcoming trip to Europe. This chatter irritated his colleagues.

OR

His constant talk about his upcoming European vacation irritated his colleagues.

QUOTATION MARKS

In technical writing, you can use quotation marks for three main reasons:

1. To draw attention to particular words
2. To indicate passages taken directly from another source
3. To enclose titles of short documents such as reports or book chapters

As for punctuation, periods and commas go inside quotation marks. Semicolons and colons go outside of quotation marks. Examples:

- His presentation included the term "fuzzy logic"; however, he only spent a minute on the topic.
- In the section called "Closing," he included the following sentence: "Plant 624 will reopen next year."
- He mentioned the following criteria in his section entitled "Rationale": costs, productivity, and quality.

REGRETTABLY/REGRETFULLY

Regrettably means "unfortunately," whereas *regretfully* means "with regret." When you are unsure of which word to use, substitute the above definitions to determine correct usage. Examples:

- *Regrettably,* the team members omitted their résumés from the proposal.
- Hank submitted his résumé to the investment firm, but, *regrettably,* he forgot to include a cover letter.
- I *regretfully* climbed on the plane to return home from Hawaii.

RESPECTIVELY

Some good writers may use *respectively* to connect sets of related information. Yet such usage creates extra work for readers by making them reread previous passages. It is best to avoid *respectively* by rewriting the sentence, as shown in the several following options. Examples:

Original: Appendices A, G, H, and R contain the topographical maps for Sites 6, 7, 8, and 10, respectively.

Revision—Option 1: Appendix A contains the topographical map for Site 6; Appendix G contains the map for Site 7; Appendix H contains the map for Site 8; and Appendix R contains the map for Site 10.

Revision—Option 2: Appendix A contains the topographical map for Site 6; Appendix G for Site 7; Appendix H for Site 8; and Appendix R for Site 10.

Revision—Option 3: Topographical maps are contained in the Appendixes, as shown in the following list:

Appendix	*Site*
A	6
G	7
H	8
R	10

SEMICOLONS

Consider the semicolon to be a modified period. Its most frequent use is in situations where grammar would allow you to use a period but where stylistic preference may be for a less abrupt connector. Example:

Five engineers left the convention hotel after dinner; only two returned by midnight.

One of the most common punctuation errors is the comma splice. It occurs when a comma instead of a semicolon or period is used in compound sentences connected by words like *however, therefore, thus,* and *then*. When these connectors separate two main clauses, either use a semicolon or start a new sentence. Example:

We made it to the project site by the agreed-upon time; however, [or, "time. However,"] the rain forced us to stay in our trucks for two hours.

As noted in the "Lists: Punctuation" entry in this Appendix, there is another instance in which you might use semicolons. Place them after the items in a list when you are treating the list like a sentence and when any one of the items contains internal commas.

SENTENCE STRUCTURE: TERMINOLOGY

All writers have their own approach to sentence style. Yet every one of us has the same tools with which to work: words, phrases, clauses, and different sentence patterns. This entry defines some basic terms. The next entry includes specific guidelines for organizing information in sentences. See the "Parts of Speech" entry for a complete description of terms for words. Only the most important ones—subjects and verbs—are discussed below.

Subjects and Verbs

The most important parts of the sentence are the subject and the verb:

- *Subject:* names the person doing the action or the thing being discussed (*He* completed the study. / The *figure* contains his data.)
- *Verb:* conveys action or state of being (She *visited* the site. / He *was* the manager.)

Phrases and Clauses

Words can be grouped into two main units, phrases and clauses:

- *Phrase:* lacks either a subject or a verb and thus must always relate to or modify another part of the sentence (She went *to the office. As project manager,* he had to write the report.)
- *Clause:* has both a subject and a verb. It may stand by itself as a *main clause* and thus can be a complete sentence (*He talked to the group.*). Or it may rely on another part of the sentence for its meaning and thus is a *dependent clause* (*After he left the site,* he went home.).

Sentence Types

There are four main types of sentences:

- *Simple:* contains one main clause (*He completed his work.*)
- *Compound:* includes two or more main clauses connected by conjunctions (*Joe completed his work, but Mary stayed at the office to begin another job.*)
- *Complex:* includes one main clause and at least one dependent clause (*After he finished the project, Jamal headed for home.*)
- *Compound-complex:* contains at least two main clauses and at least one dependent clause (*After they studied the maps, they left the project site, but they were unable to travel much farther that night.*)

SENTENCE STRUCTURE: GUIDELINES

How you write and arrange sentences is much a matter of personal writing style. Yet there are a few fundamental guidelines for all good business and technical writing:

Place the Main Point near the Beginning

One way to satisfy this criterion for good sentence style is to avoid excessive use of the passive voice (see the "Active and Passive Voice" entry in this Appendix). Another way is to avoid lengthy introductory phrases or clauses at the beginnings of sentences. The reader usually wants the most important information first.

> **Original:** After discussing the report submitted by the engineering consultant, it was decided by the committee to open a new office.
>
> **Revision:** The committee decided to open a new office after discussing the consultant's report.

Focus on One Main Clause in Each Sentence

When you start stringing together too many clauses with *and* or *but,* you dilute the meaning of your text. An occasional compound or compound-complex sentence is acceptable, just for variety, but most sentences should be simple or complex.

Vary Sentence Length, but Average No More than 15 to 20 Words

Place important points in short, emphatic sentences. Reserve longer sentences for qualifications and support of your main points. If you find your sentences run too long, there is a simple technique for shortening them. First find some long compound sentences connected by conjunctions like *and, but,* or *so.* Then separate them into shorter sentences by breaking them at the conjunction. Another strategy is to break sentences in two by separating the main point being made from supporting information.

> **Original:** Last week the human resources staff announced that the company is offering three new health plans because employees have complained about the cost of the previous plans and the poor service provided.
>
> **Revision:** Last week the human resources staff announced that the company is offering three new health plans. The change came about because of the cost and poor service of previous plans.

SET/SIT

Like *lie* and *lay,* these two verbs are distinguished by form and use. Here are the basic differences:

1. *Set* means "to place in a particular spot" or "to adjust." It is a transitive verb and thus takes a direct object to which it conveys action. Its main

parts are *set* (present), *set* (past tense), *set* (past participle), and *setting* (present participle).

2. *Sit* means "to be seated." It is usually an intransitive verb and thus does not take a direct object. Its main parts are *sit* (present), *sat* (past), *sat* (past participle), and *sitting* (present participle). It can be transitive when used casually as a direction to be seated. ("Sit yourself down and take a break.")

Examples:

- He *set* the computer on the table yesterday.
- While *setting* the computer on the table, he sprained his back.
- The technician had *set* the thermostat at 75 degrees.
- She plans to *sit* exactly where she *sat* last year.
- While *sitting* at her desk, she saw the computer.

SEXIST LANGUAGE: HOW TO AVOID IT

Language usually *follows* changes in culture, rather than *anticipating* such changes. A case in point is today's shift away from sexist language in business and technical writing—indeed, in all writing and speaking. The change reflects the increasing number of women entering previously male-dominated professions such as engineering, management, medicine, and law.

This section defines sexist and nonsexist language and suggests ways to avoid using gender-offensive language in your writing.

Background on Sexism and Language

Sexist language is the use of wording, especially pronouns like *he* or *him*, to represent positions or individuals who could be either men or women. For many years, it was common to use *he, his, him*, or other male words in sentences such as those that follow.

Examples of poor usage:

- The operations specialist should check page 5 of his manual before flipping the switch.
- Every physician was asked to renew his membership in the medical association before next month.
- Each new student at the military academy was asked to leave his personal possessions in the front hallway of the administrative building.

These examples of obsolete usage assume that male pronouns and adjectives can stand for any persons—male or female. There are two good reasons to avoid such usage:

1. The entry of many more women into the professions has called attention to the exclusionary nature of using male pronouns for indefinite use. Many readers will be bothered by such writing.
2. The use of male pronouns in an indefinite context can be viewed as one way women are constrained from achieving equal status in the professions and, generally, in the culture. That is, such use of male pronouns fosters sexism in the society as a whole.

If you fail to rid your writing of sexist language, you risk drawing more attention to your style than to your ideas. Common sense argues for following some basic style rules to avoid sexist language.

Guidelines for Nonsexist Language

This section offers techniques to help you shift from sexist to nonsexist language. Some of these strategies may not suit your taste in writing style; choose the ones that work for you.

Avoid Personal Pronouns Altogether

An easy way to avoid problems with sexist language is to delete unnecessary pronouns from your writing.

> **Sexist Language:** During his first day on the job, any new employee in the toxic-waste laboratory must report to the company doctor for his employment physical.
>
> **Nonsexist Language:** During the first day on the job, each new employee in the toxic-waste laboratory must report to the company doctor for a physical.

Use Plural Pronouns instead of Singular

Often you can shift from singular to plural pronouns without changing meaning.

> **Sexist Language:** Each geologist should submit his time sheet by noon on the Thursday before checks are issued.
>
> **Nonsexist Language:** All geologists should submit their time sheets on the Thursday before checks are issued.

Note also that you may encounter sexist language that inappropriately uses female pronouns in a generic manner. Such usage is just as flawed as male-oriented language.

> **Sexist Language:** Each nurse should make every effort to complete her rounds each hour.

Nonsexist Language: Nurses should make every effort to complete their rounds each hour.

Alternate Masculine and Feminine Pronouns

You can avoid sexist use by alternating *he* and *him* with *she* and *her*. However, do not switch pronoun use within too brief a passage, such as a paragraph or page. Instead, change every few pages, or every section or chapter. The drawback of this technique is that the alternating use of masculine and feminine pronouns tends to draw attention to itself. Also, the writer must work hard to balance the use of masculine and feminine pronouns, in a sense to give "equal treatment."

Use Forms like He or She

This technique requires the writer to include both genders of pronouns each time indefinite use is required.

Sexist Language: The president made it clear that each branch manager will be responsible for the balance sheet of his respective office.

Nonsexist Language: The president made it clear that each branch manager will be responsible for the balance sheet of his or her respective office.

However, it is important to note that this style is bothersome to many writers who feel that *his or her* is wordy and awkward. Many readers are bothered even more by the forms *he/she, his/her,* and *him/her.*

Shift to Second-Person Pronouns

Change to *you* and *your*, which are words without any sexual bias. For this technique to be effective, you need to be writing documents in which it is appropriate to use an instructions-related "command" tone associated with the use of *you*.

Sexist Language: After selecting her insurance option in the benefit plan, each new nurse should submit her paperwork to the Human Resources Department.

Nonsexist Language: Submit your paperwork to the Human Resources Department after selecting your insurance option in the benefit plan.

Be Especially Careful of Titles and Letter Salutations

When you do not know how a particular woman prefers to be addressed, always use *Ms*. Even better, call the person's employer to ask whether *Miss, Mrs., Ms.,* or some other title is appropriate. (When calling, also check on the correct spelling of the person's name and her current job title.) When you do not know who will read your letter, never use *Dear Sir* or *Gentlemen* as a generic greeting. *Dear Sir or Madam* is also inappropriate. Instead, call the organization and get the name of a particular person to whom you can direct your letter. If you must write to a group of people, replace the generic greeting with an "attention" line that denotes the name of the group.

Sexist Language: Dear Sir: [to a collective audience]

Nonsexist Language: Attention: Admissions Committee

Sexist Language: Dear Miss Finnigan: [to a single woman for whom you can determine no title preference]

Nonsexist Language: Dear Ms. Finnigan:

SIC

Latin for *thus*, this word is most often used when a quoted passage contains an error or other point that might be questioned by the reader. Inserted within brackets, *sic* indicates that the word or phrase before the *sic* was included in the original passage—and that it was not introduced by you. In other words, *sic* should be included when it is important that the reader be presented with a technically accurate quotation. Examples:

- The customer's letter to our Sales Department claimed that "there are too [*sic*] or three main flaws in the product."
- The proposal we received includes the following statement: "Work on each project will be overseen by a principle [*sic*] of the firm."

SPELLING

All writers have words they find difficult to spell, and some writers have major spelling problems. Spell-checking software can help solve the problem. Yet you still must remain vigilant during the proofreading stage. Misspelled words in an otherwise well-written document cause readers to question the quality of the document and the professionalism of the writer.

This entry includes a list of commonly misspelled words. However, you should keep your own list of words you often have trouble spelling. Most of us have a relatively short list of words that give us repeated difficulty.

absence
accessible
accommodate
accumulate
accustomed
achievement

acknowledgment
acquaintance
admittance
advisable
aisle
allotting
analysis
analyze
Arctic
athlete
athletic
awful
basically
believable
benefited
bulletin
calendar
career
changeable
channel
column
commitment
committee
compatible
compelled
conscience
conscientious
conscious
controlled
convenient
definitely
dependable
descend
dilemma
disappear
disappoint
disaster
disastrous
efficient
eligible
embarrass
endurance
environment
equipment
equipped
essential
exaggerate
existence
experience
familiar
favorite
February
foreign
foresee
forfeit
forty
fourth
genius
government
guarantee
guidance
handicapped
harass
height
illogical
incidentally
independence
indispensable

ingenious
initially
initiative
insistence
interfered
interference
interrupt
irrelevant
judgment
knowledge
later
latter
liable
liaison
library
lightning
likely
loneliness
maintenance
manageable
maneuver
mathematics
medieval
mileage
miscellaneous
misspelled
mortgage
movable
necessary
noticeable
nuisance
numerous
occasionally
occurred
occurrence
omission
pamphlet
parallel
pastime
peculiar
possess
practically
preference
preferred
privilege
profession
professor
pronunciation
publicly
quantity
questionnaire
recession
reference
safety
similar
sincerely
specifically
subtle
temperament
temperature
thorough
tolerance
transferred
truly
undoubtedly
unmistakably
until
useful

usually
valuable
various
vehicle
wholly
writing
written

STATIONARY/STATIONERY

Stationary means "fixed" or "unchanging," whereas *stationery* refers to paper and envelopes used in writing or typing letters. Examples:

- To perform the test correctly, one of the workers had to remain *stationary* while the other one moved around the job site.
- When she began her own business, Julie purchased *stationery* with her new logo on each envelope and piece of paper.

SUBJECT-VERB AGREEMENT

Subject-verb agreement errors are common in technical writing. They occur when writers fail to make the subject of a clause agree in number with the verb. ("The company president, along with his wife, are attending the meeting.") The verb *are* is *not* correct. The subject is *president,* so the verb should be *is.*

If you have agreement problems in your own writing, you can solve them by (1) isolating the subjects and verbs of all clauses in the document and (2) making certain that they agree. The main subject-verb agreement rules follow:

Subjects Connected by and Take Plural Verbs

This rule applies to two or more words or phrases that, together, form one subject phrase. Example:

> The site preparation section and the foundation design portion of the report are to be written by the same person.

Verbs after Either/Or Agree with the Nearest Subject

Subjects connected by *either/or* (or *neither/nor*) confuse many writers, but the rule is very clear. Your verb choice depends on the subject nearest the verb.

Examples:

- He told his group that either the three reports or the proposal was to be completed this week.
- He told his group that either the proposal or the three reports were to be completed this week.

In the first example, the part of the subject closest to the verb is *proposal;* thus the correct verb form is *was.* In the second example, the part of the subject closest to the verb is *reports;* thus the correct verb form is *were.* Although both sentences are grammatically correct, the second is preferred because readers often view mixed *either/or* constructions as plurals. Singular verbs may sound awkward in such sentences.

Verbs Agree with the Subject, Not with the Subjective Complement

Sometimes called a predicate noun or adjective, a subjective complement renames the subject and occurs after verbs like *is, are, was,* and *were.* Examples:

- The topic of the report is our high profits last year.
- Our high profits last year are the topic of the report.

Prepositional Phrases Do Not Affect Matters of Agreement

As long as, in addition to, and *as well as* are prepositions, not conjunctions. A verb agrees with its subject, not with the object of a prepositional phrase. Example:

> The manager of human resources, as well as the technical managers, is supposed to meet with the three applicants.

Collective Nouns Usually Take Singular Verbs

Collective nouns have singular form but usually refer to a group of persons or things (for example, *team, committee,* or *crew*). When a collective noun refers to a group as a whole, use a singular verb. Example:

> The project crew was ready to complete the assignment.

Occasionally, a collective noun refers to the members of the group acting in their separate capacities. In this case, either use a plural verb or, to avoid awkwardness, reword the sentence. Examples:

- The crew were not in agreement about the survey locations. OR
- Members of the crew were not in agreement about the survey locations.

Foreign Plurals Usually Take Plural Verbs

Although usage is gradually changing, most careful writers still use plural verbs with *data, strata, phenomena, media,* and other irregular plurals. Example:

The data he requested are incorporated into the three tables.

Indefinite Pronouns like Each and Anyone Take Singular Verbs

Writers often fail to follow this rule when they make the verb agree with the object of a prepositional phrase, instead of with the subject. Examples:

- Each of the committee members are ready to adjourn. (incorrect)
- Each of the committee members is ready to adjourn. (correct)

THERE/THEIR/THEY'RE

These words can be easily misused by accident, even by those who know their correct use. Do a careful job of editing to make sure you have followed these guidelines:

1. Use *there* as an adverb that indicates direction or that is part of the phrases *there is* and *there are.*
2. Use *their* to indicate possession or ownership.
3. Use *they're* as a contraction for *they are.*

Examples:

- You'll find the new forms over *there* in the file cabinet.
- *There is* only one road to that village in Nepal.
- The secretaries and word processors were proud of *their* successful effort to rewrite the company's style manual.
- As for the board members, *they're* all planning to attend the reception tonight.

TO/TOO/TWO

To is either part of the infinitive verb form ("to go") or a preposition in a prepositional phrase ("to the office"). *Too* is an adverb that either suggests an excessive amount or that conveys the meaning "also." *Two* is a noun or adjective that stands for the numeral 2. Examples:

- He volunteered *to* go [infinitive verb] *to* Alaska [prepositional phrase] *to* work [another infinitive verb form] on the project.
- Stephanie explained that the proposed hazardous waste dump would pose *too* many risks to the water supply. Scott made this point *too*.
- When *two* water mains broke, the city experienced a crisis.

UTILIZE/USE

Utilize is simply a long form for the preferred verb *use*. Although some verbs that end in *-ize* are useful words, most are simply wordy substitutes for shorter forms. As some writing teachers say, "Why use *utilize* when you can use *use?*" Examples:

- She *used* [not *utilized*] the Internet for her research.
- Three different drills were *used* [not *utilized*] to drill through the rock.

WHICH/THAT

Which is used to introduce nonrestrictive clauses, which are defined as clauses not essential to the meaning (as in this sentence). Note that such clauses require a comma before the *which* and a slight pause in speech. *That* is used to introduce restrictive clauses that are essential to the meaning of the sentence (as in this sentence). Note that such clauses have no comma before the *that* and are read without a pause. *Which* and *that* can produce different meanings, as the following examples show:

- Our benefits package, *which* is the best in our industry, includes several options for medical care.
- The benefits package *that* our firm provides includes several options for medical care.
- My daughter's school, *which* is in Cobb County, has an excellent math program.
- The school *that* my daughter attends is in Cobb County and has an excellent math program.

Note that the above examples with *that* might be considered wordy by some readers. Indeed, such sentences often can be made more concise by deleting the *that* introducing the restrictive clause. However, delete *that* only if you can do so without creating an awkward, choppy sentence.

WHO/WHOM

Who is a subjective form that can only be used in the subject slot of a clause; *whom* is an objective form that can only be used as a direct object or other nonsubject noun form of a sentence. Examples:

- The man *who* you said called me yesterday is a good customer of the firm. [The clause "who . . . called me yesterday" modifies *man.* Within this clause, *who* is the subject of the verb *called.* Note that the subject role of *who* is not affected by the two words "you said," which interrupt the clause.]
- They could not remember the name of the person *whom* they interviewed. [The clause "whom they interviewed" modifies *person.* Within this clause, *whom* is the direct object of the verb *interviewed.* Grammatically, the clause could be turned around to read "they interviewed whom."]

WHO'S/WHOSE

Who's is a contraction that replaces *who is,* whereas *whose* is a possessive adjective. Examples:

- *Who's* planning to attend the annual meeting?
- Susan is the manager *who's* responsible for training.
- *Whose* budget includes training?
- Susan is the manager *whose* budget includes training.

WORDINESS

Some experts believe that careful attention to conciseness would shorten technical documents considerably—perhaps as much as 40% to 50%. As a result, reports and proposals would take less time to read and cost less to produce. This entry offers several techniques for reducing verbiage without changing meaning.

Replace Abstract Nouns with Verbs

Concise writing depends more on verbs than it does on nouns. Sentences that contain abstract nouns, especially ones with more than two syllables, can be shortened by focusing on strong verbs. By converting an abstract noun to an action verb, you can eliminate extra words in each wordy sentence below:

> **Original:** The *acquisition* of the property was accomplished through long and hard negotiations.
>
> **Revision:** The property was *acquired* through long and hard negotiations.
>
> **Original:** *Confirmation* of the contract occurred yesterday.
>
> **Revision:** The contract was *confirmed* yesterday.
>
> **Original:** *Exploration* of the region had to be effected before the end of the year.
>
> **Revision:** The region had to be *explored* before the end of the year.
>
> **Original:** *Replacement* of the transmission was achieved only three hours before the race.
>
> **Revision:** The transmission was *replaced* only three hours before the race.

You can see that abstract nouns often end with *-tion* or *-ment.* Although such words are not always "bad" usage, they do cause problems when they replace the action verbs from which they are derived. In the following examples, abstract nouns are listed in the left column and the preferred verb forms are listed in the right column:

assessment	assess
classification	classify
computation	compute
delegation	delegate
development	develop
disbursement	disburse
documentation	document
elimination	eliminate
establishment	establish
negotiation	negotiate
observation	observe
requirement	require
verification	verify

Shorten Wordy Phrases

Many wordy phrases have worked their way into business and technical writing. Such weighty expressions add extra words and rob prose of clarity. Here are some of the culprits, along with their concise substitutes:

afford an opportunity to	permit
along the lines of	like
an additional	another
at a later date	later
at this point in time	now
by means of	by
come to an end	end
due to the fact that	because
during the course of	during
for the purpose of	for
give consideration to	consider
in advance of	before
in the amount of	for
in the event that	if
in the final analysis	finally
in the proximity of	near
prior to	before
subsequent to	later
with regard to	about

Replace Long Words with Short Ones

In school, most students rightly are taught to experiment with more sophisticated words. Although this effort helps build vocabularies, it also can encourage the lifelong tendency to use long words when short ones will do. As a rule, the following long words in the left column should be replaced by the short words in the right column:

advantageous	helpful
alleviate	lessen, lighten
approximately	about
cognizant	aware
commence	start, begin

demonstrate	show
discontinue	end, stop
endeavor	try
finalize	end, complete
implement	do, carry out
initiate	start, begin
inquire	ask
modification	change
prioritize	rank, rate
procure	buy
terminate	end, fire
transport	move
undertake	try, attempt
utilize	use

Leave Out Clichés

Clichés are worn-out expressions that add extra words to your writing. Although they once were fresh phrases, they became clichés when they no longer conveyed their original meaning. You can make writing more concise by replacing them with a good adjective or two. Here are some clichés to avoid:

as plain as day
ballpark figure
efficient and effective
few and far between
last but not least
leaps and bounds
needless to say
reinvent the wheel
skyrocketing costs
step in the right direction

Write like You Talk

Much wordiness results from talking around the topic. Sometimes called *circumlocution,* this flaw arises from a tendency to write indirectly. It can be avoided by reading passages aloud. Almost invariably, the sound of the words will make problems of wordiness quite apparent. Ask yourself, "How would I say this if I were talking to the reader in person?" Asking this question helps condense all kinds of inflated language. However, remember that even direct writing must retain a tactful, diplomatic tone when it contains negative or sensitive information.

Original: We would like to suggest that you consider directing your attention toward completing the project before the commencement of the seasonal monsoon rains in the region of the project area.

Revision: We suggest you complete the project before the monsoons begin.

Original: At the close of the last phase of the project, a bill for your services should be expedited to our central office for payment.

Revision: After the project ends, please send your bill immediately to our central office.

Original: It is possible that the well-water samples collected during our investigation of the well on the site of the subdivision could possibly contain some chemicals in concentrations higher than is allowable according to the state laws now in effect.

Revision: Our samples from the subdivision's well might contain chemical concentrations beyond that permitted by the state.

Avoid There Are, It Is, and Similar Constructions

There are and *it is* are not good substitutes for concrete subjects and action verbs. Such constructions delay the delivery of information about who or what is doing something. They tend to make your writing lifeless and abstract. Avoid them by creating (1) main subjects that are concrete nouns and (2) main verbs that are action words. The revised passages below give readers a clear idea of "who is doing what" in the subject and verb positions.

Original: There are many McDuff projects that could be considered for design awards.

Revision: Many McDuff projects could be considered for design awards.

Original: It is clear to the hiring committee that writing skills are an important criterion for every technical position.

Revision: The hiring committee believes that writing skills are an important criterion for every technical position.

Original: There were seven people who attended the meeting at the client's office in Charlotte.

Revision: Seven people attended the meeting at the client's office in Charlotte.

Cut Out Extra Words

Delete extra words or redundant phrasing in your work. Sometimes the problem comes in the form of needless connecting words, like *to be* or *that.* Other times it shows itself as points made earlier that do not need repeating. Delete extra words when their use (1) does not add a necessary transition or (2) does not provide new information. (One important exception is the intentional repetition of main points for emphasis, as in repeating important conclusions in different parts of a report.) The examples below display a variety of examples of wordy writing, with corrections made in longhand:

- Preparing the client's final bill involves ~~the~~ checking ~~of~~ all project invoices ~~for the project~~.
- The report examined what the ABC project manager considered ~~to be a~~ technically acceptable risk.
- During ~~the course of~~ its field work, the ABC team will ~~be engaged in the process of~~ reviewing all ~~of the~~ notes ~~that have been~~ accumulated in previous studies.
- ~~Because of his position~~ As head of ~~the~~ ABC public relations group, ~~at ABC~~, he planned ~~such that he would be able~~ to attend the meeting.
- She believed ~~that the~~ recruiting ~~of~~ more minorities for the technical staff is essential.
- The department must determine its ~~aims and~~ goals so that they can be included in ABC's 2002 ~~the~~ annual strategic plan. ~~produced by ABC for the year of 2002.~~
- Most ABC managers ~~generally~~ agree that all ~~of the~~ company's employees ~~at all of the offices~~ deserve ~~at least~~ some ~~degree of~~ training each year. ~~that they work for the firm.~~

WORDS THAT AREN'T

Many nonwords have worked their way into informal and formal usage. Listed below are some common examples.

Don't Use	*Use*
alot	a lot
anyways	anyway

anywheres	anywhere
can not	cannot
complected	complexioned
could of	could have
different than	different from
enthused	enthusiastic
hisself	himself
in regards to	regarding *or* about
irregardless	regardless
refer back to	refer to
repeat again	repeat
somewheres	somewhere
theirselves	themselves
towards	toward
use to *or* suppose to	used to *or* supposed to
would of	would have

YOUR/YOU'RE

Your is an adjective that shows ownership, whereas *you're* is a contraction for *you are*. Examples:

- *Your* office will be remodeled next week.
- *You're* responsible for giving performance appraisals.

EXERCISE 1: GRAMMAR AND MECHANICS

The following passages contain a variety of grammatical and mechanical errors covered in the handbook. The major focus is punctuation. Rewrite each passage.

1. Some concerns regarding plumbing design are mentioned in our report, however, no unusual design problems are expected.
2. An estimate of the total charges for an audit and for three site visits are based on our standard fee schedules.
3. The drill bit was efficient cheap and available.

4. The plan unless we have completely misjudged it, will increase sales markedly.
5. Our proposal contains design information for these two parts of the project; Phase 1 (evaluating the 3 computers) and Phase 2 (installing the computer selected).
6. If conditions require the use of all-terrain equipment to reach the construction locations, this will increase the cost of the project slightly.
7. An asbestos survey was beyond the scope of this project, if you want one, we would be happy to submit a proposal.
8. Jones-Simon Company, the owners of the new building, were informed of the problem with the foundation.
9. Also provided is the number and type of tests to be given at the office.
10. Calculating the standard usages by the current purchase order prices result in a downward adjustment of $0.65.
11. Data showing the standard uses of the steel, including allowances for scrap, waste and end pieces of the tube rolls, are included for your convenience at the end of this report in Table 7.
12. This equipment has not been in operation for 3 months, and therefore, its condition could not be determined by a quick visual inspection.
13. Arthur Jones Manager of the Atlanta branch wrote that three proposals had been accepted.
14. The generator that broke yesterday has been shipped to Tampa already by Harry Thompson.
15. The first computer lasted eight years the second two years.
16. He wants one thing out of their work speed.
17. On 25 September 2008 the papers were signed.
18. On March 23 2009 the proposal was accepted.
19. The meeting was held in Columbus the Capital of Ohio.
20. M-Global, Inc. completed its Indonesia project in record time.
21. He decided to write for the brochure then he changed his mind.
22. Interest by the Kettering Hospital staff in the development of a master plan for the new building wings have been expressed.
23. However much he wants to work for Gasion engineering he will turn the job down if he has to move to another state.
24. 35 computer scientists attended the convention, but only eleven of them were from private industry.
25. Working at a high salary gives him some satisfaction still he would like more emotional satisfaction from his job.
26. His handwriting is almost unreadable therefore his secretary asked him to dictate letters.
27. Any major city especially one that is as large as Chicago is bound to have problems with mass transit.

28. He ended his speech by citing the company motto; "Quality first, last, and always".
29. Houston situated on the Gulf of Mexico is an important international port.
30. The word effect is in that student's opinion a difficult one to use.
31. All persons who showed up for the retirement party, told stories about their association with Charlie over the years.
32. The data that was included in the study seems inconclusive.
33. My colleague John handled the presentation for me.
34. Before he arrived failure seemed certain.
35. While evaluating the quality of her job performance a study was made of her writing skills by her supervisor.
36. I shall contribute to the fund for I feel that the cause is worthwhile.
37. James visited the site however he found little work finished.
38. There are three stages cutting grinding and polishing.
39. The three stages are cutting grinding and polishing.
40. Writers occasionally create awkward verbs prioritize and terminate for example.
41. Either the project engineers or the consulting chemist are planning to visit with the client next week.
42. Besides Gerry Dave worked on the Peru project.
43. The corporation made a large unexpected gift to the university.
44. The reason for his early retirement are the financial incentives given by his employer.
45. Profit, safety and innovation are the factors that affect the design of many foundations.
46. No later than May 2012 the building will be finished.
47. Each of the committee members complete a review of the file submitted by the applicant.
48. The team completed their collaborative writing project on schedule.
49. Both the personnel officers and the one member of the quality team is going to attend the conference in Fargo.
50. He presented a well organized presentation but unfortunately the other speakers on the panel were not well-prepared.

EXERCISE 2: USAGE

For each of the following passages, select the correct word or phrase from the choices within the parentheses. Be ready to explain the rationale for your choice.

1. John (implied, inferred) in his report that TransAm Oil should reject the bid.

2. Before leaving on vacation, the company president left instructions for the manner in which responsibilities should be split (among, between) the three vice presidents.
3. Harold became (uninterested, disinterested) in the accounting problem after working on it for 18 straight hours.
4. A large (percent, percentage) of the tellers is dissatisfied with the revised work schedule.
5. The typist responded that he would make (less, fewer) errors if the partner would spell words correctly in the draft.
6. From her reading of the annual report, Ms. Jones (inferred, implied) that the company might expand its operations.
7. The president's decision concerning flextime will be (effected, affected) by the many conversations he is having with employees about scheduling difficulties.
8. His (principal, principle) concern was that the loan's interest and (principle, principal) remain under $500.
9. Throughout the day, his concentration was interrupted (continuously, continually) by phone calls.
10. He jogged (continuously, continually) for 20 minutes.
11. Five thousand books (compose, comprise) his personal library.
12. The clients (who, whom) he considered most important received Christmas gifts from the company.
13. The company decided to expand (its, it's) operations in the hope that (its, it's) the right time to do so.
14. The (nonflammable, flammable, inflammable) liquids were kept in a separate room, because of their danger.
15. They waited for (awhile, a while) before calling the subcontractor.
16. Caution should be taken to (ensure, insure) that the alarm system will not go off accidentally.
17. The new floors (are comprised of, are composed of, comprise) a thick concrete mixture.
18. He (expects, anticipates) that 15 new employees will be hired this year.
19. The main office offered to (augment, supplement) the annual operating budget of the Boston office with an additional $100,000 in funds.
20. It was (all together, altogether) too late to make changes in the proposal.
21. The arbitrator made sure that both parties (agreed to, agreed with) the terms and conditions of the contract before it was submitted to the board.
22. Option 1 calls for complete removal of the asbestos. (Alternately, Alternatively), Option 2 would only require that the asbestos material be thoroughly covered.
23. They had not considered the (amount, number) of cement blocks needed for the new addition.

24. (Due to, Because of) the change in weather, they had to reschedule the trip to the project site.

25. The health inspector found (too, to) many violations in that room (to, too).

26. They claimed that the old equipment (used, utilized) too much fuel.

27. Gone are the days when a major construction job gets started with a handshake and (a verbal, an oral) agreement.

28. The complex project has 18 (discreet, discrete) phases; each part deals with confidential information that must be handled (discretely, discreetly).

29. He was (definitive, definite) about the fact that he would not be able to complete the proposal by next Tuesday.

30. He usually received (complementary, complimentary) samples from his main suppliers.

31. To (lose, loose) a client for whom they had worked so hard was devastating.

32. It was (fortunate, fortuitous) he was there at the exact moment the customer needed to order a year's worth of supplies, for the sales commission was huge.

33. Among all the information on the graph, he located the one (data, datum) that shows the price of tuna on the Seattle market at 5 P.M. on August 7.

34. Each (principle, principal) of the corporation was required to buy stock.

35. He returned to the office to (assure, ensure) that the safe was locked.

Index

PLANNING FORM: TO BE USED FOR ALL TECHNICAL COMMUNICATION PROJECTS

NAME: ______________________ PROJECT: ______________________

I. Purpose: Answer each question in one sentence. ______________________

A. What is the purpose of this project? ______________________

____

B. What response do you want from it? ______________________

____

II. Audience Matrix: Fill in names and positions.

	Decision-Makers	Advisers	Receivers
Managers			
Experts			
Operators			
General Readers			

III. Information on Your Audience: Answer these questions about selected members of your audience.

1. What is this person's technical and/or educational background?

____

____

2. What main question does this person need answered?

____

____

3. What main action do you want this person to take?

____

____

4. What features of this person's personality are relevant?

____

____

5. What features does this person prefer in
   Format? ______________________
   Style? ______________________
   Organization? ______________________
   Graphics? ______________________

IV. Outline: Attach an outline (topic) to use in drafting the **body** of this document or speech.